About Jon Whale

Jon Whale is an autonomous research development scientist, these days working almost exclusively on medical and psychological applications. He is a psychologist, life script analyst, graphologist, electronic design and development engineer, experienced in a diversity of esoteric and mystical disciplines and an international author, having written and published numerous articles, monographs and books.

THE SUPERNATURAL ODYSSEY

By

Jon Whale

NAKED SPIRIT

THE PHYSICAL, PSYCHOLOGICAL, EMOTIONAL AND SPIRITUAL MAPS FOR HEALTH AND DISEASE

INCLUDING

THE ASSEMBLAGE POINT BLUEPRINTS

Contains 10 Chapters with 3 Appendixes, Supported with 271 Illustrations

NAKED SPIRIT - THE SUPER NATURAL ODYSSEY

Jon Whale, Ph.D.

ISBN: 1-873483-06-6

Layout and design by Jon Whale
Front Cover Design: Jon Whale
Copy Editor: Sharon Bridgman
Technical Editor: Roger Melhuish. M.B. Ch.B.

DragonRising Publishing
18 Marlow Avenue
Eastbourne, East Sussex
United Kingdom
www.DragonRising.com
Telephone: +44 (0) 1323 729 666
Fax: +44 (0) 8452 804 040

Printed and bound by CPI Antony Rowe, Eastbourne

Precautions For Patients And Disclaimer

Laboratory analysis providing the haematology and biochemistry data along with many other diagnostic procedures available today are paramount for the correct medical management of disease. Modern drugs and surgery are life saving.

This book is a reference work, not intended to diagnose, prescribe or treat. The information contained herein is in no way to be considered as a substitute for consultation with a professional physician.

Those who use the Assemblage Point or any other techniques described in this book do so by their own choice and, whilst if carried out according to the instructions in this book they may prove efficacious, neither the author nor the publisher promise, guarantee or accept responsibility for any specific results.

For more information see Internet websites:
www.whalemedical.com & www.theassemblagepoint.com

CONTENTS

ABOUT JON WHALE   **1**

PRECAUTIONS FOR PATIENTS AND DISCLAIMER   **4**

NOTE TO SCIENTIFIC AND MEDICAL READERS 12

PREFACE

BY JON WHALE   **13**

BIBLIOGRAPHY, REFERENCES AND FOLLOW-UP READING   **14**

INTRODUCTION

BY PROF. ELENA EVTIMOVA PH.D.   **15**

BIBLIOGRAPHY, REFERENCES AND FOLLOW-UP READING   **18**

CHAPTER 1

ATOMIC AND QUANTUM MAN   **19**

THE ULTIMATE EQUATION OF CREATIVITY 20

THE ELECTROMAGNETIC SPECTRUM 21

THE QUANTUM ENIGMA 25

THE BODY'S ATOMIC AND QUANTUM ENERGY FIELD 28

THE HUMAN ASSEMBLAGE POINT 34

BIBLIOGRAPHY, REFERENCES AND FOLLOW-UP READING 36

CHAPTER 2

EMBEZZLED HEALTH   **37**

ABORIGINAL MEDICINE MEN 37

THE SHAMAN'S BLOW 38

THE TRIGGER FOR PREVAILING ILLEGAL DRUG ISSUES? 38

NATURE'S POWER MODERATES THE HUMAN EGO 39

THE DISCOVERY OF THE FUNDAMENTAL PRINCIPLE 42

THE ASSEMBLAGE POINT AND OUR HEALTH 46
DRUGS MEDICATIONS AND SUBSTANCE DEPENDENCE 55
BIBLIOGRAPHY, REFERENCES AND FOLLOW-UP READING 58

CHAPTER 3

THE DEEP SELF OF PERSONALITY TYPES EXPOSED   **59**
THE INTROVERT AND THE EXTROVERT 59
THE INTROVERTED ARTIST 61
THE ABSTRACT CORE OF HANDWRITING ANALYSIS 64
PERSONALITY PROFILES 64
THE EXTROVERT INTUITIVE TYPE 64
THE INTROVERT INTUITIVE TYPE 65
THE EXTROVERT FEELING TYPE 65
THE INTROVERT FEELING TYPE 65
THE EXTROVERT PRACTICAL TYPE 66
THE INTROVERT PRACTICAL TYPE 66
THE EXTROVERT RATIONAL TYPE 67
THE INTROVERT RATIONAL TYPE 67
DANGEROUS LOCATIONS 68
BIBLIOGRAPHY, REFERENCES AND FOLLOW-UP READING 69

CHAPTER 4

SEVEN ATTRIBUTES OF POWER   **71**
THE SCALE OF EMOTIONAL HEALTH 71
NEGATIVE - 5. APATHY, DESPONDENCY, DISTRESS, MISERY, DISSOLUTION 73
NEGATIVE - 4. ANXIETY, SYMPATHY, APPEASEMENT, GRIEF, FEAR 73
NEGATIVE - 3. COVERT MANIPULATION, CONCEALED HOSTILITY, CLANDESTINE MALEVOLENCY 75
NEGATIVE - 2. ANGER, AGGRESSION, DELINQUENCY, INSURGENCY 76
NEGATIVE - 1. REJECTION, CONDEMNATION, CONTEMPT, CRITICISM, ANTAGONISM 77
NEUTRAL 0.0. INDIFFERENCE, BOREDOM, LETHARGY, PASSIVENESS 77
POSITIVE + 1. CONSERVATISM, PRESERVATION, MODERATION, INDEPENDENCE, DISCRETION 78
POSITIVE + 2. ENTHUSIASM, APPRECIATION, EAGERNESS, RECOGNITION, DEVOTION 78
POSITIVE + 3. EXHILARATION, RAPTURE, EXCITEMENT, VITALITY, AMBITION 79
POSITIVE + 4. EUPHORIA, HARMONY, TRIUMPH, ABUNDANCE, COHERENCE 79
POSITIVE + 5. SERENITY, COMPOSURE, TOLERANCE, DOMINION CONFIDENCE 80
USING THE SCALE OF EMOTIONAL HEALTH 81
A GRAPHOLOGICAL PROFILE OF A MINUS THREE FEMALE 82
THE MAKING OF AN EMOTIONAL HEALTHY ADULT 85
THE SEVEN DEADLY SINS V. THE SEVEN VIRTUES 86
A MAP OF THE HUMAN PSYCHE 87
ENERGY ATTRIBUTE 1, INSTINCT 89
ENERGY ATTRIBUTE 2, PASSION 90
ENERGY ATTRIBUTE 3, INTENT 90
ENERGY ATTRIBUTE 4, COMPASSION 91

ENERGY ATTRIBUTE 5, EXPRESSION 92
ENERGY ATTRIBUTE 6, INTUITION 94
ENERGY ATTRIBUTE 7, WISDOM 94
EMOTIONAL HEALTH V. ATTRIBUTE ACTIVITY 94
DOMAINS OF CONSCIOUSNESS 95
ACCOMPLISHED INDEPENDENCE 95
BASIC SURVIVAL 95
AGGRAVATED CONFORMITY 96
OVERWHELMING DISTRESS 97
THE ATTRIBUTES WITHIN RELATIONSHIPS 98
RELATIONSHIPS BASED ON POSITIVE LEVELS OF EMOTIONAL HEALTH 99
RELATIONSHIPS BASED ON NEGATIVE LEVELS OF EMOTIONAL HEALTH 100
RELATIONSHIPS BASED ON NEGATIVE AND POSITIVE LEVELS OF EMOTIONAL HEALTH 100
DIADIC AND GROUP POWER 101
YOUR INTERACTIVE EMOTIONAL LEVEL OF HEALTH 102
EMOTIONAL LEVELS OF HEALTH AND ASSEMBLAGE POINT LOCATIONS 103
BIBLIOGRAPHY, REFERENCES AND FOLLOW-UP READING 104

CHAPTER 5

BIOELECTRIC MAN — 105

SOUND PRESSURE WAVES 105
THE MUSICAL FREQUENCY SPECTRUM 105
MICROAMPS OF CONSCIOUSNESS 108
THE PSYCHOLOGY OF BRAIN FREQUENCIES 111
THE LEFT BRAIN 114
THE RIGHT BRAIN: 114
HIGH BETA BRAIN FREQUENCIES 114
BETA BRAIN FREQUENCIES 114
ALPHA BRAIN FREQUENCIES 115
THETA BRAIN FREQUENCIES 115
DELTA BRAIN FREQUENCIES 116
EARTH'S ELECTROMAGNETIC FREQUENCIES INFLUENCE BRAIN FREQUENCIES 116
PLANETARY ORBITS AFFECT OUR BRAIN FREQUENCIES AND ASSEMBLAGE POINT LOCATIONS . 117
BIOELECTRONICS AND THE ASSEMBLAGE POINT 118
ASSEMBLAGE POINT LOCATIONS 118
BIBLIOGRAPHY, REFERENCES AND FOLLOW-UP READING 121

CHAPTER 6

FINDING THE ASSEMBLAGE POINT — 123

WHERE TO LOOK FOR THE ASSEMBLAGE POINT 126
FEELING THE LOCATION OF THE ASSEMBLAGE POINT 128
REFLEX TESTING 129
SEEING THE LOCATION 131
MAGNETIC PENDULUM LOCATING 132

Confirming the Location 132
Bibliography, References and Follow-Up Reading 133

CHAPTER 7

RECOVERING THE ASSEMBLAGE POINT   135
Definitions Of Types of Assemblage Point Shifts 137
Realignment Aids 138
Realignment Using The Sliding Shift 143
How To Instruct Your Subject 148
Realignment Using Stage Shifting 149
Confirming The New Location 150
Patients' Considerations 150
Youngsters And Juveniles 151
Future Rewarding Applications 152
Bibliography, References And Follow-Up Reading 153

CHAPTER 8

SUPERNATURAL MAN AND WOMEN   155
Mystical Disciplines And The Assemblage Point 162
Zeus, Apollo And Hermes 163
The Caduceus 167
Crown Chakra 173
Brow Chakra 174
Throat Chakra 175
Heart Chakra 176
Solar Plexus Chakra 177
Sacral Chakra 178
Root Chakra 179
Persons With All Chakras Functioning Are Extraordinary 180
The Intrinsic Human Quest 181
Positive Levels Of Conscious Being 183
Trans Universal Consciousness. 99:1 % Essence v. Ego Ratio. 183
Universal Consciousness. 90:10 % Essence v. Ego Ratio. 184
Spiritual Consciousness. 85:15% Essence v. Ego Ratio. 184
Professional Consciousness. 75:25% Essence v. Ego Ratio. 185
Survival Consciousness. 50:50% Essence v. Ego Ratio. 185
Negative Levels Of Consciousness 186
Negative Levels: Aggravated Conformity. 25:75% Essence v. Ego Ratio. 186
Negative Levels: Overwhelming Distress. 15: 85% Essence v. Ego Ratio. 186
Negative Levels: Concentrated Persecution. 10:90% Essence v. Ego Ratio. 187
Negative Levels: Eternal Inferno. 1:99% Essence v. Ego Ratio. 187
Increasing Positive States And Reducing Negative States 187
Bibliography, References And Follow-Up Reading 191

CONTENTS

CHAPTER 9

JOURNEYS OUT OF THE BODY   **193**
THE SCIENCE OF THE DEATH PROCESS 195
THE MYSTERY OF THE TWO APERTURES 197
BIBLIOGRAPHY, REFERENCES AND FOLLOW-UP READING 200

CHAPTER 10

THE AFTERLIFE   **201**
SEVEN HEAVENS AND SEVEN HELLS 202
SEVEN HEAVENS OF EGYPT 203
SEVEN HEAVENS OF HINDU AND BUDDHIST RELIGIONS 204
SEVEN HEAVENS OF ISLAM 205
SEVEN HEAVENS OF THE EARLY CHRISTIANS 206
DESCENT AND ASCENT OF CHRIST THROUGH THE SEVEN HEAVENS 206
JEWISH SEVEN HALLS 209
MYSTERIOUS NUMBER SEVEN 210
SEVEN-HEADED SERPENT 212
SEVEN HELLS 213
THE SPIRITUAL CRISIS OF MAN 213
THE PROVINCE OF THE MIND HAS NO LIMITS 216
BIBLIOGRAPHY, REFERENCES AND FOLLOW-UP READING 219

EPILOGUE   221
SEEKING ASSEMBLAGE POINT CORRECTION OR TRAINING 222

APPENDIX I

ASSEMBLAGE POINT PROFILES   **223**
1. CLINICAL DEPRESSION FOLLOWING CONCUSSION 223
2. CHRONIC PANIC ATTACKS 224
3. HYPERTENSION (STRESS) 225
4. FEELING OF DETACHMENT, ANXIETY AND DEPRESSION 226
5. AGORAPHOBIA AND CLINICAL DEPRESSION 226
6. CHRONIC MENTAL ILLNESS WITH DEPRESSION 227
7. CONCUSSION RELATED SOCIAL AND ALCOHOL PROBLEMS 228
8. CLINICAL DEPRESSION 228
9. NON SPECIFIC CENTRAL SHIFT 229
10. PERIODIC DISLOCATION OF THE HIP 229
11. CONTINUAL COLD, TRAUMA, MIGRAINES AND LACK OF ENERGY 230
12. NON SPECIFIC CENTRAL SHIFT 230
13. ANXIETY 230
14. DROPPED ASSEMBLAGE POINT DUE TO DRUG OVERDOSE 231
15. SUBSTANCE ABUSE 231

16. Non Specific Central Shift 231
17. Circulation Problems With Heart Palpitations 232
18. Depression And Drug And Alcohol Dependence 233

DRUGS AND THE ASSEMBLAGE POINT   **234**
Prescribed Drugs 235
Tobacco 235
Alcohol 236
Cannabis 237
Recreational Drugs 238
Hallucinogenic Drugs 239
Toxins, Poisons And Pollution 240
Bibliography, References And Follow-Up reading 241

APPENDIX II

ADVANCED PROCEDURES FOR CORRECTING THE ASSEMBLAGE POINT

LOCATION   **243**
Case Studies Of Correcting the Assemblage Point Using The Lux IV 247
Canadian E-Mail Case Reports 247
United kingdom E-mail Case Reports (1) 248
E-mail Case Reports From Holland (EU). 250
New Zealand E-mail Case Reports 250
Bulgarian Case Report 252
UK E-mail Case Reports (2) 252
Archive Photographs 1995 252

ANCIENT AND MODERN MEDICAL USE OF GEM STONES   **254**
Correcting The Energy Of Disease And Injury 255

DOWSING ENERGY FIELDS   **263**
Chakra Dowsing 266
Some General Rules 267
Pendulum Motion 268
Using Coins To Dowse Chakra Percentages 269
Using The Electronic Dowsing Meter 270

APPENDIX III

PUBLISHED ARTICLES   **271**
Dynamic Radiometric Thermal Diagnostics And Dielectric Resonance Management
Procedures 271
The Domineering Energy Of Disease And Injury 273
From Stellar Exploration To Sub-Molecular Energy Medicine 273
The Sinister Intelligence And Power Of Disease 275
'Push-Pull' Energy Management for Disease and Injury 276

THE INFRARED BIOSCANNER   **281**

CONTENTS

ADVANTAGES IN USE 281
APPARATUS DESCRIPTION 282
HIGH DIFFERENTIAL READING 283
LOW DIFFERENTIAL READING 283
HIGH AND LOW DIFFERENTIAL READING 284
ONE EXAMPLE OF USE FOR BACK PROBLEMS 284
NOTES ON SKELETAL ALIGNMENT AND BALANCE 285
OPERATIONAL NOTES 287
USING THE INFRARED BIOSCANNER TO DETERMINE THE LUX IV TREATMENT 287
HIGH DIFFERENTIAL RECORDINGS 287
LOW DIFFERENTIAL RECORDINGS 288
RANGE AND CALIBRATION ACCURACY 288
REGIONAL TEMPERATURE DISTRIBUTION IN THE HUMAN 288
DIFFERENTIAL COMPARISON RULES 288
INFRARED BIOSCANNER MAIN PANELS AND THEIR 290

BACK IN THE SADDLE - THE INVISIBLE RADIATIONS OF INJURIES AND THEIR REPAIR   **291**

FRACTURED PELVIS 295
FRACTURED COLLARBONE 296
ABOUT WHALE MEDICAL INC.'S LUX IV 297

OTHER BOOKS BY JON WHALE   **299**

Note To Scientific And Medical Readers

This book is an economical grayscale reproduction compiled from the first edition full colour Electronic Book version (Ebook). As such, some of the graphics do not scientifically reproduce accurately as black and white images. This especially applies to the numerous infrared thermal image photographs. Those readers that are interested in the precise scientific reproduction of the high contrast colour radiometric thermal images can see and download them in full colour from the Internet Web Site:

www.whalemedical.com

Appendix III has been included to provide some technical and scientific commentaries.

Alternatively, the original full colour Ebook version can be downloaded from Dragon Rising Publishing's Internet Web Site:

www.DragonRising.com

The latest reviews, information, postscripts, discussions and blogs can be examined on the Internet Web Site:

www.nakedspirit.co.uk

Preface

BY JON WHALE

As I stated in my first published book entitled 'The Catalyst of Power - The Assemblage Point of Man', 'It is rare that a researcher has an opportunity to present an original contribution containing numerous major scientific and medical discoveries, based on some 30 years of work'.

My documented scientific, psychological and medical discoveries and procedures concerning the human Assemblage Point were first published in 1996 as a series of three short articles by the Positive Health Magazine. Some years later, one of the magazine editors, Dr. Sandra Goodman told me that never before or since has any article caused so much interest. My early publications, monographs and web pages have been of immense benefit and interest to thousands of professional and ordinary people around the world. The first edition of the Catalyst Of Power sold out in just over two years, the second edition is now available in ebook and paperback format and is also available in the Dutch and Bulgarian languages and will shortly be published in the Asian continent.

Since publishing the Assemblage Point information, I have received many thousands of congratulations, acknowledgements and deeds of appreciation. Today, many ethical scientists, doctors, therapists and professionals working in their fields of interest have taken up the work and employ it for the benefits of their families, patients or clients.

More importantly I have received a magnitude of feedback from others concerning the success and benefits relating to the application of the Assemblage Point knowledge. Being at the hub of the work so to speak, inevitably, we have all come a long way since my early publications. I have had privileged access to more knowledge and understanding. In this book I have corrected my earlier inaccuracies and deficiencies, extended the knowledge to expose more profound scientific, medical, psychological and emotional maps and procedures relating to the human Assemblage Point and the sacred realms of the self and its supernatural attributes.

The Supernatural is of profound interest to a large percentage of Earth's inhabitants. A recent United Kingdom poll confirmed that fifty five percent of those adults interviewed were either directly involved or interested in the Supernatural.

All of us at some level want to be more than we think we are or what others tell us or permit us to be.

As Willam Faulkner once said: *"Do not bother just to be better than your contemporaries or predecessors. Try to be better than yourself."*

This book provides the Global models, maps, tools and follow-up references to help ourselves and those around us to know and benefit from our inherent supernatural powers and touch immortality.

Jon Whale   July 2006

www.nakedspirit.co.uk

www.whalemedical.com

www.theassemblagepoint.com

Bibliography, References And Follow-Up Reading

Whale, Jon, Ph.D. *Core Energy - Surgery For The Electromagnetic Body.* Series of 3 articles prepared for Positive Health magazine. 1996. Website addresses:

http://www.positivehealth.com/permit/Articles/Energy%20Medicine/whale15.htm

http://www.positivehealth.com/permit/Articles/Energy%20Medicine/whale16.htm

http://www.positivehealth.com/permit/Articles/Energy%20Medicine/whale17.htm

Whale, Jon, Ph.D. *The Catalyst of Power the Assemblage Point of Man.* Second Edition. Dragon Rising Publishing. ISBN1 873483 05 8

Introduction

By Prof. Elena Evtimova Ph.D.

According to contemporary physics the Unified Field of Pure Consciousness (1) underlies All that is around us in the World. The Unified Field is infinite and it is endowed with Intelligence, Creativity, Wisdom and Love plus all the other qualities and attributes manifested into the Nature. The Unified Field is self- organizing, creating in its activities all the known separate fields, elementary particles, atoms, molecules, substances, planets, stars, galaxies and the Universe. All that is constant in the Universe are Changes, simply expressed as creation and decay. Among all of these are humans and living beings who, with our consciousness, have the ability to reflect holografically the full range of existing creative and destructive phenomena.

On the physical plane the human body is a formation of billions of constantly vibrating atoms. All the vibrating quantum particles entering humans and living systems create quantum energy waves which are expressed by de Broglie and Schroedinger equations for the relations between matter and its waves. These waves interact and interfere constructively thus producing a resulting quantum, surrounded by macroscopic energy fields. Hence the human energy field is a result of the interference of the energies of all oscillating quantum mechanical wave particles, atoms and cells constituting the human body. The spirit and the soul are included at the level of the Unified Field plane into elementary particles and fields: thus when the human energy field is formed by the amalgamation of their energy vibrations we have our spirit, soul and consciousness.

As Dr. Whale states, because of the fact that this is a vibrating quantum energy field it has an epicentre of the collective oscillations, this being the vortex of the human body and fields, called the

Assemblage Point. This is the core of all the energy strings included in the human energy body and the location through which the threads of energy beam all our perceptions to enter the human consciousness. The human energy field is our shelter and the carrier of emotions, mental, psychic and casual vibrations, determining in a subtle way all our interactions with the world as a whole. It is not by chance that Dr. Whale takes as a model of the human energy field the Earth's magnetic field, which has its epicentre in the Earth's centre though the north and south magnetic poles. As this magnetic field protects life on Earth from the harmful Solar and other Cosmic rays, so our energy field protects us against some unfriendly influences from the environment. Here one can see the application and the action of the Hermetic Principle 'As above, so below'.

Since the Assemblage Point is the epicentre of the physical body and all of its human energy fields, its location and entry angle are very important for the physical, emotional and psychological wellbeing of all of us. As the human physical body is supplied with oxygen and other nurturing substances by the heart through the blood, so the Assemblage Point supplies us with the necessary energy for our (at least) normal functioning. In this sense one can say that the Assemblage Point is the human body's spiritual heart. Dr. Whale's scientific investigations through the years led to the discovery of seven principles for the Assemblage Point and many important maps for its locations connecting them with health conditions, symptoms and diseases. Now we know when a human being is in a perfect physical and mental state then the Assemblage Point is in the centre of the chest. If the position is deviated in any way from this stable central location there may appear any kind of physical or mental problems. The book contains the full information about how to find the Assemblage Point location and correct it manually or with the electronic gem lamp therapy invented and applied by Dr. Whale and other practitioners all over the world successfully for the last twenty years. In my opinion, the Assemblage Point location maps and correction methods given in this and the previous books by Dr. Whale (2) are still to be implemented for future humanity for benefiting all life spheres.

One very interesting theme in this book is the personality types qualified by their handwriting. Learning to recognise each one enables us to apply this knowledge to better understand the people around us. The most impressive and profound characterisation is of the existing spectrum of human states of consciousness. It can be found in the given Scale of Emotional Health in Chapter 4. Here, one can see perfectly represented and exposed the diversity of human soul and spiritual expressions in society. Thus one can estimate one's own position, draw conclusions and eventually search ways to improve the situation.

For the first time in my life I have seen how the Seven Attributes of Power, Instinct, Passion, Intent, Compassion, Expression, Intuition and Wisdom are connected with the human being's chakra system. This is done at an extraordinary and deep level of understanding.

The symmetry principle appears in all existing modes of human consciousness, as many as are above zero, the same as are below. Everything in the human psyche has its opposite pole (Hermetic principle of polarity) giving people the right to exploit the whole range of positive and negative states in order to learn how to manage them. Firstly we have to be aware of this and how to operate them which can be clearly seen on the Diagram of Emotional Health. This fundamental principle has found its expression in and being developed by Dr. Whale in the cartography of Man's psyche – the maps in Chapter 4. The relations between different categories of people are discussed, relative to the map representative of their personalities. These relations are in closer functional dependence upon the existence or lack of existence of quantum resonance phenomena between the wave patterns emitted by the people. Important knowledge underlined in the book is that in the total Earth energy field are intrinsically present the highest attributes of consciousness. This affords the opportunity for each of us to synchronise our minds with the Earth's natural frequencies to stay tuned to the positive states of emotional, psychological and mental levels of health. In Chapter 5, Bioelectric Man, the frequencies operating in our brain, nervous system and body are discussed in full. A substantial fact here, appears to be the interdependence between the brain frequencies and Assemblage Point location, studied in great detail.

In Appendix I, there are cited some examples of therapeutic solutions of patient's problems unresolved by conventional medicine, homeopathy and psychiatry before the application of new and advanced methods of electronic lamp gem therapy.

The recovering of the Assemblage Point location is a crucial circumstance for healing patients of otherwise incurred symptoms and sickness or even for the purposes of self development, rapid learning and gaining power for lucid dreaming. The three types of Assemblage Point shifts are considered in Chapter 7 giving an excellent explanation of the course of action needed to execute a movement, shift or shift in depth in order to return the Assemblage Point to a healthy position.

This is a book which breaks the monotony of one's own life and by the knowledge received, it is possible to raise the level of consciousness of anyone reading it. This is an extraordinary book written by a man at his highest state of consciousness, ensuring the most comprehensive mind picture of Atomic and Quantum Man is committed to humanity. I am sure the book will give you new inspiration for further development of your own state of consciousness, intelligence and creativity. Let it be!

Elena Evtimova   March 2006

Section of Physics
Department of Language Learning
Sofia University
27 Kosta Lulchev Str.
1111 Sofia. Bulgaria
http://www.deo.uni-sofia.bg/index_en.html
http://assemblagepoint.hit.bg
aloniar@abv.bg

Bibliography, References And Follow-Up Reading

References: Consciousness the Unified Field? A Field Theorist's Perspective', Modern Science and Vedic Science 1(1): 29 87; and Proceedings of 'Towards a Science of Consciousness 1996', University of Arizona, April 8 13, (1996)

2. Dr. Whale, The Catalyst Of Power - The Assemblage Point Of Man. Findhorn Press.

Chapter 1

ATOMIC AND QUANTUM MAN

At the zero point there was infinite space, and space existed before the beginning and will exist after the end. The boundless void of space has always endured and, being infinite, extends in all directions forever without any boundaries. Even if unknown to us there are distinctions or boundaries, the question would be what is on the other side? The answer would be more space. With the exception of black holes, dark matter and dark energy, all other objects in our local universe emit energy and that is why we can detect them in the first place. Science says that energy systems are assembled from an epicentre. Galaxies, stars, planets, molecules and atoms are all energy systems that oscillate. By virtue of the fact that they are oscillating, they all have a centre of rotation. Other types of oscillating energy systems, such as electricity generating stations, radio and television transmission stations or mobile telephones also have an epicentre of rotation of the generated power. Gravity and

**Fig. 1:1. A Galaxy Spiralling Outwards
From Its Epicentre (NGC4414).**

magnetism are examples of forces and energy fields upon which the universe and our lives depend, yet the eye cannot see them. These energy fields radiate from a spinning central point called the epicentre.

For example, the Earth's magnetic field extends into space where it protects the earth's atmosphere from being blown away by magnetically deflecting solar storms. If we could see it from above, it would look like a massive doughnut and it has a hole in its field at the north and south poles, the axis of its epicentre passes through the hole. Its location in space is on three axes, X, Y and Z. The X axis is across the equator through the centre of the Earth, the Y axis is across the magnetic north and south poles while the Z axis is at 90 degrees to the X axis on the Earth equator and passes through the central core of the Earth. The crux or the cross point of the magnetic field is in the centre of the earth. This model is given as it helps to comprehend later discussions concerning the human energy field.

The Ultimate Equation Of Creativity

In 1905 Professor Albert Einstein published his famous equation $E=MC^2$. This equation means that mass multiplied by the speed of light squared equals the energy value. Mass is energy waiting to be liberated. Hidden in every object around us is a gigantic amount of energy. To release the energy inherent in mass, the nucleus of the atom must be split into neutrons and protons. The neutrons fly apart at great speed smashing into adjacent atoms, splitting them in the process. This causes a chain reaction that if not controlled will result in an explosion. Our Sun's mass over billions of years is

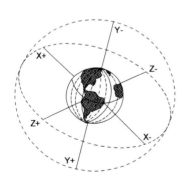

Fig. 1:2. The X, Y & Z axis of the Earth's electromagnetic field.

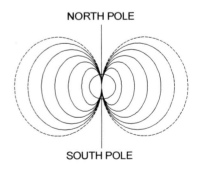

Fig. 1:3. The Earth's magnetic field epicentre.

transformed into energy, it is an ongoing fusion reaction retained by the gravity of its large mass. The energy emitted from our Sun's nuclear reactions is composed of every frequency in the electromagnetic spectrum. At the other side of Einstein's equation, the energy emitted condenses back into mass and this is why it is the ultimate equation of creativity.

The Electromagnetic Spectrum

Radio waves, infrared, ultra violet, X rays and gamma rays are all invisible electromagnetic waves that make up the frequency spectrum; their origins can all be traced back to their epicentre.

The human eye is sensitive to a very narrow band of frequencies of the overall electromagnetic spectrum. The only part of the electromagnetic spectrum that we can see is between violet, at around 3000 billion cycles per second, through the rainbow colour bands of indigo, blue, green, yellow, orange to red at 480 billion cycles per second.

Atoms and molecules emit light when their electrons make a quantum leap from one excited state to another or to their basic state. How we observe the universe will determine the outcome. If we use a wave meter to detect light, then light seems to be constructed of waves. However should we use a particle detector instead of a wave meter, light is comprised of particles or photons.

The narrow band of frequencies of white light is made up of billions of different frequencies and each individual

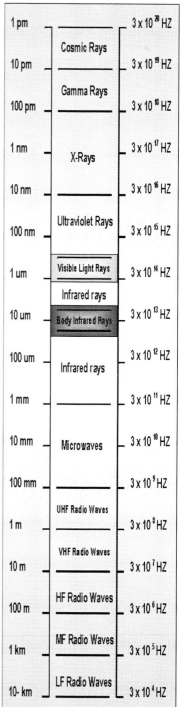

Fig. 1:4. The electromagnetic spectrum.

Hertz = cyles /se.

21

frequency represents a different colour or tone. Light is energy and modern semiconductor solar panels collect light and convert it into electricity or electron flow. Television cameras collect light and convert it into electronic pulses decoded by the television receiving set to reproduce the picture on the cathode ray tube. The eye collects light and converts it into electrical pulses that travel along the cells of the optic nerve and are then decoded by the brain. As we go about our daily lives, very few of us are aware that what we see of the world around us is not a faithful image, but a model or a hologram constructed inside our brain or mind.

The mind's model of the external reality is censored by our individual expectations and beliefs. The mind's model of consensus reality can be seriously distorted by intimidation, illness, fever, drugs, toxins or brainwashing.

Although our eyes cannot see individual electrons or atoms, they can see the frequencies at which electrons vibrate at, as colours. However the human body can also feel electron flow, and most of us have experienced the shock caused by static electricity from cars or nylon carpets. Where there are electrons flowing between adjacent atoms there is electrical current; where there is current then there are voltages and coinciding magnetic fields. Conversely, where there are electromagnetic fields they induce electron flow in conductive material from one atom to the next, generating electricity.

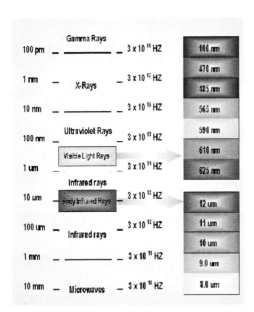

Fig. 1:5. A section of the electromagnetic spectrum illustrating the colour & infrared bands.

The atoms of the molecules that make up a living cell rhythmically exchange their outer circle or shell of orbiting electrons with electrons from adjacent atoms. They are the sub-cellular atomic engines of life. A molecule is a group of atoms linked by the outer shell of orbiting electrons. The molecule of water for example, is constructed of two atoms of hydrogen gas and one atom of oxygen. The electrons of the hydrogen and oxygen atoms rhythmically exchange their orbits at very high speeds, and this exchange of each atom's electrons electrically bonds the oxygen atom and the two hydrogen atoms together, forming water. Adding energy by passing electricity through water, it is converted back to its component gases at the anode and cathode. If this oxygen and hydrogen are mixed together and ignited they explode, forming water again.

The circulating high speed dance of the outer shell of electrons in a molecule continually defines and maintains the molecule's structure. Living cells are made up of a large structure of interactive molecules. Within the living cell, electron flow creates small magnetic

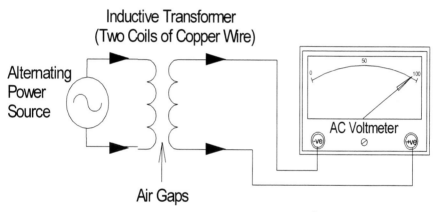

Fig. 1:6. Alternating electron flow within an isolated circuit will transmit to another isolated circuit across space by way of a combination of inductive and capacitive reactance.

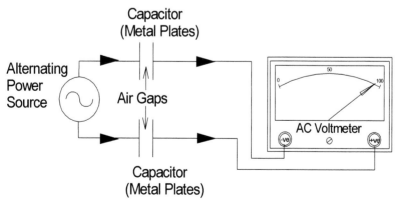

Fig. 1:7. Transmission of alternating electron flow across space by capacitive reactance.

fields. Each cell's dielectric charge is transmitted to neighbouring cells. The health and vitality of a person are reflected within the flow of energy in their cellular body. The overall flow of nervous or emotional energy in the body creates a comprehensive electromagnetic field surrounding it. This field has many smaller modulated fields inside it. These fields relate to the functions of the internal organs and glands. Electron flow pathways and energy channels, extend from the brain, to all the organs and glands, and throughout the body, to the hands and feet. The human body is a miraculous system of some 100 billion individual living and dying cells all held together by an invisible network of energy channels.

More than one hundred years ago science proved that surrounding the nucleus of every atom is a cloud of electrons. Atoms are composed of protons, neutrons and electrons. At the centre of an atom is the nucleus comprising protons that have a positive electrical charge, neutrons that do not have a charge, while the electrons have a negative charge and orbit the nucleus at high speeds. This discovery proved that everything in the material universe, including the human body, consists of electrical energy. The human body is a complex electrical energy system. Over a century later this scientific fact has largely been ignored by medical science.

The flow of electricity in the human body controls and influences this rhythmic exchange of electrons. Emotional traumas, drugs and infections, for example, can completely disrupt the body's natural

18.0 °C

10.0 °C

Fig. 1:8. Infrared image of the higher radiometric transmissions of the day's energy stored in the brickwork of a clock tower set against a cold night sky.

22.0 °C

14.0 °C

Fig. 1:9. Infrared image of the higher radiometric transmissions of people enjoying the cool sea shore.

rhythms and energy levels. This will affect or modulate the exchange of electrons and we can literally experience an emotional electric shock. The effects can be measured and recorded by sensitive electronic voltage or current meters and various electronic medical chart recorders. Besides the body's electricity, there is an unquantifiable and unseen energy factor that can exercise its will over the body's 100 billion individual living cells. This is the life force or spirit entity that is part of every living human and animal.

Electronic science, a product of quantum mechanics, proves that alternating electron flow within an isolated circuit will transmit to another isolated circuit across space by way of a combination of inductive and capacitive reactance. Since all of us have electron flow within our nervous system and gross body, then the transmissions of our quantum state will be transmitted to other individuals and this includes animals, plants and other material objects. Sensitive individuals and other living forms can detect these natural transmissions. Human psychic abilities over and above our five senses are not something yet to be proved, but an unavoidable and irrefutable scientific fact. All of us possess abilities that extend way beyond the limits of our five senses. It is only a question of our limited beliefs that limit our 'supernatural' skills. What we believe to be true is true, but our limited beliefs are a handicap to attaining our full potential as physical and spiritual beings. Our limited beliefs prevent us from attaining higher states of being.

The Quantum Enigma

As previously mentioned, surrounding every atom is a cloud of electrons orbiting the nucleus at incredibly high speeds. The valence electrons of each atom exchange their orbits and link up with adjacent atoms. These orbit exchanges bond each atom together to form molecules that are the building blocks of the material

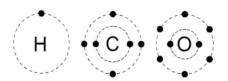

Fig. 1:10. The electron arrangement of hydrogen, carbon and oxygen.

universe, including living cells. The speed or frequency of the outer shell of electrons is what determines the colour of matter when white light is shining on it. The speed or frequency of different coloured materials matches a particular frequency of the visible light spectrum and thus, being in phase, this then reflects that colour back to the observer. The energy of those frequencies of light that are not reflected back to the observer is absorbed. When white light strikes an object, the surface of the object vibrates at a specific frequency that is equivalent to the colour reflected. For example, the colour of the light reflected by plant leaves is predominantly green, therefore the natural vibration wave length of chlorophyll is 565 nanometres long (about half a billionth of a meter) or around 530 billion cycles per second. The leaves of plants are inclined to absorb all of the other colours, except green. The plant does not absorb this frequency and reflects it back to the universe at large. Green is a cold frequency and plants require warm energy to grow, to produce carbohydrates. Therefore there is an intelligence in plants that creates chlorophyll to increase their efficiency and it appears to the observer that the plant is green. When the plant dies its life force dissipates and the frequency of the plant slows down and the leaves turn from yellow to red and then to brown. The frequencies of the plant's energy become disorganised and dissipated, as it is not being replaced by the plant's life force.

By contrast, the metal silver has the capacity to vibrate at and reflect all colours or frequencies of the light spectrum and many other frequencies besides. It is for this reason we use silver metals

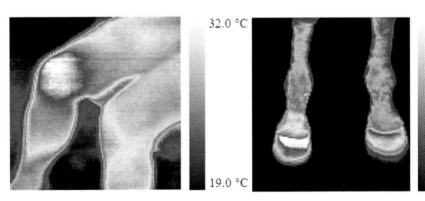

Fig. 1:11. Infrared image of the high radiometric transmissions of a right knee injury.

Fig. 1:12. Infrared image of the high radiometric transmissions of an infected right hoof and leg of a horse.

to plate the glass of mirrors. When we look into a mirror, the silver reflects back to us all of the colours of our physical form.

Question: how much energy is required to maintain the very high velocity or speed of an orbiting electron? Electrons, while spinning, exhibit the quality of mass and mass in motion consumes energy. Yet there is a scientific dilemma: the quantum of energy required to maintain the motion is more than is represented by the particle itself. This is an enigma and what is even more mystifying is that every particle radiates energy, which is why they can be detected in the first place. The energy entering an atom cannot be observed to have the equivalent value that it dissipates.

As all particles spin the problem at the universal level gets out of hand. In an instant the universe appears to rapidly consume every unit of available energy. The universe, including all of the stars, would go cold in that same moment. At absolute zero, minus 273.15 degrees Kelvin, the universe disappears or collapses to a void or empty space. Where and what is the energy coming from that maintains the universe? Is it coming from outside the universe?

Even if one could make sense of this enigma, it simply postpones the problem. According to the law of conservation of energy perpetual motion cannot exist, and yet every particle spins and it spins forever. Particle spin is exempted from this law. Why is this and what is the truth? As already stated the process that is generating the spin is much more fundamental than the mass of the universe itself and this brings us full circle again back to the enigma. Where is the energy coming from?

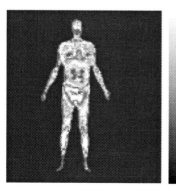

Fig. 1:13. Infrared image of the radiometric transmissions of male.

Fig. 1:14. Infrared image of the high radiometric transmissions of a female walking towards a castle.

From this observation one must deduce that mass is a secondary component or characteristic of the universe. Therefore what is the prime component or fundamental energy behind the universe that creates the orbiting electrons, by which each particle is maintaining its respective motion and differentiates itself from all other particles? What is this elementary exchange of energy that takes place at the most all-embracing level that causes the form of any given particle to reverberate in another place in the universe? What is the energy that creates this sympathetic resonance?

Naturally, adherents of oriental philosophies will claim that it is 'Chi', 'Prana' or 'Kei'; and those persons with other spiritual beliefs will tell you that it is God but this brings us full circle again, for it does not scientifically explain what is going on.

Most of us living on this planet affirm that we are spiritual beings and that we have a soul or a spiritual element extra to, or above, our gross material body. Others expound that we have an energy body and a physical body. Many of us are confident in some way that our spiritual side will transcend our death. While a few of us are so brave and self assured in our spiritual aspiration, we relinquish the material world with its rewards and devote our energies to greater undertakings for humanity or the eternal, even to giving our lives. Only a small minority of us do not hold such convictions and strive for material wealth with its pseudo gratifications. Or we moderate our consciousness with preoccupation, excessive alcohol and drugs or by somnolent living, whilst others are too ill, despairing or debilitated to participate in any undertakings in this consensus reality. Yet there is a quantum of something inexplicable inside most of us that make up the many nationalities of the human race that is conscious that we are made of more than just flesh and bones. All of us but the very young know that at some indeterminable point in time we will become ill or have an accident and will die.

There is a growing mountain of accounts to support the view that life can exist after death and that there are spiritual domains of existence; but as far as death being the absolute end, not a single piece of evidence has been presented to me or to anyone I know, to support or prove this view.

The Body's Atomic And Quantum Energy Field

If the universe including humans was only constructed of elementary particles with no supernatural force or principle more fundamental than matter, then the universe as we know it would never basically change. Existing molecules would move around and sometimes change and form new combinations but the intrinsic nature of matter would stay the same. It is only due to the existence of a supernatural force that the universe evolves. The large proportion of the mass in the universe by our standards could be said to be largely unconscious and yet we are part of a grand universal evolutionary process, therefore there are levels of consciousness and intelligence that is greater than all of us.

A key figure in the growth of quantum mechanics was Professor Einstein. His dilemma was that he could not accept that the action of observing could affect the outcome. He insisted in the belief that everything is predictable. As most of us have experienced, we cannot observe another person without affecting their behaviour, even if they are not aware that we are there. Scientists have the same dilemma: they know that their observations of their experiments affect the outcome. Observation is not a pure isolated act. When we observe an object or action there are additional forces at work. Consciousness has functions that are more than just pure awareness. Electromagnetism and gravity are the binding forces of the material universe. Human consciousness has power attributes that have

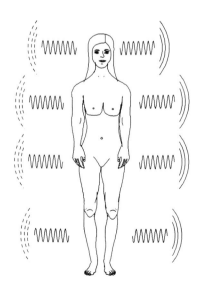

Fig. 1:15. The body emits quantum resonance frequencies in all directions.

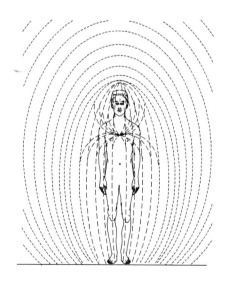

Fig. 1:16. Energy fields extend without a defined boundary.

potency like electromagnetism and gravity, but are entirely different in the way that they affect the material universe.

One key to the enigma concerning the material universe and the supernatural intelligent force, is quantum wave mechanics. Unlike the material universe where each atom is an individual and remains the same and only has external relationships with other atoms, quantum energy field systems after meeting can unite and become something larger than themselves and form a new larger entity. Another key is that conscious awareness is not simply itself. By the definition that it observes, it must project something of itself onto and into the subject of its observations and, at the same time, receive something from its observed subject. Therefore it has additional attributes other than just simple awareness. To observe there must be at the very least an element of the power of 'intent' to observe. There are other elements of power to conscious awareness besides that of 'intent'.

One question that materialises with this understanding concerns the nature of consciousness: Is our consciousness a product of our material brain or is the brain and the rest of the universe a product of our quantum consciousness? Is the true abode of our consciousness in the quantum energy fields? Does consciousness

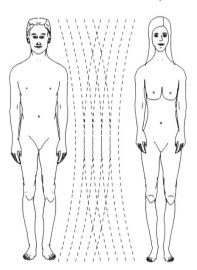

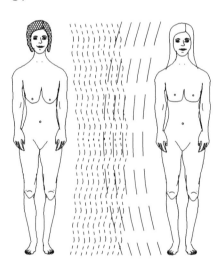

Fig. 1:17. The quantum resonance wave patterns emitted by two people in harmony exhibit the same frequency pattern as they are radiated from the same quantum state.

Fig. 1:18. The quantum resonance wave patterns emitted by two people in disharmony exhibit different frequency patterns as they are radiated from different quantum states.

exist without an object to observe? If this is the case then our consciousness could be truly eternal and our physical death, just like the rest of our experiences, could be just entirely imagined episodes of change for the entertainment of quantum consciousness to counteract the eternity and boredom of its everlasting existence.

The human body transmits energy at various frequencies and it can be detected even from a considerable distance by many types of electronic apparatus. At the atomic and quantum level, surrounding and permeating every cell of a living person, is a vibrating energy field. It is an energy field that contains and characterises our individual physical form and state of being from that of others and the universe at large. We are all individuals with an individual energy system that can move around and function independently in the world, under the direction of our will. While we are alive our physical body is permeated with an oscillating energy field that may or may not have a boundary. Some scientists call it the unified field or morphogenic fields.

The human energy field is more fundamental than magnetic or electromagnetic fields. The individual characteristics of each person's physical and psychological character will be modulated on the frequency transmissions of their energy field. We all transmit energy and it is a fact that our energy transmission frequencies will be modulated with data containing information about our emotional and physical state. Our field transmissions may even be modulated with our most private thoughts or intent. Besides transmitting energy we also receive energy. Some of us claim to be psychic and by entering into altered receptive states of consciousness can decode data transmitted, or inherent in, the energy fields of other people.

Animals and isolated tribal natives are able to tune into a sixth sense, to sense and decode energy fields. For example they can foretell and take the necessary action to avoid the consequences of natural disasters. Western man retains this ability, but today our senses are attenuated to withstand the pandemonium, commotion and pollution of modern life. If we retreat into a quite natural environment, after some days have passed, and by degrees, our brain frequencies and our thinking processes slow down and our senses open and we regain our natural super-receptivity.

The Earth's atmospheric cavity has a peak resonant frequency of 7.83 cycles per second (7.83 Hz). Schumann Frequencies are those natural frequencies that are generated and fed continually by lightning strikes around the world, and bounce between the earth's surface and the ionosphere. Because the ionosphere has many layers, the frequencies have differing wavelengths which translates into frequencies: 1.0 Hz, 7.83 Hz, 14 Hz, 21 Hz, 26 Hz, 33 Hz and 39 Hz.

If we completely relax in a quiet place in nature and slow our brain frequencies to the Theta range of 7.5 cycles per second, we can synchronise our consciousness with the resonating frequency of the planet and can tune into its fields and experience an expanded state of consciousness. Some people can in this state decode information carried on the planet's frequencies. Meditation is a disciplined method to slow our brain's electrical activity deliberately to suspend our thinking process by which we can develop our super sensitivity and gain access to the so-called psychic and spiritual powers.

Most of us have experienced a close friend vocalise our exact thoughts before we have had time to speak them. This connection occurs when the other person temporarily suspends their internal dialogue. Often close family members will experience simultaneous dreams and thoughts about the same subject. Recently, people who have received organ transplants, especially in the case of heart transplants, have been reporting that they experience the thoughts, feelings and emotions of the donor. The question is: Are these memories recorded in the cells of the donated organ, or is there a quantum connection from the donor's spirit to the recipient? If the former is true then the current belief system that 'the mind is contained in the brain' is inadequate. If the latter case is true and can be proved, then the current attitude to organ donations and transplants may

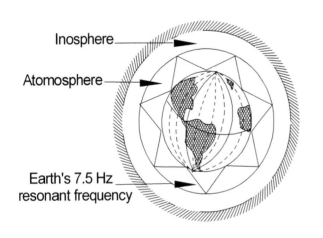

Fig. 1:19. The Earth's Atmosphere is a resonant cavity. It resonates at a frequency of 7.5 Hz, which is in the Theta brain-wave frequency range.

Inosphere

Atomosphere

Earth's 7.5 Hz resonant frequency

substantially change. Donors and their recipients may not want to be connected to each other in life or in death. The problem being that the donor has no control over what happens to their organs once they have been harvested after their death. Spiritual minded people may not want to be tied to earth by a living recipient. They may not like the idea of being trapped in some spiritual limbo land whilst being shackled for years by the thoughts, feelings and emotions of an earth-side personality.

Morphogenic field transmissions and receptions may not be limited or weakened by distance or delayed by time. For persons who are sympathetic with each other, they can be effective from one side of the earth to the other. As the distance between two or more sympathetic individuals increases, the morphogenic field energy transfer seems to increase. For people in love and who are apart the tension at times can be quite unbearable. This phenomenon exists in the behaviour of static electricity: if two metal plates that are in close proximity are charged with electricity and then are moved some distance apart, the electrical charge on them dramatically increases in voltage. This natural law is responsible for the very high voltages of the lightning of thunderstorms. Also, highly ionized hydrogen particles spewed out from the sun cause electrical current flow to the Earth. The positive charges, which are basically protons, have a relatively high mass as compared to the negatively charged electrons. These massive positive charges blast through deep space to the atmosphere and land on the Earth as electrical current.

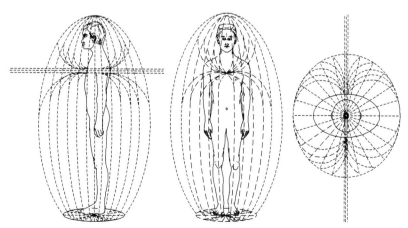

Fig. 1:20. The epicentre of the human energy field showing the Assemblage Point passing through the chest.

The Human Assemblage Point

Every living person has an oscillating energy field and scientifically and in reality all of us have an energy epicentre of this field. The human energy field epicentre is a concentrated spot of high energy that the trained person can feel or even see. The vortex or epicentre of the human energy system is called the Assemblage Point of man.

It is called the Assemblage Point because we are assembled in the womb from the umbilical cord that connects us to the placenta of our mother. The major supply of energy enters the developing foetus via the navel aperture. At the moment of birth, the Assemblage Point is positioned at the navel aperture but, with our first breaths of air, it moves upwards into the chest area. The Assemblage Point location for those of us who possess good physical and mental health is just below the thymus gland slightly to the right of the centre of the chest. For those of us who suffer from mental or physical disease, the Assemblage Point will be found in a different location.

The Assemblage Point can be thought of as like the north and south pole of earth's magnetic field. As we approach our time of death our Assemblage Point moves slowly or suddenly down towards the navel. The speed of the movement downwards depends on the reasons for us dying. If the circumstance of our death is due perhaps to old age or a terminal disease then the movement downwards may take years. On the other hand if our death is the result of a fatal accident or gunshot wound, the movement downward will be swift. As the Assemblage Point traverses the navel line our quantum energy field collapses and withdraws from the body by means of the navel aperture and death occurs instantaneously. However, as this book will demonstrate, there is another exit or aperture through which our life force or vital energy can escape when departing from our dead body.

Fig. 1:21. Albert Einstein (March 14, 1879 – April 18, 1955) was a German born theoretical physicist. He is widely regarded as one of the greatest physicists of all time. He played a leading role in formulating the special and general theories of relativity. He made significant contributions to quantum theory and statistical mechanics. While best known for the Theory of Relativity, he was awarded the 1921 Nobel Prize for Physics for his explanation of the photoelectric effect in 1905.

Fig. 1:22. Erwin Rudolf Josef Alexander Schrödinger (August 12, 1887 – January 4, 1961), an Austrian physicist, he received the Nobel Prize in 1933, for his contributions to quantum mechanics, especially the Schrödinger equation, for which In 1935 he proposed the Schrödinger's cat thought experiment.

Fig. 1:23. Louis Victor Pierre Raymond, 7th duc de Broglie, generally known as Louis de Broglie (August 15, 1892–March 19, 1987), a French physicist and Nobel Prize laureate. He received a doctorate with the thesis that put forward his theory of electron waves, based on the work of Einstein and Planck.

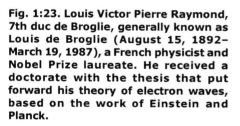

Bibliography, References And Follow-Up Reading

Notes: for more information frequencies refer to Chapter 5, for infrared frequencies see Appendix VI and VII.

Anbar, Michael. *Quantitative Telethermometry in Medical Diagnosis and Management.* CRC Press.

Andrews, C. L., PhD. *Optics of The Electromagnetic Spectrum*. Prentice-Hall Inc.

Barrel, Jean-Pierre. *Manual of Thermal Diagnosis.* Eastland Press.

Becker, Robert, MD. *The Body Electric - Electromagnetism and the Foundation of Life.* Quill, William Morror, New York.

Lederman, Leon and Dick Teresi. *The God Particle- If The Universe Is The Answer, What Is The Question?* Bantam Press.

Lilly, John C. MD. *Simulations of God - The Science of Beliefs.* Batam Books.

Iannini. Robert. *Fiberoptic, Infrared and Laser Space Age Projects*. Tab Books Inc.

Merrell-Wolf, Franklin. *Pathways Through To Space - An Experiential Journal.* Julian Press.

NASA Galaxy NGC 4414 Photograph. hhttp://upload.wikimedia.org/wikipedia/commons/c/c3/NGC_4414_%28NASA med%29.jpg

Reichenbach, Baron, Karl, Von. *The Mysterious Odic Force.* The Aquarian Press.

Sheldrake, Rupert. *The Sense of Being Stared - And Other Aspects of The Extended Mind.* Hutchinson.

Snellgrove, Brian. *The Unseen Self - Kirlian Photography Explained.* Saffron Walden.

Zohar, Danah. *The Quantum Self - A Revolutionary View of Human Nature and Consciousness Rooted in the New Physics.* Bloomsbury Publishing Ltd.

Chapter 2

EMBEZZLED HEALTH

In the time between our birth and our death a manifold of events and experiences occur. The location of our Assemblage Point and its entry angle have domineering implications not only for the quality of our living and our wealth but, more importantly, it also imposes a profound effect over our mental and physical health. Understanding and integrating the Assemblage Point information can make a significant contribution not only to our own lives but also to those with whom we interact.

Aboriginal Medicine Men

The Assemblage Point is not a recent fabrication nor a product of the New Age phenomena. It has some interesting and obscure roots that can be traced back at least several centuries. The Assemblage Point knowledge and teachings have been a closely guarded secret held by American aboriginal medicine men. Only in recent times has the knowledge begun to infiltrate into western culture. Many patented medical drugs have been derived from the herbal and mineral cures discovered and used by aboriginal medicine men and women. Drug companies are actively gathering information and samples of herbal medicines and their uses from remote aboriginal tribes around the world. They chemically extract the active principals and synthesise the drug in their laboratories. A large bulk of modern drugs owe their invention to the perceptive powers and bravery of our ancient tribal medicine men and women to 'see' and explore the plant and mineral kingdom for the health benefits of their tribal group.

Tribal medicine men and shamans can be men of outstanding character and personality. They are masters at controlling and using the power of morphogenic fields and altered states of consciousness both for medical and spiritual purposes. Their psychic powers and knowledge extend far beyond that of the average western male. Many aboriginal medicine men are specialists in the workings of the human mind and its influence on the body. Some of them have undertaken disciplined investigation and developed techniques where mind works on mind. For some American Indian medicine men the Assemblage Point, the epicentre of the human energy field, is one of the fundamental principles of their power and knowledge. Their belief systems are not in contention with atomic and quantum science.

The Shaman's Blow

The anthropologist and best-selling author Carlos Castaneda wrote ten books that sold millions of copies world wide in seventeen different languages. Castaneda, who held a PhD in anthropology from the University of California, Los Angeles, said that in the early 1960's while researching medicinal plants in Arizona, he met a Shaman that he portrayed in his books as Don Juan Matus. Later Don Juan moved to Sonora, Mexico and Castaneda followed. For more than three decades, Castaneda claimed to have been the apprentice of the Yaqui Indian sorcerer Don Juan, who said that the old sorcerers shifted their apprentices' assemblage points to move them into states of heightened, keenest, most impressionable awareness as well as to keep them in apprenticeship bondage.

Throughout this time Castaneda continued publishing books about his apprenticeship with Don Juan. In the beginning of his association Don Juan had used 'power plants' containing powerful hallucinogenic alkaloids to loosen Carlos Castaneda's Assemblage Point. Don Juan claimed that Castaneda's Assemblage Point was so stubbornly fixed that only power plants had sufficient power to shift it to another location.

The Trigger For Prevailing Illegal Drug Issues?

In his book, 'The Fire From Within', his benefactor and Shaman, Don Juan, warns Castaneda about the extreme dangers of an 'involuntary' shift of the Assemblage Point due to perhaps disease, physical exhaustion, the unwitting use of drugs, hunger, thirst, or even an emotional or physical crisis. A fact of great importance, claims Don Juan, is that it is the position of the Assemblage Point that dictates *'how we feel and how we behave'*.

Although Don Juan used powerful hallucinogenic plants to shift Castaneda's Assemblage Point, he gave Castaneda stern warnings of the dangers of uninformed use of drugs and other adverse incidents that can cause an involuntary shift. Throughout his book Castaneda records Don Juan's intimations that an involuntary or unconscious shift of the Assemblage Point can cause serious physical and mental problems, and even be life-threatening. On another occasion in his book Don Juan says that people who unwittingly shift their Assemblage Point by taking drugs can induce a feeling of numbness and cold, and have difficulty in talking and thinking, as if they were frozen from inside. Despite these warnings, the 60's burgeoning drug culture adopted Castaneda's books and work as a licence to use drugs. Don Juan clearly knew what he was talking about, but at no point throughout his books, does Castaneda demonstrate to his readers how a dropped or misaligned Assemblage Point can be corrected.

Don Juan also spoke extensively to Castaneda about the process of death and the gap at the navel. Unfortunately Castaneda does not elaborate nor provide any practical or useful scientific information that enables the reader to assimilate Don Juan's medical knowledge of the Assemblage Point. Perhaps Don Juan gave more details about the dangers to health than Castaneda has related to his readers but, considering that Castaneda's books about Don Juan and drug induced mysticism attracted millions of enthusiasts, this is extremely valuable information and it begs many questions:

1. What is the Assemblage Point?

2. What is its significance with physical and mental disease?

3. What is the essence of the extreme danger?

4. How can we check the location of our Assemblage Point?

5. How can we shift and correct its location if this is detrimental?

6. How can we gain stability of our Assemblage Point location?

Nature's Power Moderates The Human Ego

In 1945 the American military proved to the world the validity of Einstein's equation $E=MC^2$ by dropping Atomic bombs on Hiroshima and Nagasaki. A tiny amount of mass equivalent to 0.6 grammes was converted into the energy equivalent to 12,500 tons of TNT explosive. The initial explosion killed 70,000 Japanese and razed the city to the ground.

The volcanic eruption of Krakatoa off the west coast of Java, in 1883 caused an explosion the equivalent of at least 200 million tons of TNT. The resulting tsunami wave reached a height of 37 metres and killed some 36,000 people in the region. The tsunami of Christmas 2004 killed an estimated 250,000 thousand people. By contrast the pandemic outbreak of influenza in 1918 to 1919 killed more than 40 million people worldwide. Did the grief and tragedy felt by so many families in Europe after the First World War, when added to the economic privations of the post war period, reduce the position of the Assemblage Point in so many people that the communal resistance to infection dropped dramatically? Might this be one of the reasons why the influenza became a pandemic, rather than remaining a localised epidemic? If a similar outbreak was to occur in western countries today, the tragic death toll would leave countless homes and offices empty and debts unpaid. The resulting crash in the value of property and businesses would be catastrophic for the banking system and could even trigger global bankruptcy. Nature can deliver humanity an unforeseen blow that makes man's inhumanities look like child's play. These catastrophes cause millions to suffer post traumatic incident syndrome.

Such traumas always lead to a drop in the position of the Assemblage Point.

In the UK there are more than two million people with chronic depression and fatigue equivalent to 1.5 percent of our population. Over the last two centuries, despite countless billions of tax payer's money and billions of man hours of research, medical organizations around the world have not discovered the root cause, nor effective modalities of treatment for conditions such as post traumatic incident syndrome, depression, anxiety, panic, manic depression (Bipolar disorder), postnatal depression, chronic fatigue syndrome, psychotic behaviour, psychosis and the hundreds of other mental and physical conditions that torment not only those suffering but, by interdependency, millions of healthy people worldwide.

Sufferers are not able to lead normal happy productive lives, and this is a tragic waste of human potential. These diseases and conditions are enormous burdens to society, public health services, social services, tax payers, infrastructure maintenance and development, employers, insurance companies and families.

These afflictions can often follow a severe shock, traumatic incident, infection, accident, surgery, bereavement, divorce or childbirth. They can also occur soon after an incident of violence, legal or financial intimidation; rape, substance abuse or a drug overdose.

One common factor that many victims of traumatic incidents attempt to convey is that some inexplicable fundamental thing deep inside them has changed or shifted at the time of the incident. Many also report that no matter how hard they try, what medications and therapies they undertake, they are unable to return to their former health, state of mind, personality and good humour.

Medical science has neglected in asking and answering the single, most important question: Why, when following any type of traumatic incident, does the victim become mentally and physically ill? What is the 'Fundamental Principle' that changes inside a person following a traumatic incident that can cause disease?

It is quite understandable that this question has never been asked or resolved since the problem is that the 'Fundamental Principle' that changes is not a psychological, biological or a material element. It cannot be dissected by the scalpel, nor manipulated by the rational mind and it is not visible to the untrained eye. Neither does it help how much a patient nor practitioner rationalises or analyses a traumatic incident, the symptoms often do not diminish. They may with time become more serious and trigger the onset of disease. Frequently the drugs, medications, therapy, diet supplements, counselling, psychotherapy, or other management modalities prescribed by a medical professional do not correct the situation or return the patient to health.

As a result the enormous number of patients with unresolved mental and physical health problems has virtually bankrupted and paralysed the United Kingdom's National Health Service and Social Services. This is supported by the fact that some 25% of hospital beds are occupied with patients suffering with iatrogenic disease, which is disease caused by previous medications, surgery or therapies. Also, neither psychiatry nor psychology, counselling, drugs and other medication can reverse or cure diseases such as for example, myalgic encephalomyelitis, chronic fatigue syndrome or Bipolar disorder. Usually the medical treatment modalities provide only management of the patient's condition, but not a satisfactory solution.

A friend suffering from myalgic encephalomyelitis for many years administered a charitable telephone help line for patients suffering from ME and chronic fatigue, she told me:

"Over the many years I spent talking and listening to women on the telephone about myalgic encephalomyelitis and chronic fatigue, out of all of the different medicines and therapies we tried to get well, nothing worked, none of us could regain our former health and energy."

The Discovery Of The Fundamental Principle

The earliest memory of my childhood is of putting my fingers into an electric wall socket in my bedroom. All I can remember is a bright blue light - perhaps sparks- searing pain and the stench of burnt flesh. My muscular system locked rigid. I lost planetside consciousness and entered another domain. Fortunately for me, my father was home from work and he unplugged me from the 240 volt mains. Even to this day I still wear small scars on my index and second fingers.

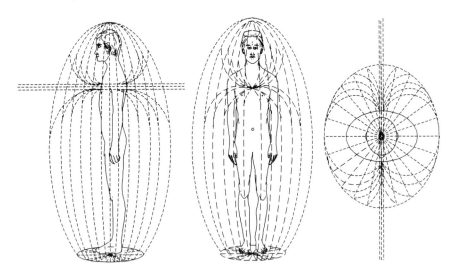

Fig. 2:1. An excellent healthy location and entry angle for the Assemblage Point.

I am, among many other interests, an electronics enthusiast, and over the years I have received more electric shocks than I can remember. They go with the territory. Some of them were severe yet they have never bothered me at all, being at times even humorous. Several decades ago I received a mild electric shock to the back of my head while experimenting with faulty battery powered electronic apparatus, supplied to me by an acquaintance. This was a mild shock of low current, but of a high voltage. The current was insufficient to cause me any actual physical damage, but it did trigger a serious health condition.

At the time I felt something in the right side of my chest shift

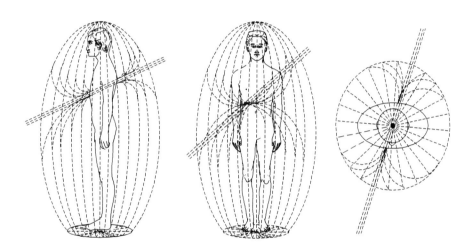

Fig. 2:2. An uncomfortable and depressive location and entry angle for the Assemblage Point.

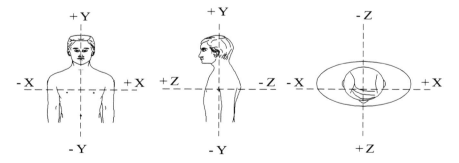

Fig. 2:3. This drawing illustrates how to plot the location of the Assemblage point on the X, Y axises, front and rear. This is essential for determining the entry and exit angles on the Z axis.

downwards into the area around the top of my liver. As the weeks passed I became ill with physical fatigue and malaise, and I watched helpless as my professional, financial, social and family life disintegrated with each passing week. I required many months to recover and during that period I was aware of a vortex of energy and pressure move upwards by degrees from my liver area. This energy vortex is the 'Fundamental Principle 'which can dislocate during a traumatic incident. This is accountable for, and associated with, the many types of mental and physical symptoms that can later manifest following a trauma.

The research that followed the discovery was exciting and intense. Now, twenty years on, mostly we now know what this energy vortex is and how it functions. We now have a comparatively accurate working map of the various locations for the dislocated energy vortex that can trigger various mental and physical symptoms that follow traumatic incidents. This 'Fundamental Principle' or the 'energy vortex ' is the human Assemblage Point.

I published a series of papers and drawings more than ten years ago (1996), after several years of research, giving explicit instructions on how to locate and shift the Assemblage Point for improving health and to increase personal performance and wealth. I had spent the previous decade (1986-96) researching and mapping the Assemblage Point locations for various mental and physical diseases and symptoms. The diagram is the original published map of the approximate Assemblage Point locations for various symptoms and states of consciousness.

(These papers were extensively published in several languages

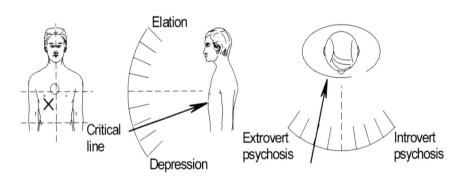

Fig. 2:4. The approximate location and entry angle of the author's Assemblage Point after the electric shock.

and later in my book entitled: 'The Catalyst of Power - The Assemblage Point of Man').

A drawing is necessary to illustrate and record the Assemblage Point location and entry angles for each individual's health problems. It must show the location on the X and Y axis and also the entry angle on the Z axis.

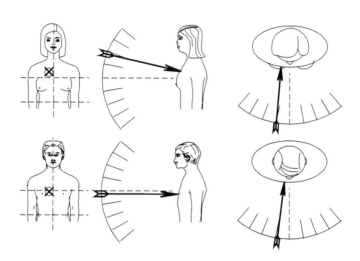

Fig. 2:5. The average location for a healthy female is slightly higher on the right side of the chest than for a healthy male.

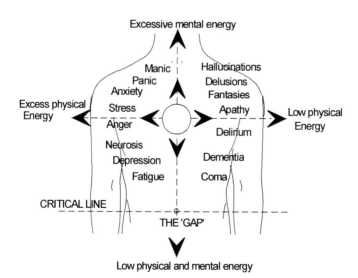

Fig. 2:6. The original published map of approximate Assemblage Point locations for numerous symptoms (1995).

45

The location of the Assemblage Point on the body is marked on the left frontal image of the drawings with a cross. It is also necessary to show the middle side view image and the right top view image on the drawing because the Assemblage Point can enter the chest and exit at the back at many possible angles on the Z axis,

Today, hundreds of doctors and professional therapists around the world have verified this map and use my original Assemblage Point diagnostic and correction procedures for the benefit of their patients and clients. Today, I have vastly improved on those original published methods and developed more efficient and subtle procedures (see Appendix I and III).

The Assemblage Point And Our Health

During my youth I would occasionally find myself in the company of a very stable person, they seemed to have something that I wanted to acquire. I paid attention to them and wanted to be like them. Unconsciously I enjoyed and indulged in their energy field but I confused my fascination with perhaps their personality, environment or their conversations. Later in life when I had integrated the knowledge of the Assemblage Point and had stabilised my own Assemblage Point location, I realised that the thing that they

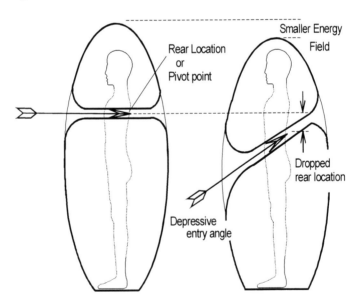

Fig. 2:7. Side view schematics illustrating a normal entry angle and a depressed entry angle and location.

possessed which I wanted was something they could never ever give me. They had no knowledge of the Assemblage Point and I often think how much better my life, and that of those close to me, would have been if they had possessed the knowledge to pass on to me.

The idea that how we behave and how we feel might be beyond our rational control is largely unbelievable to most healthy people. Such people are extremely fortunate as they have a stable, near central Assemblage Point.

This idea is acceptable and can be easily comprehended by anyone us who has experienced any of the following:

1) Serious accident, bereavement, disease, fever, tragedy, chronic stress or depression.

2) Distressed or oppressed childhood, rape or sexual assault, violent intimidation, kidnapping, abduction, enslavement.

3) Self laceration, mutilation or poisoning, attempted suicide, substance and drug, indulgence, drug overdose, mental institution.

4) Mugging, robbery, burglary, fraud, identity theft.

5) Genocide, war, terrorism, homicide, torture, post military combat trauma, imprisonment.

6) Physical or psychological intimidation, interrogation, brainwashing.

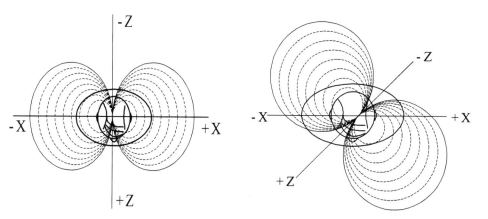

Fig. 2:8. Schematic to illustrate the cross point of the Assemblage Point on the Z axis (view: from above).

Fig. 2:9. Entry angle twisted to the right on the Z axis.

47

7) Betrayal, financial or legal intimidation, blackmail, malicious divorce, bankruptcy, redundancy, home repossession, arrest, prosecution.

Under any of these circumstances many people can undergo a serious or seemingly permanent change of their mood or even a personality change. They may also develop physical symptoms and illness. This may eventually lead to more serious disease.

Any of these incident types can and do cause an involuntary shift of the Assemblage Point to a dangerous location.

Our Assemblage Point location fixes in a healthy, stationary, near-central position at around the age of seven if we are brought up in a stable home environment and positively identify with good mother- and father-figures.

But an unstable and displaced Assemblage Point is likely if we had a consistently negative relationship with our parents or there was a background of divorce, having a single parent or having a displaced upbringing. Genetic reasons or disease can similarly produce abnormal and unstable Assemblage Points.

Sufferers of an involuntary Assemblage Point shift downwards experience that "something" deep inside them has changed. Although they can remember how they behaved and felt before the incident, returning to their former energetic and happy self is impossible for them. That indescribable "something" deep inside all of us that can suddenly shift following an adversity, changing our whole perception of reality and our physical health, is the location and entry angle of our Assemblage Point.

If the Assemblage Point drops beyond a certain distance for example, with chronic fatigue, down to or below the liver area, despite what medications or therapies are employed, it is very difficult for the individual to recover their former health and state of being. This is because, without direct intervention, their Assemblage Point is most unlikely to return to its previous healthy location. Literally the biological energy levels are too low, so preventing recovery. Raising the Assemblage Point location and angle upwards, closer to the centre of the chest, is an essential consideration in such cases. Unfortunately, accepted orthodox medical diagnostic and management procedures do not take the patient's Assemblage Point location into consideration.

Gross misalignment of the Assemblage Point location is present in many diseases such as: Depression, post natal depression, bipolar syndrome, paranoia, schizophrenia, drug and alcohol addiction, epilepsy, senile dementia, coma, Parkinsonism, toxicity, leukaemia, cancer, auto immune deficiency syndrome, myalgic encephalomyelitis, multiple sclerosis, and many others. Many of these conditions are accompanied by compromised pathology of the patient's haematology and biochemistry.

Extreme locations to the right side of the chest with an acute angle are associated with extrovert psychotic behaviour such as violence, bullying, rape, stalking, murder, terrorism or fanaticism.

Extreme locations to the left side of the chest are associated with introvert psychotic behaviour such as hallucinations, autism and downs syndrome.

High locations are accompanied by symptoms of hyperactivity, anxiety, panic, insomnia and so on, along with hyper liver/adrenal

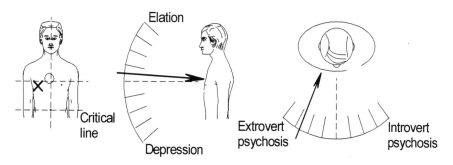

Fig. 2:10. Location and entry angle for the hypertension spectrum (extrovert psychosis, anger, violent behaviour, etc. far right side of the chest).

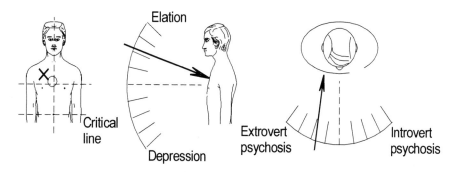

Fig. 2:11. Location and entry angle for hypertension spectrum, (the anxiety, panic, etc. high on the right side of the chest).

activity. Attention deficit hyper activity disorder (ADHD) in children is now very common and is an example of this.

Low locations are accompanied with hypoactivity, the depressive illness spectrum and hypo liver/adrenal/thyroid activity.

The bipolar disorder spectrum or manic depression is accompanied by an oscillating Assemblage Point location which

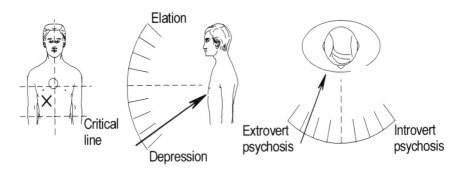

Fig. 2:12. Location and entry angle for the hypotension spectrum (depression, low on the right side of the chest).

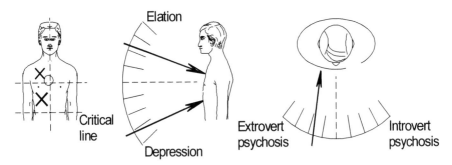

Fig. 2:13. Locations and entry angles for bipolar conditions (manic phase: high on the right side, depressive phase: low on the right side).

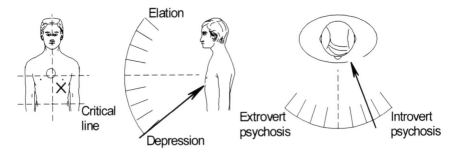

Fig. 2:14. Location and entry angle for the dementia spectrum (low on the left side of the chest).

switches between a high manic location to a low depressive position on the right side of the chest.

With the autistic spectrum the Assemblage Point will almost certainly be found on the left.

With the schizophrenic spectrum there may be several Assemblage Point locations, as often happens with the epilepsy spectrum.

The Assemblage Point has a critical relationship with our embryonic life force. A good stable physical location near the centre of the chest is essential for good mental and physical health.

The location for an average healthy woman is slightly higher than that of an average healthy man.

If, for whatever reason, the Assemblage Point shifts outside the average location, distressing physical and mental symptoms can and do frequently occur. For example, following a traumatic incident, should the Assemblage Point drop down into the liver area, then the liver will become disturbed and will not function correctly. We will feel tired, lacking energy and the body will not respond to our mental commands. This can cause clinical depression, postnatal depression and chronic fatigue syndrome. Further, the liver's blood supply is by way of the spleen via the portal circulation, and should the spleen's blood pathways become constricted or congested, perhaps because of a previous chronic infection, then the liver will not function as it should and the Assemblage Point will drop downwards.

Concerning high blood pressure: the liver demands blood and if the spleen is congested or diseased then to satisfy its needs, the liver may change the blood's chemistry in order to raise the heart rate and force more blood through the spleen.

On the other hand, should the Assemblage Point shift to the right and upper part of the chest the person will be feeling anxious and nervous and experience disturbed sleep. Here the liver and adrenals will be overactive. Manic depression is a bipolar condition where the Assemblage Point oscillates between a high location in the manic phase and a low liver location in the depressive phase.

The Assemblage Point is the unknown factor that is absent in all

51

current medical, psychological, scientific, philosophical and spiritual models.

The public's criticism of current medicines, therapies and treatment procedures can be addressed by the application of Assemblage Point diagnosis and correction procedures, especially if combined with good medical and psychological diagnostic and management procedures.

Hunger, thirst, shock, trauma, drugs, alcohol, accidents, violence, intimidation can and do cause the Assemblage Point to drop to a dangerously low location. If the Assemblage Point location is not corrected soon after the incident that was responsible for it to drop, then the victim's haematology and biochemistry can change to levels outside the normal range of that of a healthy person. This may create the conditions for serious physical and mental disease to take hold such as cancer and leukaemia. When these serious diseases occur, the Assemblage Point location becomes even further depressed towards the critical line at the umbilical region. Ironically the drugs and therapies used in treatments for these diseases often depress the patient's Assemblage Point location even further down towards the critical line. Death results when the Assemblage Point crosses the umbilical region. In the case of comatose patients on life support systems, regardless of any electroencephalogram tests, the patient will not be brain-dead until their Assemblage Point has traversed the umbilical region. It is advisable to take into consideration the location of the victim's Assemblage Point as soon as possible after the incident that caused it to drop.

With all serious diseases in their chronic phase, the patient's Assemblage Point will be found in a low location perhaps as much as 20 centimetres or more below that of a healthy person. Likewise, for those patients that have a serious physical or mental disease it is imperative for their recovery to adjust the location of their Assemblage Point back up to a location of that of a normal healthy person. This simple action will greatly help the patient's restoration of normal haematology and biochemistry levels that are essential for good health. Not only are the Assemblage Point diagnostics and correction principals applicable to mental and physical disease but, for a normal healthy person, regular correction to the central location can dramatically improve mental and physical efficiency. This helps to produce stable and efficient functioning of the liver, spleen and other organs and glands and produces a stable state of well being that is most beneficial.

Some Examples Of Approximate Assemblage Point Locations For Chronic Diseases

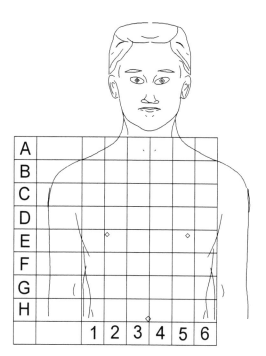

Fig. 2:15. The quadrant map for the approximate Assemblage Point frontal location for diagnosed diseases (see text). Note that the rear location must be established to determine the entry angle).

It is important to take into account the entry angle, this can only be determined by establishing the Assemblage Point location not only on the front but also on the back. Extreme high, right side, left side and low locations will have a corresponding acute entry angle.

Alzheimer's Disease	D4, D5, E4, E5
Anorexia	B2, B,3
Attention Deficit Hyperactive Disorder	B2, B3, C1, C2, D1, D2, E1, E2
Anxiety/Panic	B2, B3
Autism	B4, B5, C4, C5
Bipolar Disorders (Manic Phase)	B4, B5, C4, C5

Bipolar Disorders (Depressive Phase)	E2, E3, F2, F3, G2, G3
Cancer (s)	E1, E2, E3, F1, F2, F3, G1, G2, G3
Chronic Fatigue Syndrome	E2, E3, F2, F3, G2, G3
Clinical Depression	E2, E3, F2, F3, G2, G3
Coma	G4, G5, H4, H5
Dementia	D4, D5, E4, E5
Downs Syndrome	C4, C5, C6, E4, E5, E6
Hyper Activity	B2, B3, C1, C2, D, E1
Hypertension	B2, B3, C1, C2, D1, E1
Hypotension	E2, E3, F2, F3, G2, G3
Leukemia (s)	E3, E4, E5, F3, F4, F5
M.E. (Myalgic Encephalomyelitis)	E1, E2, E3, F1, F2, F3,
M.S. (Multiple Sclerosis	E1, E2, E3, F1, F2, F3, G1, G2, G3
Parkinson's Disease	D4, D5, E4, E5
Post Natal Depression	E2, E3, F2, F3, G2, G3
Schizophrenia:-	
a) Psychosis Extrovert Spectrum	B2, B3, C1, C2, D1, E1
b) Psychosis Introverted Spectrum	B4, B5, C4, C5, C6, E4, E5, E6

You will be able to determine the entry location of your Assemblage Point. Here is what to look for: when light to firm pressure is applied with a finger tip to the exact location of the point of entry on the chest, you will experience slight soreness, pain or discomfort and this discomfort extends deep into the body and often through to the back. The entry point and area of soreness is very small in diameter, typically only about 1.0 centimetre. If you are in good physical and psychological health, feeling and pressing with your index finger around the average location for male and female as shown on the map and diagrams, you will discover your own Assemblage Point.

(For further details see: 'Finding the Assemblage Point' in chapter 6 of this book).

For those of you who are experiencing medical and psychological problems, you will have to explore the area shown on the maps which corresponds with your symptoms.

The Seven Rules Of The Human Assemblage Point

1. At the physical, emotional, atomic and quantum levels, a human being is an independent oscillating energy field. All oscillating energy fields, by virtue of the fact that they are oscillating, must have an epicentre or vortex of the rotation. The epicentre of the human energy field is called the Assemblage Point.

2. The location and entry angle of the Assemblage Point with respect to the physical body dictates the shape and distribution of the human energy field.

3. The shape and distribution of the human energy field are directly proportional to the biological energy and activity of the organs and glands in the physical body, and to the quality of the emotional energy.

4. The biological activity of the organs and glands determines the position of the Assemblage Point, and thus the shape and distribution of biological energy throughout the physical body.

5. The location and entry angle of the Assemblage Point has a direct influence over the biological activity of all of the organs and glands including the brain and these have a direct influence on the location of the Assemblage Point.

6. The location and entry angle of the Assemblage Point regulates how we feel and behave. Disease also dictates the Assemblage Point location and entry angle.

7. The way we feel and the manner in which we behave; our state of health or disease and our ability to recover is reflected in the location and entry angle of our Assemblage Point.

Drugs Medications And Substance Dependence

A small number of readers of my previous publications opposed to drug medications concluded that I also disagree with the use of drugs. I must state here that I am not.

Pharmaceuticals are indispensable in the management of medical emergencies, accidents and the like. If you need an anaesthetic, pain killers, antibiotics, sleeping pills in the short term, then that is what you have to have.

The National Health Service, by and large, deals with emergencies very well.

My issue is the management of long-term conditions. While pharmaceuticals are gallantly offered to manage e.g. Hypertension, Rheumatoid Arthritis, Crohn's Disease, Asthma, Eczema, Depressions, Panic Attacks, Bipolar Disorder, Schizophrenia etc. etc., once you stop the drugs the condition usually comes back. So the drugs may have reduced the symptoms or risks associated with that condition, but have they significantly changed it?

The burgeoning costs of maintaining people on these medications is bankrupting the NHS and medical insurance companies.

Surely it is time for some mature studies to be carried out to assess the true value of other approaches to illness and disease management; studies which would include a thorough evaluation of techniques which shift the Assemblage Point.

In my previous publications and this one I have stated that, for many conditions, preliminary attention to the patient's Assemblage Point location contributes towards:

1. Efficient rapid economic management of a broad spectrum of health problems reducing the demand on vital medical skills and facilities.

2. Prevention of unnecessary suffering and expense for the patient and their families.

3. Elimination or a reduction of the medication requirements and surgical procedures.

4. Contribution towards the prevention of inception of serious disease and a decrease of the incidents of iatrogenic disease.

5. Decrease in dependence of alcohol, tobacco and illegal drugs, together with the associated social and economic problems.

6. Increased personal and professional satisfaction of all vocational health personnel.

7. Reduction of the incidence of civil or judicial litigation against medical services and personnel.

Fig. 6:16. Sigmund Freud (May 6, 1856 – September 23, 1939). The Austrian neurologist and the founder of the psychoanalytic school of psychology. Freud is best known for his theories of the unconscious mind, especially involving the mechanism of repression. He redefined sexual desire as a force that can be projected on a wide variety of objects.

He is commonly referred to as "the father of psychoanalysis" and his work has been tremendously influential in the popular imagination. He was responsible for popularizing such notions as the unconscious defence mechanisms, Freudian slips and dream symbolism.

Freud was an early user and proponent of cocaine as a stimulant. He wrote several articles on the antidepressant qualities of the drug. Freud felt that cocaine would work as a cure-all for many disorders and wrote a well received paper, "On Coca," explaining its virtues. He prescribed it to his friend Ernst von Fleisch Marxow to help him overcome a morphine addiction (low right side Assemblage Point Location). Freud's medical reputation became somewhat tarnished because of this early enthusiasm. Freud's friend Fleisch Marxow developed an acute case of "cocaine psychosis" as a result (high right side Assemblage Point Location).

Fig. 6:17. Carl Gustav Jung (July 26, 1875 – June 6, 1961). He developed a distinctive approach to the study of the human psyche. Through his early years working in a Swiss hospital with schizophrenic patients and collaborating with Sigmund Freud, he gained a closer look at the mysterious depths of the human unconscious.

Fascinated by what he saw, he devoted his life to the exploration of the unconscious but did not feel that experimental natural science was the best means to understand the human soul.

Many pioneering psychological concepts were originally proposed by Jung, including: The Collective Unconscious (Quantum Consciousness) which is composed of archetypes. The mechanics of the collective unconscious are essential to human society and culture. Devoting his life to the task of exploring and understanding the collective unconscious, Jung theorized that certain symbolic themes exist across all cultures, all epochs, and in every individual.

Fig. 6:18. Carlos Castaneda (December 25, 1925 – April 27, 1998). He was the author of a series of books that claimed to describe his training with a Yaqui Indian shaman named Don Juan Matus. In Castaneda's first books: 'The Teachings of Don Juan: A Yaqui Way of Knowledge (1968)', he describes the use of powerful indigenous plants, such as peyote, datura and psilocybin mushrooms to induce altered states of awareness.

He employed numerous Toltec magic rituals for shape-shifting into an animal form, and to 'shift' the Assemblage Point to gain access to other domains of consciousness.

His books sold more than 8 million copies in 17 languages and for many readers, they provided the inspiration and 'licence' to experiment with psycho-active drugs, such as mescaline, psilocybin and LSD.

Bibliography, References And Follow-Up Reading

Notes: for more information on the effect of drugs on the Assemblage Point location refer Appendix IV and for case studies Appendix I.

Anderson, Edward. *Peyote - The Divine Cactus.* Arizona Press.

Castaneda, Carlos, PhD, *The Teachings of Don Juan: A Yaqui Way of Knowledge.* The University of California Press.

Castaneda, Carlos, PhD, T*he Fire From Within.* Black Swan.

Harner, Michael, *The Way Of The Shaman.* Bantam Books.

Leary, Timothy. *The Politics of Ecstasy.* Paladin.

Lilly, John, C. Lilly MD. *The Human Biocomputer.* Abacus.

Pallister, C, J, *Haematology.* Butterworth-Heinmann.

Scults, Richard Evans. *Hofmann, Albert. Plants of the Gods. Origins of Hallucinogenic Use.* Hutchinson.

Stafford, Peter. *Psychedelics Encyclopedia.* Tarcher.

Swiftdeer Reagan, Harley, Ph.D. *Training Manual for Aura Perceptual Analysis.* Gold Horse Unlimited, USA.

Whale, Jon, Ph.D. *Core Energy - Surgery For The Electromagnetic Body.* Series of 3 articles prepared for Positive Health magazine. 1996. Website addresses:

http://www.positivehealth.com/permit/Articles/Energy%20Medicine/whale15.htm

Whale, Jon, Ph.D. *The Catalyst of Power the Assemblage Point of Man.* Second Edition. Dragon Rising Publishing. ISBN1 873483 05 8

Chapter 3

THE DEEP SELF OF PERSONALITY TYPES EXPOSED

Our personality type and the level of our emotional and psychological health are key factors that can affect the stability and location of our Assemblage Point. They are also important considerations concerning how deeply we can be affected by a traumatic incident.

Maps are aids to help us reach a destination. They are not the geography, they are not the terrain but they are still useful. This section enables us to map our personality type, and that of other people.

One useful tool is graphology, which is the analysis of handwriting. Our handwriting is a graphical representation of our psyche expressed through our nervous and muscular coordination system. It expresses our emotional, rational, intuitive and practical characteristics. A good graphologist can tell more about a person than they can know about themselves.

This is widely used in Europe for the selection of the person with the appropriate personality type for a particular vacancy in a company. Further counsel is often taken from life script bureaux to give greater depth to that selection process.

European companies also find this useful in developing the most relevant strategy for dealing with contacts or clients from outside of their company. These companies then find their employees are more contented and more productive. Such techniques are largely ignored in the UK.

The Introvert And The Extrovert

The first distinction to establish concerning the sample of handwriting or the person under examination is: Are they an introvert or extrovert personality type?

INTROVERT

- Abides within and confers with the inner realities of their mind.

- Can never become or behave like an Extrovert.

- Is vexed by an Extrovert telling them how to be or what to do in life.

- Feels vulnerable and exposed when the above happens.

- Negatively or ambivalently identified with parent(s).

- Has a greater propensity for having a misplaced, unstable Assemblage Point with a low point of entry.

EXTROVERT

- Abides in and interacts with the external world.

- Can never understand or become like an introvert, (unless he has a deep understanding of personality types, expressed with ethical considerations).

- Is vexed by the emotional, intuitive, rational necessities and good intentions of the Introvert.

- Feels held back, compromised, smothered, when the above happens.

- Positively identified with their parent(s).

- Is likely to have a central, stable Assemblage Point with a normal entry angle.

Introverts and Extroverts will forge relationships with, and are dependent on, each other. Also, whether we are an introvert or an extrovert the chances of our Assemblage Point dropping to a low, dangerous location following a traumatic incident are greatly increased if our psychological and emotional health level is already below average before that event (see Chapter 4).

For our prospects and opportunities in life, establishing whether we are an extrovert or introvert type, together with ascertaining the sub category whether we are an emotional, intuitive, practical or a rational type is profoundly important.

So the second objective is to find out if we are:

- an emotional feeling type,

- an intuitive seeing type,
- a practical handy type,
- a rational thinking type?

To illustrate these points: it would be useless to employ an introverted emotional feeling personality type in a job in charge of a team of construction workers. Yet for the building project in hand to be a remarkable edifice the insights and anxieties of an introvert type in the early design and costing stages may be desirable.

By knowing in advance our personality type and those that we associate with, we can avoid the pitfalls of living by the trials and errors of inexperience. In knowing ourselves we can understand others better and circumvent traumatic situations that are detrimental to our wellbeing, our family, business or profession.

The following is a requested handwriting report prepared for a young female with an introvert emotional feeling type personality who was experiencing problems in a relationship with an extrovert male. Her level of emotional health at the time was occupied with anxiety and appeasement with a depressed Assemblage Point entry angle.

The Introverted Artist

This is the handwriting of an artistic, creative, individualistic person and as such has a completely natural affinity to be introverted and

Fig. 3:1. The Introvert In The Tower.

depressed at times.

She is, when at her best, introspective, self aware, searching for her true self and in touch with her feelings and inner impulses. Sensitive and intuitive to both herself and others, she is tactful, discrete and respectful. She has a highly personal and individualistic way of expressing herself and can be tender and passionate. At other times she can become emotionally overwhelmed and becomes self absorbed, self conscious and shy. At this point she begins to question herself and take everything personally, feeling that she is different, an outsider and can be moody, easily hurt and emotionally vulnerable. Criticism or manipulation by extrovert insensitive types can exacerbate her situation. She can become angry with herself

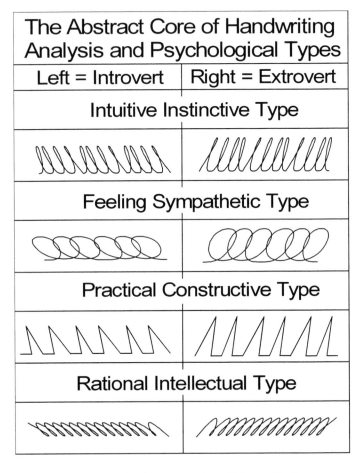

Fig. 3:2. Schematic of handwriting samples. Schematic diagram on the flip board easel.

and severely depressed with profound mental fatigue and confusion, unable to work, with a deep sense of futility and meaninglessness. The artist person when feeling worthless and hopeless is more inclined to despair and resort to abusing alcohol or drugs to escape their crushing negative self hatred that can occasionally lead to an emotional breakdown.

She negatively identified with both parents, perhaps feeling that they had abandoned or misunderstood her in some way. Due to this, in her early development, she lacked parental role models to structure her formation and was forced to create her own identities by looking inwards to her feelings and imagination. She has a basic fear of being defective or inadequate in some way and a basic desire to comprehend herself. She knows that she is a sensitive intuitive person and at the same time feels that she is different and does not really fit in. Her defensive mechanisms are introspection, displacement and turning against herself. She is envious of people that seem normal and easy-going (extrovert types). Due to her script, she unconsciously associates with personality types that seem strong and direct hoping that some how, they can compensate for her entirely imagined deficiencies, she will look to them for extrovert role models to assimilate. Strong extrovert personality associations are in her case counterproductive as they lack the knowledge and sensitivity to help her and, as previously stated, will exacerbate her psychological balance.

Out of all of the personality types, she has the greatest capacity for emotional balance and does not have to be tossed around by

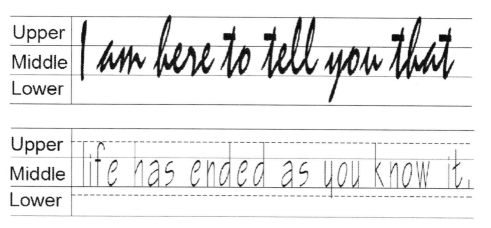

Fig. 3:3. Two Examples of handwriting occupying different zone positions.

her every feeling and can transform everything, even the negative, into something worthwhile.

The Abstract Core Of Handwriting Analysis

In the past I have conducted many training workshops and seminars about the Assemblage Point. Within a group of perhaps twenty people attending, one critical or hostile person would always be disrupting the proceedings. To prevent this, I devised a small form that everyone filled in on their arrival and this provided me with samples of their handwriting. I would open the seminar with a large diagram on the flip board easel entitled: 'The Abstract Core of Handwriting Analysis and Psychological Types'. I would then proceed with a short talk about personality types. This guaranteed that the seminar would run smoothly. This also had the benefit that everyone paid attention and if someone became disruptive or upset, I would have their handwriting to hand, enabling me to adopt a positive handling strategy for their personality type.

Personality Profiles

All personality types have their good and bad points and my comments in this section should not be taken as a moralistic stand. No two people look the same and everyone has different handwriting. What is given here concerning handwriting structures is only a general simplistic explanation, a 'map' so that you can gain an overview.

The Extrovert Intuitive Type

Handwriting: generally angles forwards, reaching high into upper zones.

- Great vision.
- Great planning.
- Gifted virtuoso
- Many interests; prodigious skills.
- Deep sense of the excellence in life.
- Reach out into the unknown, making it visible for all of us to see, use and enjoy.
- They have an active sixth sense.

- Can attain high or altered states of consciousness
- Assemblage Point location not as stable as that of the practical personality type listed below.

The Introvert Intuitive Type

Handwriting: mostly leans backwards or slopes to the left, or is embellished with backward strokes. It extends into the upper zone.

- Calming influence, people feel at ease.
- Foresight, dignity, serenity, genuine contentment.
- Can form deep relationships.
- Diplomatic, peacemakers, good counsellors, mediators, public relations negotiators.
- Assemblage Point location and entry angle can be easily affected by a traumatic incident.

The Extrovert Feeling Type

Handwriting: Generally slopes forwards, has round circles and loops that dominate the middle zone.

- Unselfish, loving, helpful, thoughtful.
- Does not expect rewards.
- Work for charities, hospitals, clinics, etc.
- Good Samaritans to the suffering or less fortunate.
- Assemblage Point and entry angle can be jolted more easily than in practical, rational types, because they are feeling, emotional types.

The Introvert Feeling Type

Handwriting: similar to the Extrovert Feeling type, except it slopes backwards and can extend further into the lower zone.

- Highly individualistic.
- Passionate.
- Can intensify reality by projecting their fantasies and inner realities onto the external world.
- Creative, Artistic, Aesthetic.

- Express deep emotions and passions through e.g. writing, composing, creating works of art.
- Their Assemblage Points are very susceptible to dramatic shifts.

The Extrovert Practical Type

Handwriting: slopes forwards, has angular and square formations, occupies the middle zone but is limited in its extensions into the upper and lower zones.

- They love challenges.
- Self starters.
- Resourceful, decisive, authoritarian.
- Make things happen, get results.
- Undemonstrative in emotions and feelings.
- High tolerance to pain and hard physical work.
- Good at construction and engineering.
- Tend to be leaders and managers.
- Lack depth of vision, feelings and emotions of the Intuitive and Feeling types.
- Unable to comprehend the distress and exhilaration that feeling and intuitive types can at times experience.
- Assemblage Point is very resilient to change.

The Introvert Practical Type

Handwriting: slopes backwards, otherwise similar to extrovert type, above.

- Good at concentrating on minute essential technical details.
- Good at design.
- Problem solvers.
- Practical
- Servicing, maintenance, repair in engineering, construction, hardware.
- Less likely to be managers or leaders. (They are introverts so would feel exposed).

- Down to earth.
- Assemblage Point location relatively stable, but more vulnerable to shift during trauma than that of the extrovert practical type.

The Extrovert Rational Type

Handwriting: small, slopes forwards, is disciplined, organised and makes economic use of the paper.

- Moderate.
- Reasonable.
- Disciplined: controlled and restrained by rational thinking.
- Logical approach to life, hence emotions and feelings are suppressed.
- Their standards can make them moralistic.
- Extrovert, so can crusade for idealistic causes.
- May even be dictatorial.
- Can become magistrates, judges, chair of committees etc.
- Assemblage point location is more vulnerable to change with trauma than the extrovert practical type, despite the regulation of their feelings and emotions by rationality.

The Introvert Rational Type

Handwriting: slopes backwards, or if forward it is characterised backward hook and lines, small, less disciplined and organised than the extrovert rational type and makes greater economic use of the paper and ink.

- Moderate and reasonable, yet somewhat nervous.
- Controlled and restrained by rational thinking.
- Logical approach to life, hence emotions and feelings are suppressed.
- Prefer sheltered situations and positions where others are in control.
- Experience difficulty in making quick decisions.
- Can be bankers, solicitors, teachers, accountants and book keepers.

- Assemblage Point is less exposed to traumatic incidents as they take sheltered and regulated positions in life.

Dangerous Locations

Hopefully from reading this you now have some useful insights about the different personality types, and their relationship with the location and entry angle of the Assemblage Point.

Basically some of the personality types, following a traumatic incident, are more vulnerable to an accidental shift of their Assemblage Point downwards to a dangerous location and entry angle. Should this occur, it should also be understood that no matter how much love, good intentions, psychological or psychiatric analysis or counselling is given to the person, it is most unlikely to correct and realign their Assemblage Point location. Paying direct attention to and correcting this Assemblage Point location can prevent a lifetime of suffering and expense, both for the sufferers and everyone associated with them.

Fig. 3:4. Louis Pasteur (December 27, 1822 – September 28, 1895) was a French microbiologist and chemist. He is best known for demonstrating how to prevent milk and wine from going sour, which came to be called pasteurization. His experiments confirmed the germ theory of disease, and he created the first vaccine for rabies. He became one of the founders of bacteriology. He made many discoveries in the field of chemistry, including the asymmetry of crystals.

His Autograph indicates that he was a Rational Type with Extrovert and Introvert characteristics.

Fig. 3:5. Heinrich Rudolf Hertz (February 22, 1857 - January 1, 1894), was the German physicist and mechanician for whom the hertz, an SI unit (Cycle Per Second, see Chapter 5), is named. In 1888, he was the first to demonstrate the existence of electromagnetic radiation by building apparatus to produce UHF radio waves.

His Autograph indicates that he was an Extrovert Intuitive Type.

Bibliography, References And Follow-Up Reading

Berne, Eric, MD. *Games People Play - The basic handbook of Transactional Analysis*. Penguin Books Ltd.

Forrest, Lynne. *The Three Faces of Victim - The Three Roles on the Drama Triangle Persecutor, Rescuer and Victim*. http://lynneforrest.com/html/the_faces_of_victim.html

Harris, Thomas A. MD. *I'm OK - You're OK -Climbing Out Of The Cellar Of Your Mind.* Pan Books

Hertz Heinrich, Rudolf. http://en.wikipedia.org/wiki/Heinrich_Rudolf_Hertz.

Palmer, Helen. *Enneagram - Understanding Yourself and Others in Your Life*. Harper Collins.

Renna, Nezos, *Graphology - the Interpretation of Handwriting.* Rider and Company Ltd.

Riso, Don, Richard, *Personality Types - Using the Enneagram for Self-Discovery*. The Aquarian Press.

Riso, Don, Richard. *The Practical Guide To Personality Types.* Aquarian Press.

Steiner, Claude, M, Ph.D. *Games Alcoholics Play.* Ballantine Books.

Wilson, Robert, Anton. *Promethus Rising.* Falcon Press, USA.

Fig. 3:6. Masks Of The Psyche
(Oil on canvas: 600 x 840 mm)

Chapter 4

SEVEN ATTRIBUTES OF POWER

When I look back to the early years of my life and the thousands of encounters with others, it is awesome to realise that a few of those people wise with years or other abilities and skills embraced the ability to see and know more in an instant about me than I knew about myself. I can still picture them as if I had a photograph. Perhaps they were sitting behind a desk at an interview, or we were around a dinner table, or listening to me on the telephone. Now when I recollect some of those encounters, I become embarrassed at my behaviour and disclosures and I reminisce at lost opportunities.

I always wondered what it was that they possessed and where they obtained their abilities. In those early years little did I know how naive I was, feeling conceited and sure of myself not knowing how ignorant I truly was. Thankfully some of them had the good grace to seek out the best in me and provide beneficial opportunities for me to rise and discover the levels of my ignorance that I am aware of today.

The Scale Of Emotional Health

The following description of the scale of emotional health is a rudimentary overview and exposure, that I know will serve as a most useful map. Individuals who inhabit the upper positive levels of emotional health can employ or drop into any level including the negative levels if required to do so. They will only stay there just as long as they need to achieve a solution. The negative levels can be chronic, i.e. long-standing. Anyone who habituates to any of them may find it arduous to find authentic help or techniques to rise to the higher, positive levels. They are often trapped in the chronic negative levels for the duration of their life. Nevertheless, using this map, many of you will be able to pinpoint your location and that of family, friends and acquaintances. With it there is no doubt

The Scale of Emotional Health 'Key Words'	
Positive +5	Serenity, Composure, Tolerance, Dominion, Confidence,
+4	Euphoria, Harmony, Triumph, Abundance, Coherence,
+3	Exhilaration, Rapture, Excitement, Vitality, Ambition
+2	Enthusiasm, Appreciation, Eagerness, Recognition, Devotion
+1	Conservatism, Preservation, Moderation, Independence, Discretion
Neutral 0.0	Indifference, Boredom, Lethargy, Passiveness,
-1	Rejection, Condemnation, Contempt, Criticism, Antagonism
-2	Anger, Aggression, Delinquency, Insurgency
-3	Covert Manipulation, Concealed Hostility, Clandestine Malevolency
-4	Anxiety, Sympathy, Appeasement, Grief, Fear
Negative -5	Apathy, Despondency, Distress, Misery, Dissolution

Fig. 4:1. Scale of Emotional Health.

that using common sense and the application of the Assemblage Point methods, you will be able to navigate your way out of the wilderness and provide positive assistance to others to find their way through. The list starts at the bottom of the ladder, the lowest level of emotional health.

Negative - 5. Apathy, Despondency, Distress, Misery, Dissolution

The lowest level of Emotional Health.

- All emotions are turned off or chemically attenuated.

- The core of antisocial behaviour.

- Many are drug addicts, alcoholics, compulsive gamblers, suicidal psychotics, vagrants, petty drug dealers and lawbreakers, failures, bankrupts, social dependants, institutionalised inmates, the minimalist, or apathetic intellectuals.

- They see no point in owning anything, run up debts which are seldom paid

- Allow property and possessions to decay.

- Feel helpless and unable to care for themselves.

- Slowly self-destruct, bringing down everyone around them.

- Rely on handouts and charity.

- Never improve, keep making the same mistakes.

- Are often actively supported and subsidised by individuals lower on the scale at – 4.

- They are fed up with life, the world and society, which are to them superficial and no longer interesting.

Negative - 4. Anxiety, Sympathy, Appeasement, Grief, Fear

- In deep fear.

- Here individuals and groups smother creativity and enthusiasm by using pseudo-kindness, leniency, sympathy and generosity.

- This creates, and fosters in others, the lowest negative

emotional level of apathy.

- They collect and help losers, the sick, down and outs or good causes for the purpose of using them to demonstrate their merciful and compassionate generosity and good intentions.

- These self-righteous strategies are used to induce feelings of guilt and shame in people of higher positive emotional levels.

- They have an overwhelming fear of hurting others and they never turn their back on anyone they deem is in need.

- They provide infinite justifications for failure, they presume nobody is all bad and always give the benefit of the doubt.

- Pampering everyone, waiting on them, doing favours for them, refusing to accept anything in return, they prevent unfortunate individuals from regaining self reliance, self worth and dignity.

- Their children are treated in exactly the same way. This results in those children wanting continual sympathetic attention and so they are always crying, screaming, fighting, or throwing tantrums to get it, never learning to entertain nor educate themselves.

- They cling to sentimentality, grief and pain to protect themselves and attract pity, sympathy and empathy.

- They constantly worry about health, accidents, crime and disasters.

- Paranoid and suspicious, nearly everything is threatening: germs, disease and criminals are just around every corner waiting to strike.

- So they never take chances and are too careful as they never know what might happen.

- Life has treated them terribly, they whine, are melancholic, dwell in the past, feel betrayed.

- Everything is painful. No money, no job and nobody loves them.

- They are afraid of hurting others and are caught in indecision.

- Show blind loyalty and compulsive agreement.

Negative - 3. Covert Manipulation, Concealed Hostility, Clandestine Malevolency

- This is probably the most populated chronic emotional level in these times.

- Problem: difficult to immediately assess that they are in this category; only time reveals this to individuals higher on the scale as their game strategy unfolds.

- Those in chronic grief and apathy (- 3 and - 4), never comprehend their strategies.

- Always present a cheerful facade, often with a nervous laugh and constant smile.

- Appear calm, pleasant and resourceful.

- Seem to be sympathetically or morally concerned in politely asking probing personal questions about you, your work, your relationships, your sex life, your politics or your religion.

- Their anger remains invisible, yet they are petrified of anyone in anger.

- Jealous and extremely dangerous.

- Cruel cowards.

- Manipulative, they engage in gossip readily but have no qualm in covertly twisting facts around, to knife into the back whenever, wherever and to whomever they can.

- When confronted, they change the subject to move away from the point and are always rewriting history or changing the truth about past events to suit their current position. They will do and say anything to avoid exposure.

- Through their appearance, word, propaganda or advertising they present themselves, their services or products as being 'so nice, so charming, so condescending and so helpful'.

- For objectives that they are too lazy or fearful to undertake themselves, they covertly manipulate and subjugate individuals at chronic -4, -5 and -2 to do their bidding and dirty work.

- Their targets are any individual, families, groups, companies or nations that they consider high on the scale (e.g.+3's; +4's etc.), attempting to bring them down to chronic appeasement, grief and apathy (- 4 and - 5 levels). They would like everyone on the planet at this level so that they can feel power.

- They have little time for children unless they can use them as an introduction or a weapon for manipulation towards their strategy of introverting others down to -3 and minus 4.

- Their unstated aim is to cause ruin, discredit achievements and split up relationships.

- At this they can be very successful and gloat when their victims go down into the lower chronic levels of - 4 and -5.

- Males at this level subconsciously know their fearful limitations. They can be slothful, but have a need to control and suppress women down to the -4 and -5 levels so that they can feel secure in their sexuality, (as also happens in males at -1 and -2).

- Males at this level occupying influential or powerful offices can instigate acts of terrorism and war.

- You cannot trust anyone at this level with your health, your money, your reputation, your safety, your husband, your wife, your children, your business, your company, your country, or this planet.

Negative - 2. Anger, Aggression, Delinquency, Insurgency

- Individuals at this chronic level are consumed with animosity and are furious.

- They dominate and intimidate others into submission and obedience.

- They blame everyone else for their problems.

- They collect grudges to justify their anger and dump them on anyone or anything that passes their way.

- They destroy property, social conveniences and lives.

- Everyone they meet is wrong or obstructing their ambitions.

- Expressing no kindness, no consideration, being blatantly dishonest and disloyal, they lie, use intimidation and ambiguity to destroy creativity and satisfaction.

- They cause sabotage by deliberately instigating situations or circumstances where others will fail; afterwards they accept no blame, excuse or explanation.

- They handle children by tyranny, sometimes with brutal punishment to force them, by means of pain, into what they want.

- Not being interested in any viewpoints unless it reinforces their position, they do not listen and continually interrupt others' discussions.

Negative - 1. Rejection, Condemnation, Contempt, Criticism, Antagonism

- Interacting with a person that habituates this level can be amusing for a short time, any longer and it can become boring or enraging.

- They enjoy, even laugh at, the misfortune of others and never play for the pleasure.

- They want to dominate every activity involving others.

- Being resentful and mocking, their subsistence depends on finding and engaging a contestant.

- Children are there for them to torment and provoke.

- They are insensitive, undiplomatic and unsporting.

- They love to argue and dispute everything and get a kick out of reducing others to acute anger and lower.

- They never listen, continually interrupt, never permitting the other person to establish their point.

- They twist facts to defend and satisfy their own reality, doing their utmost to sabotage the position of others.

Neutral 0.0. Indifference, Boredom, Lethargy, Passiveness

- They are observers being indifferent, mildly pleasant, inoffensive, purposeless and unconcerned about any issue.

- Everything is too much trouble.

- With poor concentration and no ambition, they never achieve any outstanding feat.

- Not having any purpose, being lazy and careless, neither content nor discontent, they are not particularly helpful and never intimidating.
- Like all of the lower negative levels, they want more affluence but cannot consent to own much.
- Largely unnoticed, they amble along stuck at some routine job never upsetting anyone and are accepted by most people.

Positive + 1. Conservatism, Preservation, Moderation, Independence, Discretion

- The conformist, reticent individual who considers everything with careful deliberation.
- They demand proof before believing or acting.
- They invariably take the soft, safe option to maintain contentment and rely on the authorities to protect them and do their prosecuting.
- They resist change and discourage exploration and innovation.
- They are not very tolerant of others in the chronic negative levels, insisting that laws should be made to contain them.

Positive + 2. Enthusiasm, Appreciation, Eagerness, Recognition, Devotion

- The genuinely helpful and constructive active person with good personal conviction.
- They have a quiet sense of wellbeing and look forward to the day's activities and work.
- They can express a wide range of emotions when called for.
- Although not yet a leader, not wanting to take sides, they are active people who inspire others to action.
- Are always willing to accept more responsibility towards a larger horizon.
- They like a good standard of living.
- They can spend time with the low emotional levels of people without getting depressed, compulsively sympathetic or exhausted.

Positive + 3. Exhilaration, Rapture, Excitement, Vitality, Ambition

- Charismatic personality.
- Attract people without effort.
- Loved by almost everyone.
- Can maintain a strong, sustained interest in their subjects.
- Preoccupied with involvement and creativity, they never start something and give in easily.
- They are not grasping nor greedy, but are not afraid of possessions.
- Not able to tolerate gossip or defamation.
- They expect honest facts and, if not forthcoming, they cease communication.
- They dislike generalities, insinuations and assumptions.
- Have broad spectrum and novel interests.
- They can conceive influential plans and ideas that thrust toward a better future for themselves and others.
- For them making a fortune is easy and can normally embrace abundant ambitions for survival.

Positive + 4. Euphoria, Harmony, Triumph, Abundance, Coherence

- These individuals believe and respect the rights of others.
- Honesty, affection, ethics, trustworthy, diplomatic, confidential, discrete, discriminating, communicative, are some of the credits of this level.
- They do not interfere with or damage others' lives, business or personal affairs, being more concerned about the survival and future of society and the environment.
- Always striving for higher standards for people at lower levels on the scale, they listen to others and understand them easily and can help low level people upwards, without being critical or derogatory.
- Enjoying and encouraging children to express themselves, they care for their mental and physical well being.

- They direct their interests and efforts to improve culture and set up institutions and situations for the deprived to have a better chance.

- This inspiring high level is contagious, promoting easily understood communications containing constructive solutions.

- Although they are targets to be shot at by individuals, agencies and institutions lower on the scale, they will not settle for mediocrity nor tolerate poverty.

- They accumulate more than their immediate needs.

- If they are brought down, they recover easily by finding diverse means to achieve their objectives.

Positive + 5. Serenity, Composure, Tolerance, Dominion Confidence

- This is the highest emotional level.

- The benevolent hero and champion.

- Individuals at this level are rare and priceless.

- They can look at new ideas, change viewpoints, being intuitively spontaneous, light-hearted and humorous.

- Neither modest nor egotistical, avoiding snooping and investigation.

- They know their abilities and what they are worth.

- They like themselves and do not care what others think.

- They can follow orders but under no circumstances will they compromise their ethics, but if forced to do so will fight with determination.

- Should they decide to do something it will be done and should anyone try to stop them, they do so at their own peril.

- They never hold grudges and stay on good terms with most people by reserving a magnanimous and light-hearted nature.

- They excel, having no need to control or dominate people to satisfy their own ego.

- Their enthusiasm and confidence inspires others to reach higher levels and do things for themselves.

- They possess tremendous personal power to calm worried or

troubled people and find resolutions to the world's problems.

Using The Scale Of Emotional Health

It is a simple matter to integrate the eleven emotional levels of health into your life. Make a list of people that you have known or know well. They can be relations, neighbours, colleagues, politicians, prime ministers, presidents, historical characters, TV and other media personalities, news reporters and commentators; in fact anyone that you know, living or dead. For example, many television soap operas comprise characters acting in the chronic low levels of emotional health on the scale; while the script writers of situation comedies often use characters acting in the higher levels of emotional health.

When you have made the list, compare each person's behaviour to the eleven levels of emotional health to determine their chronic or long standing emotional level.

When I first tried this exercise, I made a list of all of the people past and present who directly and indirectly participated or affected my life. I was very disheartened to discover that over seventy percent of those on my list categorised in the chronic negative levels.

Previously, I scarcely knew anyone on the scale much higher than 'chronic conservatism'. The reason for my resulting melancholy was partly due to my certainty of the rarity of people high on the scale of emotional health and the abundance of people low on the scale.

I was disappointed to discover that love and peace was not the solution. Extending these sentiments, showing others the 'pink light' only provided an invitation for individuals low on the scale, (-3, 4 &5), to gain access and manipulate my inherent good nature. Before long I would find myself in their same negative states. Along with this came the realisation that I had frittered away many years of my life in the company, and under the influence, of intensely negative people.

I have a conscience. Perhaps I was born with one. My error was to believe that everyone else also possessed a conscience. It was one of the greatest moments in my life when I realised this was not so. Suddenly I became able to expose all of the covert hostile minus threes belonging to my past, and understand where and why I went wrong.

Several years passed before I had mastered the ability to spot and prevent minus threes from introverting me, ruining my affairs and involving me in their schemes and problems.

A Graphological Profile Of A Minus Three Female

"During her early formation she positively identified with her mother or a mother figure (at - 4), who lavished attention and praise on her. She was the centre of attraction, the 'peacock' and as a child,

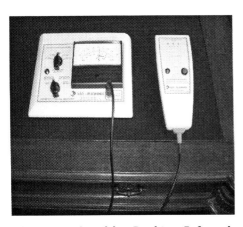

Fig. 4:2. A Sensitive Desktop Infrared Microwave Scanner & Meter .

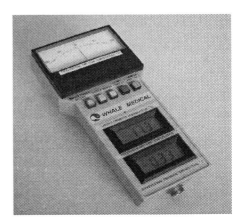

Fig. 4:3. Infrared Microwave Scanner & Meter (earlier design).

Example: due to higher biological activity in the forebrain, Intuitive Personality Type's microwave emissions are generally higher than the Emotional Feeling Types, or the Rational and Practical Types.

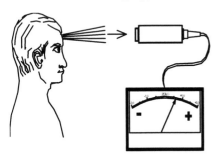

Fig. 4:4. Intuitive Personality Type (high meter reading).

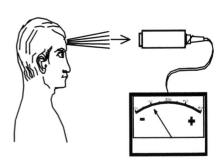

Fig. 4:5. Emotional Feeling Type, Rational Type and Practical Type (low meter reading).

with her mother's approval, had total reign.

Her early mismanaged upbringing guaranteed that she would grow up believing that 'applause' is 'love', and without an audience she feels empty inside. Her basic fear is to be rejected and she at all times demands to be accepted. She craves to be admired and to impress others, to use or do whatever she needs to stay on top, to ruin others if she cannot be superior. Her hidden complaint is: "I am a superior person and other people are jealous of me". She enjoys the feeling of triumph when she is able to put others down into ruin, as this proves her superiority to her dominated admirers (- 4's and - 5's). Unconsciously she is deluded and jealous of others higher on the scale, and is devious and duplicitous to protect her image. She needs to feel sure, at any cost, that her deceptions will not be exposed. She is vindictive, diabolically sadistic and attempts to ruin others whom she sees as superior to herself. She at all times wants to be on the centre stage and she demands that the audience applauds her and God help them if they don't.

Her unconscious temptation is to compete with others high on the scale to maintain her high self esteem and feeling of superiority. She uses simplistic overt bullying and deceptive covert strategies to achieve this. Her main goal is to surround herself with a grovelling propitiative audience. Anyone higher than doormat appeasement is her enemy. She is a sloth to self-development and personal education, lacking professional qualified status and direction. This creates a facade of charm and deceitfulness to cover up her incompetence. She never feels guilt as she will always rewrite history or blame others for the endless predicaments that she creates.

Her inevitable consequences are ego inflation (manic phase) and then rejection as everyone she interacts with will, eventually, discover that she is not the paragon she wishes to be. They will see her as a fraudulent, incompetent, empty, menacing person. This results in self- aggrandising narcissism, exploitative opportunism, malicious deception and sadistic psychopathic behaviour. This creates recurring catastrophes, (depressive phase).

In short, she is an extrovert extravagant inconsiderate type with a self assured, ambitious, narcissistic, sadistic, and psychopathic personality."

This is a true profile of a charming, mendacious and dangerous person. Once she gets her teeth into someone she can't dominate and thus wants to destroy, like a Rottweiler, she will never let go.

Males are even more dangerous. If they are in a position of power minus three's can resort to murder, even to war, to protect their reputation and estate.

Do not attempt to negotiate with them as behind your back they will twist anything that you do, say or write against you. The only safe handling strategy is to cut off all communication with them and everyone they associate with. Get every last one of them out of your circle, regardless of the losses or expense, otherwise be prepared to face ruin.

Inevitably, not a day will pass when at some point we have to interact with persons low on the scale. Developing the necessary handling strategies to prevent them from infiltrating too close gets easier with time and experience.

In the twenty-twenty vision of hindsight, if there were four subjects that I wish, with all my heart, that my school teachers could have introduced me to or even have hinted at their existence, they would be:

1. The Assemblage Point, i.e. the epicentre, the axis of rotation of the human morphogenic field.

2. A basic understanding of psychological script types and the eleven levels of emotional health.

3. An introduction to graphology and the possibility to decipher handwriting to uncover the psychological structure and the level of emotional health of others.

4. A description of the psychic attributes of the human species and the possibilities associated with them.

It has taken up the best part of my life, with years of dedicated work, research and a large proportion of my income bootstrapped at every turning point, to acquire these skills and knowledge.

If I had been in a position to possess and employ them earlier in my life, not only would I have been able to avoid many detrimental and expensive situations, but everyone with whom I have ever interacted would have benefited.

My family, friends and even my enemies would have been spared hardship, financial losses, unhappiness and health problems.

In as much that I am now familiar with them and admit that they are vast subjects with far reaching implications for humanity, I make no apologies for compressing them into this small volume as easy to read details, maps and instructions.

The Making Of An Emotional Healthy Adult

A healthy adult comprises five balanced entities:

1) a free child;

2) an adaptive child;

3) a critical parent;

4) a nurturing parent.

These four entities, when balanced and expressed correctly, make the fifth entity: a healthy balanced adult.

The early childhood formation of a healthy adult entity is illustrated by the following story:

Little John gets a new bicycle for his birthday. On his first excursion, his 'free child' decides to try and ride it down the garden steps.

His critical mother seeing this shouts to him to get off and walk the bicycle down the steps otherwise he will have an accident.

John's 'free child' rebels and goes for it, falling off in his attempt.

His nurturing father, hearing his cries rushes to his aid to attend his discomfort.

When John recovers, his 'adaptive child' decides that his mother was correct. John eventually grows up to become an emotionally healthy balanced adult high on the scale.

A remarkable adult consists of a balance between:

- a state of nurturing consciousness;
- analytical critical consciousness;
- combined with free expression;
- the determination and humour of their youthful free child;
- All moderated by their adaptive child entity.

If during their early formation, an adult develops an overt nurturing parent entity with a weak critical parent entity, then their resultant chronic emotional health level on the scale will be -3, -4 or -5.

Conversely: if during their early formation, an adult develops an overt critical parent entity with a weak nurturing parent entity, then their resultant chronic emotional health level on the scale will be -1, -2 or -3.

Parental figures with a low level of emotional health will have a dysfunctional adult entity.

Children who are raised by single, married or divorced or multiple parents low on the scale, will fail to develop properly. They are most likely to experience the consequences of an unstable Assemblage Point and can turn to using drugs, excess alcohol, casual sex, crime and the host of other traps out there to catch the naive and the emotionally vulnerable.

We all need to wake up to the fact that the emotional and mental health of our young people is in crisis.

This is almost entirely due to the disintegrating standards of ethics and behaviour of the adult population in all walks of life, including professions such as politics, medicine, law enforcement, solicitors, government agencies, defence, councils, management, business, ecclesiasts, media, entertainment, education and sports. Everyday, we hear about individuals in public service compromising themselves (and us) for hedonistic gratification, money, sex, power or applause.

Where are the heroes of today? Where are the noble and exemplary role models that our young can turn to or look up to?

The Seven Deadly Sins v. The Seven Virtues

Our emotional level of health can deteriorate for many natural occurring reasons such as bereavement over the death of a loved one, disease, intimidation or totalitarian manipulation. If prior to an incident our emotional level of health was a positive level on the scale, the chances of recovery are very good. For those of us already in a chronic negative level then the question is: what can we do to climb up the ladder to a more healthy level? What is it about the chronic low levels that sustains them? Why are there millions of people living in, and enduring, the lower levels?

If we review the levels from chronic boredom downwards to -5, we will discover that each of them contains substantial elements of 'The Seven Deadly Sins' which are: Countered by the Seven Virtues

• **Pride,**	**Prudence**
• **Envy,**	**Temperance**
• **Anger,**	**Justice**
• **Sloth,**	**Fortitude**
• **Greed,**	**Charity**
• **Gluttony,**	**Hope**
• **Lust.**	**Faith**

As old fashioned and religious as it may seem today and although there may be other good reasons, this is actually true in most situations.

What old-fashioned perspectives apply to the high positive levels? The answer is: The seven virtues. For many people, the problem today with these types of generalised religious quotations is that on their own they do not provide us an easy means to understand or improve ourselves.

And beside this, without the benefits of quantum mechanics and morphogenic fields, Darwin's theory of evolution, which is often taken out of context by not including these, has provided many people with an excuse to transgress by believing that life and its death is all there is. So why bother, lets grab what we can while living, runs the rationalisation. Why strive to live a virtuous life when I can take what I want and enjoy life without effort?

In these times, many people simply do not have the faith to apply the old methods for self development. The truth is that individuals with chronic low levels of emotional health do not enjoy life or achieve and get what they want. The reasons for this at the quantum consciousness level are easily explained.

A Map Of The Human Psyche

As mentioned earlier, human consciousness has functions that are more than just pure awareness. Human consciousness has elements or power attributes that have a potency that intrudes into and affects the material universe. Our quantum energy field endows us all with natural psychic and spiritual powers.

Evolution insists that nature's benefits will prevail. We may not be interested in believing in or developing our psychic and spiritual abilities. And why should we, if life is satisfying and we are content with our station? However, circumstances and events naturally occur that force the universal principles onto us. For example, the mortal consequences of global warming caused by human gluttony is invoking the scientific 'square law of energy' causing thermal runaway threatening all life as we know it. Should the environmental ambient temperature rise to a level and the human deep brain temperature rises from 37.5 to above 40 Celsius, everyone affected will enter a coma and could die. Due to the square law of energy, global warming is not a linear slope but a steeply rising curve. In the summer of 2003 in France, more than twenty thousand people died from this effect. The future will see many more high pressure, high temperature weather systems manifesting over large towns unless we make urgent changes.

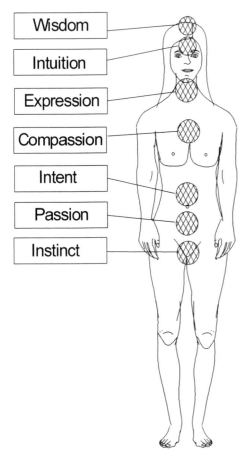

Fig. 4:6. The Physical Location for the Seven Attributes.

Many people today are desperately spending fortunes looking for methods that they can employ to improve their health and happiness. Many more are fighting, determined to raise public and government awareness. As Darwin said, the universe is evolving, we ignore it at the peril of extinction.

The abilities and variations of the human psyche seem immense and the accounts of the possibilities of experience are confusing.

For low emotional level agnostics, sceptics and critics, the ethical, psychic and spiritual domains are fertile territory for their amusement and capitalisation. It permits the promotion of their destructive propaganda for materialistic gain by encouraging demoralisation of the higher positive levels. Inasmuch as their emotional health is at -1, -2 and especially -3 on the scale, they can be ignored. If we divide down our diverse natural quantum energy abilities into a few easy comprehensible domains, we can pigeonhole the sceptics and their propaganda and free ourselves from their intimidation and transcend and enjoy the positive levels of emotional health and the rewards that these bring.

If the human psyche is condensed to the basic quantum energy functions and expressed as simple group labels or 'key words', we can then construct an understandable map. With the help of a map it is easy to understand and navigate the territory and we stand a better chance to arrive at our destination.

For this map we can use a description of seven key recognisable inherent energy attributes available to all of us. Assigning each of these attributes a specific station or plexus in the physical body makes the map easy to remember and understand. The functional energy levels of each of these attributes for any given individual can be non existent, weak, average, good or overt. The combination of an individual's seven attribute energy activity levels is directly related to their personality type.

Using a sensitive infrared microwave scanner to measure the body's microwave emissions demonstrates that individuals have higher and lower levels of biological activity according to their personality and level of emotional health. For example, in the case of the intuitive type, microwave energy levels emitted from the centre of their forehead are generally higher than in an emotional feeling type or practical type. Whereas the energy levels emitted from the chest and palms of their hands by the emotional feeling type will generally be greater than in the intuitive type, or the practical and rational types.

Energy Attribute 1, Instinct

The Instinctive energy of survival is a natural ability in all of the animal kingdom. Contemporary humans are the only exception where this energy can be weak or non existent. The survival instincts of aboriginals are of no use in western society. Western survival instincts by necessity have developed into something alien to our aboriginal origins. Our instincts now have to consist of abilities to secure money, property, transport, all types of electrical and mechanical appliances, including the know-how to operate and service them. We are forced to acquire the skills of reading and writing, mathematics, safety skills for handling chemicals and electricity, legal and banking skills, the list is endless. Males in particular have adapted well and these abilities function instinctively. In these times, the female of our species is vulnerable and is in the unenviable position of being dependent on males to substitute the energy of this attribute.

Energy Attribute 2, Passion

The energy of passion for most of us is almost unmanageable and at times defies our best efforts. It is gluttonous and devouring and yet has within it the ability to create the abundance and diversity of the myriad of life forms on this planet. Some of its qualities maybe defined as love but definitely not compassion. When functioning at its full glory it has elements of jealousy, lust, anger, gluttony, in fact all of the seven deadly sins that explode in orgasms of creativity followed by a short lived contentment. Uncontrolled or overt levels of passion extend into lustful gratification, avaricious nest building, anger, jealousy, possessiveness, material gluttony, territory accumulation, the acquisition of ego boosting symbols and tokens.

Energy Attribute 3, Intent

The energy of personal intent is uncompromising. It can only be impeded by the more gross quantum energy of universal intent (fate) that may have a greater or different objective to the individual.

Intent can be said to be willpower, but at the quantum level it is not the mental power of thought, although thinking can influence intent when it is active. It is a powerful energy that extends from the navel area and has more to do with silent concentration or fervour. Thinking, especially intellectualisation, is noisy and it disrupts and weakens intent. The power of intent arranges and provides us with everything material, the necessary coincidences and opportunities that are essential to continue with our purpose, provided that they are in harmony with cosmic intent. Otherwise overt personal intent can be self destructive.

Energy Attribute 4, Compassion

The energy of true compassion forces itself on no man. It is an eternal form of energy that patiently waits for us to take it up or ignore it as we see fit. Compassion is often confused with the binding force of the energy of passion. Compassion is true benevolence and it is not contaminated with expectations of reward or even reciprocation. Compassion is true love that flows freely. The energy can be so blissful that we, those of us who are in touch with it,

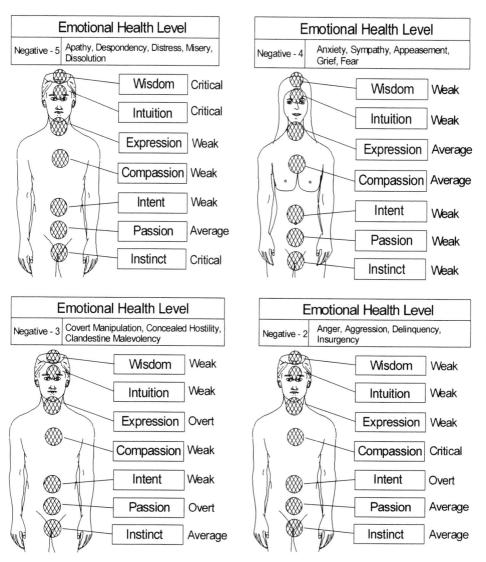

Fig. 4:7 - 10. Emotional Health and Attribute Activity Charts.

experience the most profound contentment. When compassion becomes excessive it can become destructive as it transgresses into sympathy and eventually apathy.

Energy Attribute 5, Expression

Expression is an energy that gives form to our creativity. At this level we can express ourselves, our visions, ideas, plans or expertise in the material world. Through the energy of expression, we can gather others to assist us. Human expression and creativity takes a

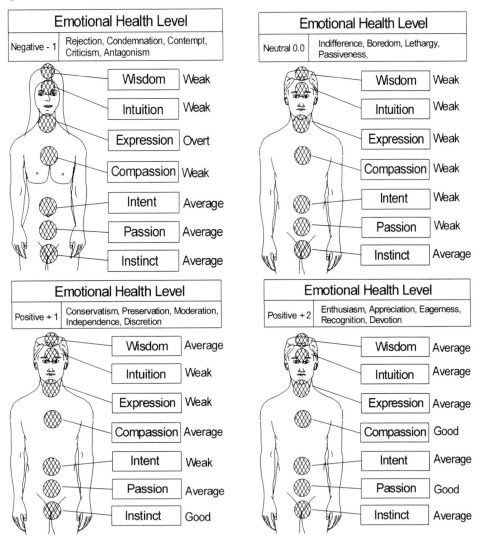

Fig. 4:11 - 14. Emotional Health and Attribute Activity Charts.

myriad of forms. It can be through art, music, gardening, construction, sports, cooking, conversation, politics, metaphysical or religious aspirations, literally anything that we do or aspire to do.

If our expression and creativity are driven by the other six energy elements of wisdom, intuition, compassion, intent, passion and instinct, the product will be an innovative masterpiece for others to appreciate.

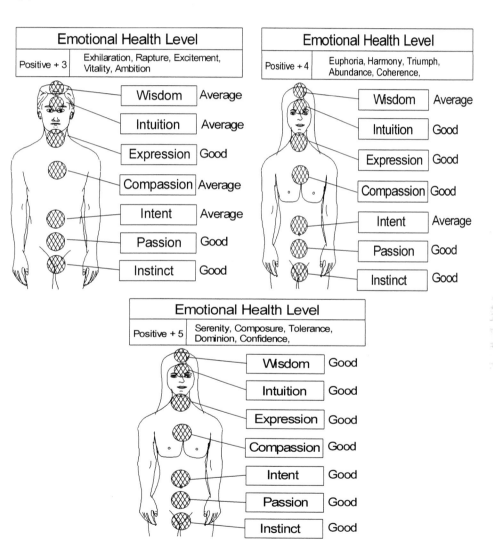

Fig. 4:15 - 17. Emotional Health and Attribute Activity Charts.

The degree of the success of our expression is dependant on the efficiency and number of other energy attributes that are functioning within us. When not controlled with wisdom, intuition and compassion, expression can easily become contaminated by the seven deadly sins. It can be very destructive, especially if driven by an overt passion-energy.

Energy Attribute 6, Intuition

The Intuition attribute is the precognitive energetic ability to tune into the quantum energy fields of wisdom and see what is concealed, what will be revealed in the future and what has been obscured in the past.

It is clarity and permits us to see and know others, their deepest thoughts and feelings and most importantly, their intent. If this attribute is active in us, it enables us to see the pitfalls and benefits of any situation and diminishes the risks of living. We can avoid stepping into costly or dangerous situations, accidents and disasters, including naturally occurring catastrophes.

Energy Attribute 7, Wisdom

The attribute of wisdom at the quantum energy field level is the ability to synchronise with universal quantum consciousness. This comprises all our individual fields and the planet's field and other domains, realities, matrixes or universes. By harmonising at this level we acquire discernment, genius and virtuosity.

Eventually, with sufficient exposure, we will arrive at the position of philosophers and sages where we acquire the state of consciousness of 'pure knowing'. This state does not depend on and should not be confused with cleverness or intellectual masteries which are actually handicaps to entering the level of pure knowledge.

Emotional Health v. Attribute Activity

If our emotional level of health declines, or for whatever reason our Assemblage Point should shift to a detrimental location, the power of our functional attributes deteriorates and we experience a decline in every aspect of our life.

Domains Of Consciousness

The following map is not a definitive list of the levels of consciousness available to us. These are the commonplace levels that all of us experience. Higher positive and lower negative levels of non-ordinary and uncommon states are available to us and these are discussed later. This map is useful as it allows us to navigate though our past experiences. We can identify and rationalise them and reduce the risks of entering into the negative levels in the future.

Accomplished Independence

This is a state of consciousness that has a profound level of professionalism and freedom about it. If we are in this state, we are absorbed and preoccupied with pleasurable and interesting activities concerning our profession, work, relationships, sports, hobbies and other physical, mental, intellectual or metaphysical endeavours. We are engaged in what we know how to do and like to do best. All of the skills and information required for what we are engaged in have been learnt and they function automatically providing a sense of freedom that permits a high degree of humour to be expressed.

We preserve this state by exercising impeccable ethical principles at all levels of interaction. Our experiences are invigorating, exhilarating, thrilling, stimulating and rewarding. The Assemblage Point location will be slightly on the right side close to, or in the centre of, the chest. When we are operating in this state, we are at the top levels on the emotional health scale at +5, +4 and +3.

This is a level that champions the highest functions of physical and mental health and we are much less likely to succumb to infections, disease or accidents. The quantum energy fields of this level ensure that we enjoy abundance and influence, also that we are in harmony with or connected to the higher levels of consciousness, (discussed later in chapter eight).

Basic Survival

At a lower level, we are engaged in learning, absorbing or teaching skills and information. We can be working on a demanding task or a project requiring the acquisition of new information and skills. The self is uncompromising about maintaining good standards but humour is less prevalent. This is because personal energy is demanded for the self discipline and the need to stick to the rules, principles and the attention to detail for the task in hand. This is often not so much an enjoyable level, but it can often be a moral and social commitment.

The Assemblage Point will be in the average male or female position or if the stress levels are high, the entry angle may bend to the right. When we are functioning in this state, we are at the intermediate levels of +2 and +1 on the scale of emotional health. When we have completed the task or absorbed the lesson, we are again free to allow our energy and consciousness to expand and allow us to withdraw from this level into levels +3 and higher.

This state is not an easy state to sustain for long periods due to a tendency to drop into the negative states of consciousness, perhaps because of the energy demands of hard work and concentration.

There is also the desire to escape up to higher states whenever possible. I do not particularly enjoy this level. When I have to pay a visit to this state, I am always reminded of the saying:

'When the going gets tough, the tough get going'.

I feel obliged to work as hard as possible so that I can exit it quickly, otherwise I may drop down into the negative levels should I become exhausted or bored.

Aggravated Conformity

This level and the next following level are lower than emotional level 0.0, the neutral level on the emotional health scale. Although very common, this is not a pleasant state to be in but many of us can spend months or even years at this level and our emotional health can be said to be chronic. Some social groups spend their entire lives at this level of consciousness.

Here we are functioning, working and living in a negative depressive state. We continue to execute our routine chores, but we are working and existing in a state of hypotension or even hypertension. We can be experiencing stress, emotional distress, fear, pain, guilt, anger, anxiety, fatigue or torment or a mixture of these. Illness and disability can trap and constrain us at this level. In my experience irritable bowel syndrome, back pain, migraine, eczema, psoriasis or gut parasites, such as H. Pylori or Giardia lamblia, just to mention a few, can restrict our freedom to higher levels.

If a person is habitually in this state, then the Assemblage Point location and entry angle will doubtless be incorrect and misaligned. It is likely to be in a low right side location or too far to the right, or too high. When we are functioning in this state, we are on the scale of emotional health at the negative levels of -1, -2 and -3.

At the quantum field level, we are more susceptible to accidents, infections and disease and insufficiency. We are more likely to mix with the wrong types of people or take their advice and perhaps get involved in circumstances that may be outside the law. Indulging in excessive alcohol or drugs is a common means to attenuate the pain and the dreariness of living at this level.

Sometimes, I think that for many people who chronically patronise this level, part of the problem is that they may feel that they do not possess skills or professional abilities and may see the Basic Survival State above as a formidable barrier or obstacle too difficult to overcome to realise higher levels.

In reality all of the positive and negative levels are the natural inheritance of humanity. There are no rules or barriers to any of the levels. Any barriers are not real, they should be seen for what they are, self limiting, third party or culturally imposed beliefs, prejudices and restrictions. Countless people who do not possess any particular skills or wealth naturally enjoy the higher levels.

Overwhelming Distress

The self is in an extremely negative state.

We are locked into our body and overwhelmed with emotional or physical pain, fatigue and malaise. The distress is at such a high level that working or concentrating on any external affairs is impossible. We are unable to attend to normal duties or daily tasks. We may be confined to bed or are housebound, requiring the support of family members and perhaps nursing staff. The pain and distress can be at such high levels that thoughts of suicide are one considered option for escape.

Disease, acute infections, accidents, bereavement, tragedy, are some of the common precursors to this state.

Fortunately as the body retains a capacity to heal itself and the mind to forget, we do not spend too much time at this level. In fact for many people who have experienced this level it has resulted in life changing consequences. The negativity and pain being so profound that it has subsequently moved them into very high levels of appreciation for life (the spring board effect of the 'dark night of the soul').

When this state is sustained for a lengthy time, the Assemblage Point may drop down into a dangerous location that should be checked. The scale of emotional health at the negative levels is -4 and -5.

The Attributes Within Relationships

The circumstances of our genetic origins, or perhaps the parental influences on our early formation, or even the standard of our education and the development of our personality, will determine the number of functioning attributes and their potency within relationships.

Relationships are the binding of individuals through complementary active and deficient quantum energy attributes. Each member compensates for the deficient or absent elements of the other. The relationship thus is more powerful and complete than its individual members.

Passion is very strong immediately following puberty, but the waning of passion as we get older allows other attributes such as intuition or compassion to develop and take precedence, and our former relationship that perhaps was based on passion may become redundant.

Not all of us are intuitive or perhaps very expressive. Others may not be compassionate or even passionate. The active attributes are limited or dependant on our chronic level of emotional health and to some degree, our psychological type is in turn dependent on the number and efficiency of functioning attributes. Women usually embody more compassion and intuition than men, whereas men are better at basic survival instincts and expression. Both complement each other. Therefore, a relationship may form. At their best, relationships can be a mutual exchange of energy, skills and needs that are beneficial to all parties. At their worst, when the emotional level of health is low, they can be a contentious dependency of coercion and extortion based on the needs and weaknesses of one or all parties.

Relationships Based On Positive Levels Of Emotional Health

Relationships where all parties are higher than the level of boredom, and the low or weak attributes of one member are complemented by the high operating attributes of another member can function very well. This spontaneous and natural occurrence will form a new quantum entity many times more effective and more powerful than the sum of the separate individuals.

At the gross material level each member is, and remains, a separate being but, at the quantum field level, things are much different. Quantum fields unite and form a new entity. The high and low attributes are compensated by the energy transmission to and from each member forming a new combined quantum field entity many times larger than each member's personal field.

Conscious knowledge of what is actually taking place at the supernatural level will permit each member to rationalise and

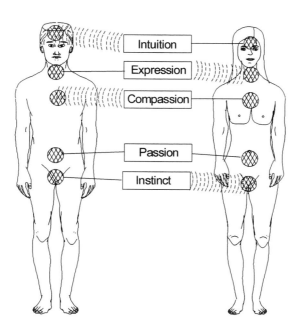

Fig. 4:18. An example of Attribute compensation within an average relationship.

harmonise contentions and tensions that can arise in the relationship from third party interference. This will amplify and accelerate the relationship development, increasing the efficiency of the new quantum entity for the benefit of everyone they come into contact with. Relationships at this level are blissful, largely occupying the positive domains of consciousness. They enjoy good health and prosperity and at the same can time attract resentment and malicious interference from people low on the emotional scale, especially in impoverished small communities.

Relationships Based On Negative Levels Of Emotional Health

Relationships that are made up of members who have a low level of emotional health are fraught with recurring problems of disharmony that cause pain and loss. When they are based entirely on physical and sexual attraction and the emotional health levels are low on the negative scale, sooner or later they are likely to disintegrate into chaos. The reason is that the individual quantum field entities are unable to unite and form a new harmonious entity.

If passion forms the main force in the early stages of the relationship and the other attributes are weak and unable to temper it, eventually the by-products of pure passion will dominate, hence the so called seven deadly sins of pride, envy, anger, sloth, greed, gluttony and lust. These are contradictory to the high attributes which function in the earth's quantum field, even if in any given individual they are weak.

Deceit, adultery or appropriation for example will be transmitted in the quantum field and even if one is discrete, it will eventually be discovered. Should a third person covet or interfere in a relationship based on passion then all parties will at the quantum level become unconsciously aware of the change and problems are guaranteed to ensue. Relationships between individuals low on the scale will experience health and financial problems. They will largely occupy the negative domains of consciousness.

Relationships Based On Negative and Positive Levels Of Emotional Health

In the case of a relationship where one party has a high level of emotional health and the second party is low on the negative scale, it may well be tolerated but will not be particularly happy or auspicious. The party high on the scale without exercising ruthless compassion may become exhausted with the problems, trivia and emotional demands of the lower negative party. At best it will be a mundane existence with less than an average level of health and accomplishment.

At the quantum energy field level the positive energy party will have to compensate for the negative party's energy levels and will be severely compromised. If the negative party is very low on the scale, then the positive party will fall into the upper negative levels of anger and criticism and may even have to resort to covert manipulation to survive.

High positive individuals compromised by a relationship with a low negative party will not be so successful in their professional activities and occupation. They certainly will have to take time out from the relationship with others at a high level to renew their confidence and serenity. This in turn will create more discontent as the individual low on the scale will feel isolated and jealous.

Diadic And Group Power

The combined power of a good functioning relationship somewhat follows the square law of Einstein's famous equation of creativity $E=MC^2$. If one partner has an individual power factor of lets say 4 and the second partner is 5, then the individual's sum is 9. But power is a square law and the true power value of a high level relationship in this case might be 4 plus 5 equals 9, then squared, so the power product of the relationship is 81.

This is the reason why individuals, relationships, companies or even countries that operate at high levels of emotional health are very successful. Yet this is the very reason why they are targets for others low on the scale of emotional health to destroy or bring down.

Over the years I thought that not everyone is all bad, that all people would respond to reason, love, compassion and discussion. I was wrong and my attitude then cost me dearly.

Some years back, when I discovered that the religious canon of love and peace was not the answer to the world's problems and when I realised that my reliance on it had caused myself and my loved ones considerable harm, I became very despondent for a while.

When life's circumstances necessitate that I have to interact with people low on the scale I am very careful about what I say or disclose. I maintain a stricture of confidentiality about my personal and business affairs and especially those of my friends. Yet I am not afraid to reprimand individuals, groups or offices where their behaviour is oppressive or unethical.

Your Interactive Emotional Level Of Health

The people that we associate with all have their emotional level of health. This will affect us to a greater or lesser degree. The consensus emotional level of health of any given individual or group depends on the quality of many factors such as: The type of newspaper and TV programs consumed, the local and national political climate, the type of environment, neighbourhood and country, the economy, employment opportunities, educational and recreational facilities.

If you make a list of people who you spend time or communicate with, place each of them on the scale and assign them a plus or minus number from - 5 through zero to + 5. Add all of those with a plus value and subtract all those with a minus value to arrive at a total. With twenty people on your list you have a maximum possible positive score of + 100 and an equivalent minimum negative score of - 100.

Any positive score value higher than zero is auspicious whereas negative values are ominous.

Should you score a negative value, it is relatively easy to improve your health wealth and happiness. When I was faced with the realisation that my average score was a negative value, I proceeded to direct my attention to those on my list with a positive score. I spent much less time and energy on those with a negative score. I was astonished how quickly my circumstances improved and at the number of new people I met that were high on the scale. By degrees, life became more enjoyable, interesting and rewarding.

Initially, I felt regret and sorrow when I avoided interaction with people low on the scale. Later I realised that for people who found their way to the more positive levels, their health, vibration rate and energy levels increased quite dramatically. The energy of people high on the scale by transmission automatically raises the level of those low on the scale. It is not necessary to act sympathetically or get involved in the dramas of people low down on the scale.

Maintaining one's own high position is generally more constructive and beneficial for everyone around.

Unified fields can be fragmented by interfering people low on the scale. The troubles of the world today can mostly be attributed to the prevalence of the seven deadly sins and the accompanying low levels of emotional health. From this perspective it is advisable that persons high on the scale make available the knowledge and means for those who are low on the scale to transcend their station.

The maps in this book can be used towards providing one avenue towards solving the problems generated by low levels of emotional health.

Emotional Levels Of Health And Assemblage Point Locations

Following any traumatic incident even a person with a high level of emotional and physical health can experience an excursion down to the lower negative levels. Recovery back to the higher levels will occur with the passing of time, provided that the individual's Assemblage Point has not shifted too far towards a detrimental location because of the trauma,

If the trauma or illness is sufficiently intense leading to chronic levels of negativity, the Assemblage Point may have shifted to a location that is beyond self recovery. In these cases, direct correction of the location and entry angle of the Assemblage Point will greatly assist in the rehabilitation process.

Bibliography, References And Follow-Up Reading

Castaneda, Carlos, PhD, *The Power of Silence - Further Lessons of Don Juan.* Black Swan.

Berne, Eric, MD. *Games People Play - The basic handbook of Transactional Analysis.* Penguin Books Ltd.

Brunton, Paul, Dr. *The Wisdom Of the Overself.* Rider.

Brunton, Paul, Dr. *The Inner Reality.* Rider.

Brunton, Paul, Dr. *The Spiritual Crisis of Man.* Rider.

Forrest, Lynne. *The Three Faces of Victim - The Three Roles on the Drama Triangle Persecutor, Rescuer and Victim.* http://lynneforrest.com/html/the_faces_of_victim.html

Harris, Thomas A. MD. *I'm OK - You're OK -Climbing Out Of The Cellar Of Your Mind.* Pan Books

Korda, Michael. *Power - How to Get It, How to Use It.* Coronet Books.

Lilly, John, C. Lilly MD. *The Centre of the Cyclone.* Calder and Boyars.

Lilly, John, C. Lilly MD & Lilly, Antonietta. *The Diadic Cyclone - The Autobiography of a Couple.* Paladin.

Minshull, Ruth. *How To Chose Your People.* 1972.

Sheldrake, Rupert, *The Sense of Being Stared - And Other Aspects of The Extended Mind.* Hutchinson.

Steiner, Claude, M, Ph.D. *Games Alcoholics Play.* Ballantine Books.

Swiftdeer Reagan, Harley, Ph.D. *Training Manual for Aura Perceptual Analysis.* Gold Horse Unlimited., USA.

Wilson, Robert, Anton. *Promethus Rising.* Falcon Press, USA.

Zohar, Danah. *The Quantum Self – A revolutionary View of Human Nature and Consciousness Rooted in the New Physics.* Bloomsbury Publishing Ltd.

Chapter 5

Bioelectric Man

Electromagnetism is at the foundation of life so it is wise to know something about frequencies and the oscillating currents that pervade our physical body.

In 1994, I compiled a manuscript entitled: 'The Frequency of Health'. It occurred to me that many of you may not have had the opportunity or the electronic apparatus to study the invisible universe. This is made up of countless bands of electromagnetic frequencies, some of which can be beneficial for our health and others that can adversely affect our bioelectric selves. So this chapter is a brief summary.

Frequencies are calibrated as the number of vibrations or oscillations that occur in the time of one second. The electronic and scientific profession abbreviate cycles per second to Hertz, normally written as Hz. Frequencies are also calibrated by the length of the wave in units of metres for a single cycle or wave.

Sound Pressure Waves

The range of notes on a piano keyboard is from 27.5 Hz to 4186 Hz.

Middle C is the centre note on a standard keyboard and its frequency is 261.6 Hz. The standard pitch for A being above middle C and has a frequency of 440 Hz. Raising the pitch of a note is equivalent to doubling the frequency for each complete octave.

The Musical Frequency Spectrum

Although it has some electromagnetic properties, sound is not a true electromagnetic wave. It is a pressure wave that travels in solids, liquids or gases. The wave travels by pressing on one atom or molecule to the next. Sound travels at a speed of 332 metres per second in air at sea level. Therefore the musical note A has 27.5 cycles per second (Hz), and a single cycle has a length of 12.07 metres. This derived by dividing the speed of sound in one second by the number of cycles in each second (332 metres ÷ 27.5 Hz = 12.07 metres). The higher the frequency, the shorter the wave length.

Analogous with the colours of the rainbow and the major visible planets, there are seven notes in each octave, the eighth being the beginning of the next octave. Further, the human frequency hearing

A= 27.5	A=55.0	A=110.0	A=220.0	A=440.0
B=30.9	B=61.7	B=123.5	B=246.9	B=493.9
C=32.7	C=65.4	C=130.8	C=261.6	C=523.3
D=36.7	D=73.4	D=146.8	D=293.7	D=587.3
E=41.2	E=82.4	E=164.8	E=329.6	E=659.2
F=43.7	F=87.3	F=174.6	F=349.2	F=698.5
G=49.0	G=98.0	G=196.0	G=392.0	G=784.0

A=880.0	A=1760.0	A=3520.0
B=987.8	B=1975.5	B=3951.1
C=1046.5	C=2093.0	C=4186.0
D=1174.0	D=2344.3	
E=1318.5	E=2637.0	
F=1396.9	F=2793.8	
G=1568.0	G=3136.0	

Fig. 5:1 - 2. The frequencies of the Music Scale.

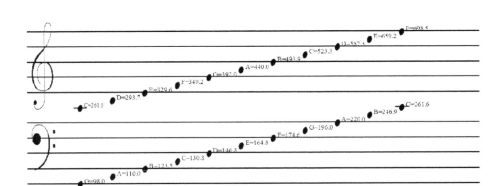

range so far as music is concerned comprises seven octaves.

Electromagnetic waves cannot be seen or heard. Electromagnetic waves travel a million times faster than sound waves. Their speed is 300,000 kilometres per second (186,000 miles per second). Electromagnetic wave lengths are calculated by dividing the frequency into the speed of light. Old fashioned radio sets were fitted with calibrated tuning dials that often displayed the frequency along with the wavelength. The United Kingdom's BBC Radio 4 station transmits on the long wave band at 198 kilohertz or a wave length of 1500 metres. As another example, the frequency of 3 mega hertz has a wave length of 100 metres (300,000 kilometres ÷ 3,000,000 Hz = 0.1 kilometres or 100 metres).

The frequency of visible light is incredibly fast, for example, blue is 618 billion cycles per second with an extremely small wave length of 485 thousand millionths of a metre in length or 485 nanometres.

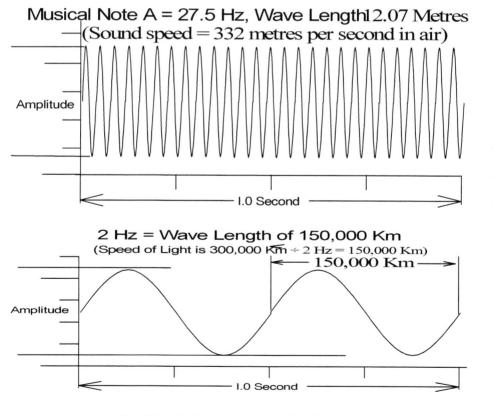

Fig. 5:3 - 4. Frequency example schematics.

Normally the frequency of blue would be written as 6.18 x 10 14 Hz and its wave length as 485 nanometres (nm).

Low frequency sound waves or base notes are inclined to penetrate and pass through solid structures. High frequency and ultra sound waves are inclined to bounce off, or are deflected by, solid structures. The same is true for electromagnetic waves. Low frequency radio waves will easily pass through most solid structures but high radar frequencies tend to bounce off solid surfaces. Higher frequencies than light such as X-rays and gamma waves have such a small wavelength that they can pass between the electrons orbits of most types of atoms. The wavelengths of gamma rays and neutron bombardment are so small that they can disrupt the nucleus of atoms and are dangerous to life.

Another important factor concerning sound and electromagnetic waves is their amplitude or power. The higher the amplitude the further they will propagate and the more harmful they can be. If we receive an electric shock from the European Mains with a voltage of 240 volts, it is much more dangerous than an electric shock from 110 volts American Mains. The European mains are far more likely to be lethal compared with the USA. Generally speaking the higher the transmission frequency and the amplitude of electromagnetic waves, the more potential they possess for causing harm to living organisms.

Microamps Of Consciousness

The human body functions on an incalculable number of frequencies

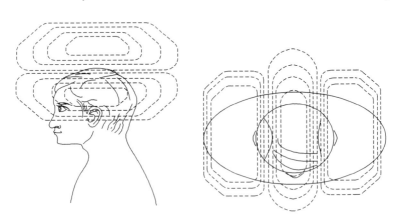

Fig. 5:5. The Brain's Electromagnetic Field.

throughout the brain and the nervous system. Minute pulses of electrical current travel from cell to cell within the brain and throughout the nervous system, so creating very weak electromagnetic fields. The voltages of these electrical currents are also very small being typically around 5 thousandths of a volt (5 millivolts). The currents are also small being only measured in millionths of an ampere (microamps).

As our nervous system depends on such tiny electrical signals, we are very susceptible to the influences of the very powerful natural and man made electromagnetic and electrostatic energy fields that pervade every area of this planet.

Scientific researchers using electroencephalographs to monitor

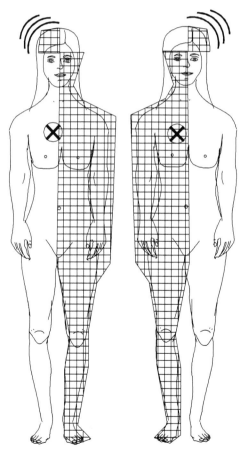

and record the electrical activities of the human brain have shown that the left and right sides of the human brain are associated with distinctly different behavioural functions.

The left brain activities are thought to be: logical thinking and extrovert pursuits.

The right brain's activities are associated with emotional feelings and introvert spatial conceptions.

Medical researchers have not been able adequately to explain the reasons for the distinctly different functions of each half of our brain. However, if we take a larger overview of the human body and include in this overview the electrical and chemical activities associated with each side of the body, then the reasons become more evident.

Fig. 5:6. The right side of the brain controls the left side of the body and the left brain the right side of the body.

Injuries to the left side of the brain affect the muscular

coordination of the right side of the body. Similarly injuries to the right side of the brain affect the left side of the body. If the left side of the brain is damaged by a blood clot or internal bleeding, resulting from a stroke or head injury, the right side of the body can become paralysed.

The left brain controls the right side of the body and the liver is largely on the right side of an adult's body. The spleen is on the left side of the body, which relates to the right side of the brain. The liver has many important functions and its healthy activity is essential for life. One of its major functions is to keep a steady concentration of glucose in the blood to replace what is consumed as fuel. The brain retains no stores of glucose and we will fall unconscious, should supplies from the liver cease.

As all stressful or intimidating situations place a heavy demand for glucose on the liver, and the liver is on the right side of the body, the situation maybe reflected in the left brain's electrical activity. Excessive electrical energy in the left side of the brain has for some years now been scientifically associated with stress. Accompanying stress is raised blood pressure, increased heart rate and muscle tension, with increased levels of adrenaline in the blood. Stressful situations prepare the body for the extrovert activities of "fight" or "flight".

Intimidation and stress unbalance the chemical and electrical functions in the body and brain. This imbalance bends the angle of the Z axis of the Assemblage Point to the right side of the body

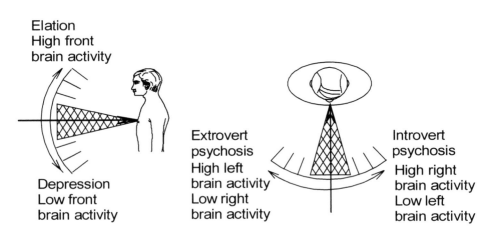

Fig. 5:7. How changes in the Z axis angle increase and decrease brain activity.

reflecting the increased electrical activity in the left brain and liver. Almost everyone who experiences a serious stressful or intimidating incident will take several days to recover. In the case where the Assemblage Point location is moved to the right, it may take months to return to normal. In extreme cases, the person experiences post traumatic shock syndrome and may never recover their original Assemblage Point location or their original mental composure.

Assemblage Point location affects the left and right brain energy levels and the brain's predominant operating frequencies. A person's state of health and consciousness is directly related to their brain frequencies and the location of their Assemblage Point. The brain frequencies of panic are very much faster than sleep.

With low brain glucose levels, we will fall asleep or can even enter a coma, when the brain's electrical activity reduces sharply and brain frequencies slow down. The liver provides the brain with glucose, therefore chronic high liver/adrenal activity will be accompanied with high electrical activity and high brain frequencies with a high Assemblage Point location and symptoms such as insomnia and anxiety.

There is a direct correlation between chronic brain frequencies and the location and entry-angle of our Assemblage Point. Therefore, our brainwave frequencies also partly determine how we feel and behave, just as the location of our Assemblage Point can affect chronic brain frequencies and their related states of consciousness. The two are intrinsic.

The Psychology Of Brain Frequencies

When I was at school, I constructed a brain wave monitoring helmet from strips of sheet aluminium that I shaped to fit my head. The strips of aluminium that made up the circular and cross braces of the helmet were fitted with several spring loaded electrical contacts. When it was placed on my head, these contacts pressed on several points of my head including the temple areas. The contacts were constructed from small copper coins and springs from ball point pens. An aluminium box containing electronic circuitry, and a battery together with several control knobs was screwed to the top of the helmet. It was fitted with a germanium transistor amplifier that powered a pair of ex-government surplus second world war headphones. The spring load contacts were padded with medical gauze soaked in isotonic salt water. The electronic circuitry of the apparatus was arranged so that the micro-volt brain frequencies picked up by the contacts were amplified and used to modulate a white noise generator that was fed into the earphones. This was a biofeedback instrument.

When I first placed it on my head, I was amazed to hear my own brain frequencies. With practice I could slow my post puberty excited Beta brain wave frequencies and enter the slower Alpha and Theta states of consciousness. This brainwave helmet was extremely popular at school and, for a short time, I was considered an eccentric star. Eventually it was confiscated and the teacher sent it to the cellar for destruction in the school coal furnace. I considered it a waste of transistors as they were expensive and difficult to come by in those days (1960's).

Brain frequencies and their related states of consciousness have been extensively researched and established by scientists.

High brain frequencies cause increases in:

- the stress response,
- the heart rate and blood pressure,
- blood flow to muscles,
- muscle tension,
- oxygen consumption,
- cortisone and glucose production.
- They reduce blood flow to the skin and organs.

Whereas low brain frequencies induce reduction in:

- heart rate, blood pressure,
- blood flow to muscles,
- muscles tension,
- oxygen consumption,
- cortisone and glucose production.
- They increase blood flow to the skin and organs.
- They increase relaxation,

Researchers have used electronic recording instruments called an electroencephalogram or EEG machines to monitor the subjects'

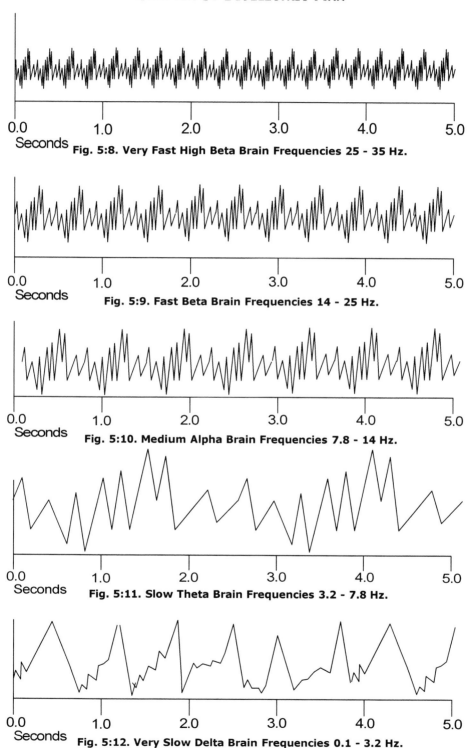

Seconds Fig. 5:8. Very Fast High Beta Brain Frequencies 25 - 35 Hz.

Seconds Fig. 5:9. Fast Beta Brain Frequencies 14 - 25 Hz.

Seconds Fig. 5:10. Medium Alpha Brain Frequencies 7.8 - 14 Hz.

Seconds Fig. 5:11. Slow Theta Brain Frequencies 3.2 - 7.8 Hz.

Seconds Fig. 5:12. Very Slow Delta Brain Frequencies 0.1 - 3.2 Hz.

113

brainwave activities and frequencies. The electroencephalogram is connected to numerous points around the skull with electrodes. These electrodes are connected to the recorder by wires in much the same way as a doctor's electrocardiogram or ECG monitor is used to monitor the electrical signals of the heart. These researchers established that:

The Left brain

- Increased activity with mental tasks e.g. Maths, Sitting Exams, Worrying,
- Produced much higher frequencies at these times.

The Right Brain:

- Increased activity with e.g. Arts or music.
- Produced lower frequencies with these activities.

In sleep the frequencies throughout the brain are very slow. While dreaming, the frequencies are midway between sleep and being relaxed.

Future researchers will confirm the following commentaries concerning the location of the Assemblage Point and the related predominant or chronic brain operating frequencies.

High Beta Brain Frequencies

Frequency:	Above 25 cycles per second.
Expressions:	Hyperactive, Hypertensive, Anxiety, Panic, Anger, Rage, Psychosis.
Thus:	Dangerous to self and others.
Needs:	To be calmed down to the lower Beta or Alpha range.
Otherwise:	May cause permanent physical damage, for example to the heart muscles in the long term.

Beta Brain Frequencies

Frequency:	14-25 cycles per second.

Expressions: the attention of the self is focused on external affairs and extrovert activities.

In Higher Beta: Behaviour less controlled. Tendency to Hyperactivity and H y p e r t e n s i o n. Benefits of rational thinking attenuated. Introvert awareness guidance reduced.

Alpha Brain Frequencies

Frequency: 7.8-14 cycles per second.

Expressions: Self and attention focus both externally and internally.

Lower frequencies: 7.8 cycles per second are conducive to introvert skills.

Thus: Meditation, telepathy, intuitive awareness and the spiritual states of consciousness. Can lower the stressful High Beta waves.

Higher Alpha: Up to 14 cycles per second.

Expressions: Effective and relaxed interaction with others. Our extrovert activities are controlled by introvert thinking.

Theta Brain Frequencies

Frequency: 3.2-7.8 cycles per second

Expressions: Dreaming, three-dimensional spatial visions. Gateway to higher states of consciousness. Trance, self hypnosis, subliminal super learning, astral and time travel, lucid dreaming, channelling, clairvoyance.

[**N.B.** 7.83 Hz is the resonant frequency of the Earth's atmospheric cavity].

Hypnosis induces Theta states of consciousness. Then:

a) The brain is susceptible to the suggestions of the hypnotherapist.

b) Emotional and physical pain are substantially reduced.

c) One may feel that the body has disappeared, i.e. one has left the constraints of the physical body to have an 'out of the body' experience or move into an astral plane of consciousness.

The shamanic traditional method to enter trance Theta states is to use drums and rattles at around 210 beats per minute, equivalent to 3.5 Hz. The low frequencies of the drum induces the trance state, while the much higher rhythmic frequency of the rattles maintains a state of heightened alertness. When the shaman enters his trance, he drops to the floor and then is able to communicate with the spirit worlds.

Delta Brain Frequencies

Frequency:	0.1 and 3.2 cycles per second.
Expressions:	Conscious, but aware of being profoundly asleep.
Around 3 Hz:	Less conscious of sleeping, maybe aware of dreaming.
Expressions:	Unconsciousness, deep sleep, anaesthesia, coma,
Thus:	Absence of feelings or pain, yet we can somehow remember having a good night's sleep.

[**N.B.** The state of unconsciousness is the condition of consciousness observing sleep].

Earth's Electromagnetic Frequencies Influence Brain Frequencies

Schumann Frequencies are generated by the millions of lightning strikes that occur around the world each day. Lightning strikes are pulses of extremely high voltage and amperage that contain many different frequencies. These Frequencies bounce between the earth's surface and the ionosphere. As the ionosphere has many layers, the multitude of frequencies are filtered by the Earth's natural resonance into frequency bands of 1 Hz, 7.83 Hz, 14 Hz, 21 Hz, 26 Hz, 33 Hz and 39 Hz. These seven bands of natural atmospheric resonant frequencies correspond to brain frequencies and our mental state.

1) 1 Hz. = 300,000,000. Metres wavelength = Delta brain frequencies = Sleep.

2) 7.83 Hz. 38,314,176 Metres wavelength = Theta brain frequencies = Dreaming and trance.

3) 14 Hz. = 21,428,571 Metres wavelength = Alpha brain frequencies = Relaxed easy-going.

4) 21 Hz. = 14,285,714 Metres wavelength = Beta brain frequencies = Alertness.

5) 26 Hz. = 11,538,461 Metres wavelength = High Beta brain frequencies = Stress.

6) 32 Hz. = 9,375,000 Metres wavelength = Very high Beta brain frequencies = Hyperactivity and agitation.

7) 39 Hz. = 7,692,307.692 Metres wavelength = Exceedingly high Beta brain frequencies = Hypertension and Psychosis.

The Earth behaves like an enormous electrical circuit, ionized hydrogen particles venting out from the sun cause electrical current flow to the Earth. The ionosphere, atmosphere, land and the sea are profoundly affected by the sun, moon and the seven major planets. Movements of the moon and planets, solar storms all influence the intensity of the Schumann Frequencies of any given band and will influence and modulate our brain frequencies and therefore the way we feel and behave. Just as the moon influences menstruation and the mood of females (and males by partnership), so the movements and positions of the major planets also play their role.

Planetary Orbits Affect Our Brain Frequencies And Assemblage Point Locations

Mental and physical human behaviour is disturbed by gravitational tension caused by the orbits of the moon and planets, as well as by solar eruptions. This is unfortunate for the average person. The greater this tension, the higher the dominant frequency, the more agitated and angry we can feel. Human behaviour, being what it is, blames anyone and anything for causing our internal state and our discomfort.

Man-made environmental pollution and climate warming exacerbate the global tension. This causes more lightning, hurricanes and tornados, with a proportional increase in hysterical and violent human behaviour. Those living closest to the equator in arid environments will be affected the most. With the current increase in global warming and environmental pollution, the future prospects for world peace look foreboding.

Maintaining a central Assemblage Point location together with a high level of emotional health will minimise the influences of planetary tension, pollution and climate change on human misconduct and fate.

Bioelectronics And The Assemblage Point

The body's network of nerves transmits modulations of the brain frequencies to every part of the body. When the mind is stressed or relaxed, the physical body follows in sympathy. The nervous system is a finely tuned feedback loop system. In situations where the physical body is stressed by illness or injury then the brain frequencies will mirror the body's condition and we experience a corresponding mental and emotional discomfort. Conversely, when we are experiencing favourable brain frequency activity, we will also experience the corresponding pleasurable physical and emotional feelings. Either way, the energy at the atomic and quantum levels are modulated with the brain frequencies, or the atomic and quantum energy is modulating the brain frequencies. In turn the frequencies that permeate our body will modulate our energy field transmissions, the axis of rotation of which is the Assemblage Point.

The location of the Assemblage Point affects the predominant brain frequencies and at the same time, the predominant brain frequencies will influence the location of the Assemblage Point.

Assemblage Point Locations

1. On the Right side of the body, the locations are associated with:

- Discomfort and distress.
- An increase in left brain activity and Beta brain frequencies.
- Extrovert attention and compulsive activities.

- Higher blood pressure, heart rate and adrenaline levels,
- Excessive physical and nervous energy.

2. On the Left body side, the locations are associated with:

- Relaxation and comfort,
- An increase in right brain activity and Theta brain frequencies,
- A preoccupation with introvert attention,
- Lower blood pressure, heart rate and increased levels of endorphins, (the body's natural pain killer).
- Little or no physical activity.

3. Central locations are very beneficial for:

- Health,
- Professional, personal and social development.
- Inducing balanced brain and bodily activities and Alpha brain frequencies.
- Relaxed and balanced internal and external attention.
- Normal blood pressure, heart rate and balanced bodily functions.

4. Low locations and depressed Z axis entry angles are very dangerous to health. They induce and are associated with:

- Low frontal and upper brain energy,
- Chronic low Alpha and Theta brain frequencies. This state can cause overcompensation with periodic high beta frequency activity that can result in behaviour associated with the hypertension spectrum (anger, anxiety, panic, etc.).

5. Low on the Right side is associated with:

- physical and mental depression.

6. Low on the left side is associated with:

- Catatonia,
- Coma
- Low blood pressure and heart rate,
- Low muscle tension.

7. High on the right side with right side Z axis entry angles

(depressed, neutral or elevated) are dangerous to health and society.

- They reflect in an increase in frontal and left brain energy,
- Excessively high Beta brain frequencies.
- Induce extrovert psychotic behaviour with increased left brain activity.

Persons who have this location can be dangerous and unpredictable. They will do literally anything to relieve their situation - acts of violence, murder, rape, road rage or substance abuse.

8. When it is high on the far left:

- Introvert psychotic behaviour,
- Increased right brain activity.

The Assemblage Point Location and its angle of alignment affect the state of the patient's consciousness and the way their internal organs function. Where pathological disease or damage is not involved, manually shifting the Assemblage Point is the fast way back to high biological energy, improved mental and physical health and normality. Realignment should be done as soon as possible after the incident that caused the misalignment. This reduces the possibility of physical damage and disease developing from any long term imbalances in the biological energy distribution.

Even with patients who have been sick for a long time, realignment can make a significant contribution to their recovery, even if disease or physical damage is prevailing. But in these cases the realignment has to be done by non-manual means, e.g. electronic gem therapy, (for further details please see Appendix I & III). Where detrimental Assemblage Point locations are associated with, or are perhaps due to the presence of, or previous chronic exposure to, electromagnetic and electrostatic fields, environmental pollution, toxins in the patient's body; or there is physical damage, infection or malfunctions of one or more of the body's organs, these problems should be addressed along with paying attention to and correcting the Assemblage Point.

Bibliography, References And Follow-Up Reading

Becker, Robert, MD, *Cross Currents - The Perils of Electropollution - The Promise of Electromedicine.* Jeremy P. Tarcher Inc.

Godwin, Joscelyn, Prof. *Cosmic Music -Musical Keys to the Interpretation of Reality.* Inner Traditions.

Hutchinson, Michael. *Megabrain New Tools and Techniques for Brain Growth and Mind Expansion.* Beech Tree Books.

Blundell, Geoffrey. *The Meaning of EEG (Electroencephalograph).* Audio.

Harner, Michael, *The Way Of The Shaman.* Bantam Books.

Fig. 5:13. Count Alessandro Giuseppe Antonio Anastasio Volta (February 18, 1745 - March 5, 1827). He was an Italian physicist known especially for the development of the electric battery in 1800. In 1800, as the result of a professional disagreement over the galvanic response advocated by Luigi Galvani, he developed the so called voltaic pile (battery) which produced a steady electric current. Volta demonstrating his battery to Napoleon in 1801. In honour of his work in the field of electricity, Napoleon made him a count in 1810. In 1815 the Emperor of Austria named him a professor of philosophy at Padova. The SI unit of electromotive force, the Volt was named after him.

Fig. 5:14. Joseph Henry (December 17, 1797 – May 13, 1878) was a Scottish American scientist. During his lifetime, he was considered one of the greatest American scientists since Benjamin Franklin. While building electromagnets, he discovered the electromagnetic phenomenon of self inductance.

He also discovered mutual inductance independently of Faraday. His work on the electromagnetic relay was the basis of the electrical telegraph, jointly invented by Samuel Morse and Charles Wheatstone. The SI unit of inductance, the Henry, is named after him.

Fig. 5:15. Sir Isaac Newton (4 January 1643- 31 March 1727). He was an English physicist, mathematician, astronomer, alchemist, and natural philosopher. Regarded by many as the greatest figure in the history of science. He layed the groundwork for classical mechanics by publishing in 1687 his treatise Philosophiae Naturalis Principia Mathematica, describing universal gravitation and the three laws of motion. By deriving Kepler's laws of planetary motion from this system, he was the first to show that the motion of objects on Earth and of celestial bodies are governed by the same set of natural laws.

The unifying and deterministic power of his laws was integral to the scientific revolution and the advancement of heliocentrism. Newton showed that gravity decreased by the inverse square of the distance.

He invented the reflecting telescope and discovered that the spectrum of colours observed when white light passes through a prism. Newton notably argued that light is composed of particles. He also formulated an empirical law of cooling, studied the speed of sound, and proposed a theory of the origin of stars.

Newton argued that light is composed of particles, but he had to associate them with waves to explain the diffraction of light. Later physicists instead favoured a purely wavelike explanation of light to account for diffraction. Contemporary quantum mechanics has restored the idea of the wave-particle duality(Chapter 1).

His greatest passions was the study of the Bible. He devoted more time to the study of the Scriptures, the Church Fathers, and to Alchemy than to science, He said, 'I have a fundamental belief in the Bible as the Word of God, written by those who were inspired'. He studied the Bible daily. He also placed the crucifixion of Jesus Christ at 3 April, AD 33, which is now the accepted traditional date.

It is almost certain that Newton experienced the highest expanded states of consciousness which endowed him with 'genius' (see chapter 8 & 10). Had he not relied on the occult idea of action at a distance, across a vacuum, he might not have developed his theory of gravity. To Newton, his scientific and religious experiments were one and the same, observing and understanding how the world functioned. Newton saw God as the master creator whose existence could not be denied in the face of the grandeur of all creation.

Chapter 6

FINDING THE ASSEMBLAGE POINT

Locating and experiencing our Assemblage Point gives us personal proof that, in addition to our physical body, we all have an energy body.

Working with the energy body is not a trivial affair. The Assemblage Point, in particular is particularly personal, directly connected to the "life force" of the individual. The Assemblage Point is not part of the physical body. Although it has serious beneficial medical applications, like the acupuncture meridians, chakras and nadis, it is an integral component, the epicentre of the energy body that saturates the physical body and is almost entirely a spiritual matter.

It should be understood that the Assemblage Point, acupuncture meridians, chakras and nadis have little place in the treatment of

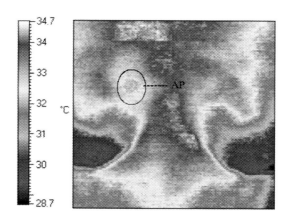

Fig. 6:1. An Infrared image scan of a healthy female location showing a reading of approx. 0.2 degrees centigrade lower than surrounding tissue.

notifiable contagious diseases such as tuberculosis, AIDS, syphilis, gonorrhoea, parasite infestations, etc..

The Assemblage Point is a cluster of strong energy lines or strings. Close to the body they have an average diameter of about 1.0 centimetre or less. These lines pass through the chest and out of the back not unlike the Earth's magnetic north and south pole. There is an energy "potential" both along the length of the lines and across their diameter. The energy potential is strongest close to the body where the lines are concentrated. Further away from the body the energy lines diverge or spread out and the energy potential spreads with them.

Where the cluster of lines enter the physical body, they induce a tender or very sensitive area of skin when pressed or touched. This

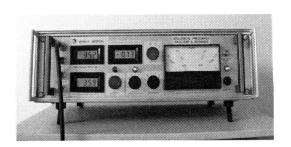

Fig. 6:2 - 3. Using a prototype Infrared radiometric differential scanner to find the Assemblage Point location (2001).

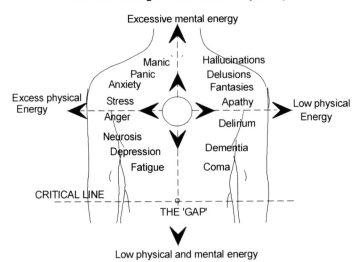

Fig. 6:4. Use this 'Off Centre' symptomatic map to find the approximate location for people with health problems.

area has only a diameter of about 0.5 to 1.0 centimetres. This tenderness can be quite uncomfortable and can penetrate through to the back.

For a healthy person, infrared digital thermometers and infrared image scanners will show a slightly lower reading of approximately 0.2 degrees centigrade at the precise location where the Assemblage Point enters the chest compared to the immediate surrounding skin.

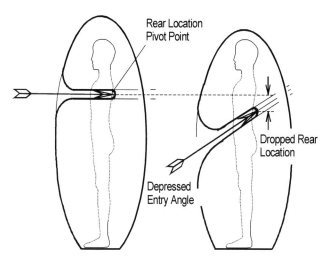

Fig. 6:5. It is important to pinpoint the front and the rear locations to enable you to determine the entry angle (on the 'Z' axis).

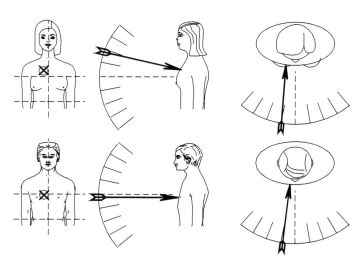

Fig. 6:6. The average location for a healthy female is slightly higher than for a healthy male.

Where To Look For The Assemblage Point

The location of a healthy woman's Assemblage Point is generally, but not always, several centimetres higher than that of a healthy man. Finding the precise location and entry angle of the average, healthy male or female is a quick and simple procedure.

Persons with a bright and energetic disposition or a high

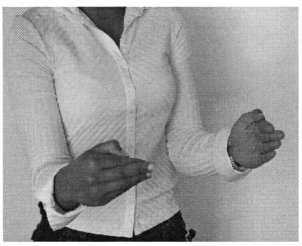

Fig. 6:7. How to form the hands to feel for the location. This is the simplest and fastest method and makes it easy to establish the Z axis angle.

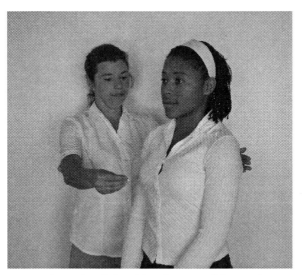

Fig. 6:8. Always stand on the right side of your subject using your left hand to locate the rear point and your right hand to find the front location.

126

vibrational rate will have a high location and slightly elevated entry angle. Depressed and lethargic persons will have a low location and a descending entry angle.

Finding the location and entry angle of a person with mental or physical disease can be difficult but gets easier with experience. Often their symptoms, posture, and tone of voice will suggest where to look. The "off centre" map gives a general overview of locations for specific symptoms. Determining the Z axis entry angle is important.

Many doctors have incorporated the procedures simply by reading my former documents and book. Investigators who are of the intuitive or feeling types generally will not experience any difficulties in finding Assemblage Points. Rational and practical personality types may find difficulties with the feeling and seeing methods described below. Confidence will develop with experience. It is best initially to work in a small team to support each other and compare results. Maintain good records for each person. Note their medication, symptoms, age, sex, and profession, make a drawing of the location and entry angle for future reference.

The following methods and procedures for locating the Assemblage Point have been confirmed and improved by other investigators. Refer to the drawings and photographs.

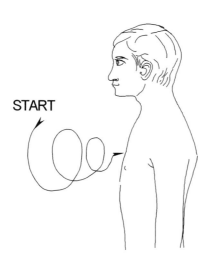

START

Fig. 6:9. Move your right hand in a slow spiralling motion to detect the Assemblage Point location on the front.

127

Feeling The Location Of The Assemblage Point

1. The person should stand upright, looking ahead at the horizon. The investigator should stand facing the person's right-hand body side.

2. Form your left hand into a shallow cup shape. Use it to "feel" for the person's Assemblage Point at the back around the area between the shoulder blades.

3. Form the fingers and thumb of your right hand into a tight, concentrated point, like a "bird's beak". Use the finger tips of the right hand to "feel" for the cluster of energy lines entering the person's chest.

4. Hold both of your arms wide apart. Hold your left hand behind the person and your right hand in front. Standing relaxed, be keenly aware of your physical feelings and your weight on the floor. It helps to close your eyes or look away. Moving both hands in a slow circular motion, slowly bring your hands towards the back and the chest, feeling for the maximum energy disturbance or potential in the finger tips of your right hand and in the palm of your left hand. Allow the person's energy lines to control your arm muscles.

5. The difference in energy potential along the collection of energy lines of the Assemblage Point is easy to distinguish,

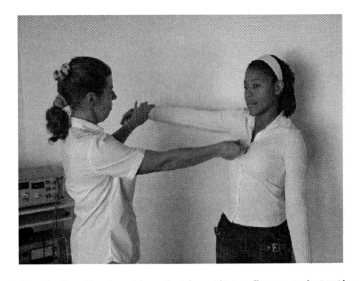

Fig. 6:10. Finding the front location by using reflex muscle testing.

being concentrated and stronger close to the chests. When your cupped left hand and right hand pointed fingers are lined up with the person's cluster of energy lines, you will experience an "energy surge". This will pass along your arms and through your chest between your shoulders.

6. Bring your hands together, feeling for the maximum power and connection with the person. Allow your hands to touch the person's back and chest at the points of maximum energy connection.

7. Move your right-hand fingers back and forth across the energy lines of the Assemblage Point. Most subjects will feel a "pulling" sensation deep inside their chest. Use small, adhesive labels to mark the front and rear position.

Reflex Testing

This procedure is not suitable for frail or exhausted subjects. Considerable energy is required by the subject to hold their arm out horizontally for any period of time.

1. Stand facing the person. With your left arm, apply slight pressure to the subject's outstretched right arm, as shown in the photograph. The person should resist your downward pressure on their arm by holding against it.

2. Grouping the fingers to a point, as before, move your right

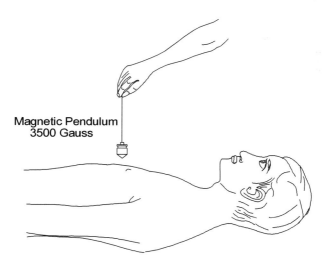

Magnetic Pendulum
3500 Gauss

Fig. 6:11. Finding the front location by using a strong magnetic pendulum. The same method is used to locate the rear location for determining the entry angle.

hand across the person's chest. Keep the hand at a distance of 5 centimetres away from the chest. The person's arm will drop when you move across the location.

3. Check the entry angle by testing the person's arm muscle strength further away from the chest. Drawing your fingers in and out along the Assemblage Point lines will reflect in the person's arm muscle tone.

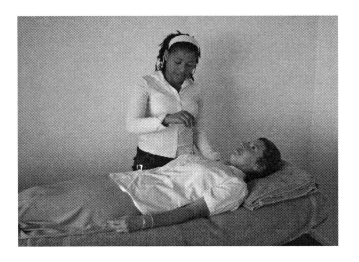

Fig. 6:12. For many practitioners, finding the front and rear locations using a high power Magnetic Pendulum is fast and very easy.

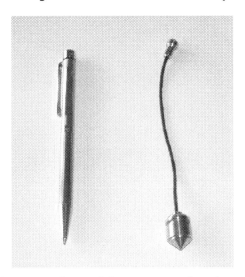

Fig. 6:13. Example of a magnetic pendulum compared against a ball point pen.

4. Touching the chest at the entry location will weaken the person's arm muscles.

Seeing The Location

This method is the most difficult to describe and comprehend yet, ironically, it is the simplest and least obtrusive way to find Assemblage Points. The method, though totally subjective, is most useful in assessment and diagnosis. If you can "see" your patient's alignment, it becomes possible, with experience, to describe to them their symptoms and experiences beforehand. A female medical doctor whose right arm had been amputated being unable to locate Assemblage Points using the methods outlined above, was an excellent authority at seeing the location and entry angle.

Always look for the Assemblage Point before you use any of the above methods to locate it. Confirming the location by using the other methods will develop your confidence and accuracy in "seeing" it. It is essential to realise that what we see "outside" is not the actual object, but a hologram or mental construct "inside" our mind. While intensely observing your subject, suspend all thinking and judgements. Perceive the space surrounding the subject as charged

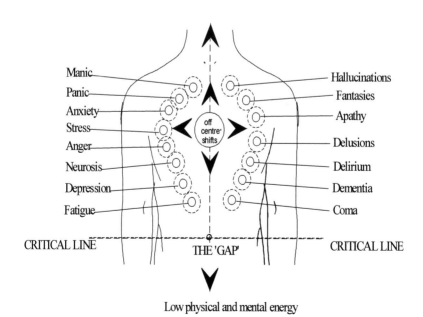

Fig. 6:14. Symptomatic Schematic Map 2.

with energy. Try to see the energy as effervescent particles. Look for a concentration of these particles in front of and on the surface of your subject. Where the particles are most concentrated, you will find the Assemblage Point location. These particles may be bright or dull. Look for lines of flux, flowing to a small concentrated bright or dull spot or even a shadow on the subject. Note the location and angle.

Magnetic Pendulum Locating

It is possible to locate the Assemblage Point with the aid of a specially constructed high power magnetic pendulum. I discovered that it produced significant sensations with respect to the human Assemblage Point. Most subjects can feel or sense their Assemblage Point location as the pendulum is moved close to it. The practitioner can also feel a distinct magnetic pulling effect as the pendulum approaches their location and when directly above the Assemblage Point, the pendulum turns in a circular motion. Although more research is scheduled, here are the basic techniques:

1) With the subject lying down, using the pendulum dowse over and around the chest area.

2) Feel for an 'attraction' sensation in your hand and arm. The subject will also feel a pulling sensation in their chest as you pass over or lock onto their Assemblage Point.

3) Turn the subject over to lie on their front and dowse their back in the same way.

4) Mark the front and back location with a small circular self adhesive paper label. This will then allow you to ascertain the entry and exit angle by comparing the relationship between the front and rear circular labels.

Notes: For more information on locating the Assemblage Point using a magnetic pendulum refer to Appendix V.

Confirming the Location

At the location of the Assemblage Point, the skin is less resilient and more painful to the touch. The skin may occasionally be blemished or marked in some way, sometimes by a small diameter reddish spot. Touching or pushing the spot with a finger tip will cause the skin to redden more than skin elsewhere on the chest.

The spot is tender, sore or uncomfortable. Pushing it causes the person a feeling of slight unease. The feeling passes deep into the chest, often right through to the shoulder blade or the place of exit at the rear.

Any sensitive person touching the precise location of a person's Assemblage point will feel an exchange of energy. It will feel like a faint or weak electric shock and often has a vibrating quality to it.

Bibliography, References and Follow-Up Reading

Locating and shifting photographs: Appreciation to therapist Ms. Sharon Bridgman and assistant Ms. Patience Matekesa.

Faraday, Michael. http://en.wikipedia.org/wiki/Image:Michael_Faraday

Whale, Jon, Ph.D. *Core Energy - Surgery For The Electromagnetic Body.* Series of 3 articles prepared for Positive Health magazine. 1996. Website addresses:

http://www.positivehealth.com/permit/Articles/Energy%20Medicine/whale15.htm

http://www.positivehealth.com/permit/Articles/Energy%20Medicine/whale16.htm

http://www.positivehealth.com/permit/Articles/Energy%20Medicine/whale17.htm

Whale, Jon, Ph.D. *The Catalyst of Power the Assemblage Point of Man.* Second Edition. Dragon Rising Publishing. ISBN1 873483 05 8

Fig. 6:15. Michael Faraday, FRS (September 22, 1791 – August 25, 1867) was an English chemist and physicist who contributed significantly to the fields of electromagnetism and electrochemistry. He established that magnetism could affect rays of light and that there was an underlying relationship between the two phenomena. The SI unit of capacitance, the farad, is named after him, as is the Faraday constant, the charge on a mole of electrons (about 96,485 coulombs). Faraday's law of induction states that a magnetic field changing in time creates a proportional electromotive force.

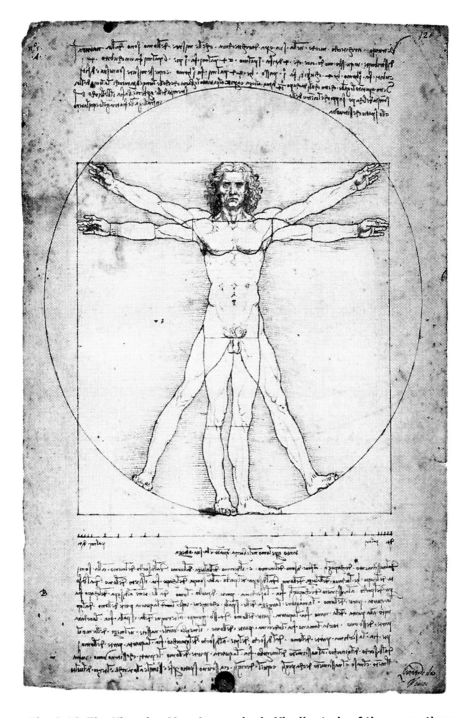

Fig. 2:16. The Vitruvian Man, Leonardo de Vinci's study of the proportions of the human body.

Chapter 7

Recovering the Assemblage Point

There are many methods to correct the Assemblage Point location and the information outlined in these documents and elsewhere will eventually lead to greatly improved medical management procedures for a wide spectrum of disease.

Shifting the Assemblage Point without any apparatus is possible for a trained person. Assemblage Point locations and their Z axis entry angle that are not too far away from the average healthy position can be easily manipulated by many methods.

For high and/or right side locations and entry angles, where the symptoms may be anxiety, panic, insomnia, hyperactivity, compulsive behaviour disorders, etc., i.e. the hyperactive spectrum, there are many medications that will relieve the symptoms and thus lower the location and entry angle of the Assemblage Point. Depressive medications such as tranquillisers, sleeping pills, certain herbal remedies are the methods most commonly used. Other methods include relaxation techniques, psychotherapy, hypnotherapy and meditation. All these can reduce the brain activity and slow down high Beta brain frequencies helping to lower the location of the Assemblage Point in the process.

However, with the exception of meditation and the numerous associated disciplines, most of these modalities will not move the assemblage point towards the coveted central position. They only move the location up or down on the Y axis. There are exceptions. Regular meditation or special relaxation techniques, perhaps combined with a compatible physical exercise or a yoga type discipline, when practised over long periods of months or years will eventually move the location on the X axis towards the left, closer to the coveted stable central location. Today, many schools teach these methods and they are designed to reduce brainwave frequencies and harmonize the mind with the body. Occasionally, where these methods are practised to an excess then the Assemblage Point can move over to the left side of the central line into the introvert realities and associated symptoms.

Where depressive drugs are used to reduce symptoms and dampen down an overactive or sensitive nervous system (hypertension spectrum), if the medication is stopped suddenly, a withdrawal crisis will follow. For chronic depressive drug users, the liver, adrenals and possibly the thyroids adapt to the presence of the drug. When the drug is withdrawn or unavailable, these organs go into "hyper-drive" causing high Beta brain frequencies with desperate hypertensive behaviour. In all such cases, the Assemblage Point location and entry angle will rapidly shift upwards and overshoot the original position prior to the drug being ingested. This results in exacerbation of the original symptoms, and dependency on the medication can result.

This is the essence of the problem for everyone who gets involved with chronic substance, illegal and prescribed drug misuse (See Appendix IV for more information).

Where low locations and entry angles, not too far down from the healthy location are present, along with the hypotension spectrum of symptoms, such as depression, post natal depression and so on, there are only limited methods that will raise the Assemblage Point location and entry angle. Antidepressants are the most common medication prescribed and they can elevate the entry angle and raise the location. In the UK millions of city dwellers are regular users who depend on antidepressants. Psychoanalytical, hypnosis, counselling, relaxation or meditation methods are not particularly helpful for sufferers with chronic hypotension due to, or in combination with low Assemblage Point locations.

An input of biological energy is required. Yoga breathing exercises can raise the location if the air is absolutely pure and free of pollutants, otherwise they may aggravate the symptoms. In these times pure clean vibrant air cannot be found in or anywhere near a city unless the weather is very windy, bringing in clean air from the countryside. Going on an activity holiday to the mountains, countryside or seaside can raise the location if the Assemblage point is in a low position.

Definitions Of Types of Assemblage Point Shifts

There are three different classifications of types of movements or shifts that can occur with the Assemblage Point, and these are:

1) A movement.

2) A shift.

3) A shift in depth.

1) A movement of the Assemblage Point happens to most of us regularly. For example, if we are aggressively intimidated or repudiated, we can develop hypertension or depression. The Assemblage Point entry angle will move to the right side, upwards or downwards and it can take several days or weeks for it to drift back to the original location. The person will gradually feel better by degrees as their systems rebalance. A movement is a change in the Assemblage Point entry angle on the Z axis. The central core of the Assemblage Point does not shift.

2) A shift is distinctly different from a movement. The Assemblage Point becomes dislodged and moves to a different location in the body. This can occur with a traumatic incident of any kind. Generally, under these circumstances the Assemblage Point does not return to its original location naturally and the recipient may become ill. A shift is a change in the location on the X and Y axes. The entry angle on the Z axis will almost certainly change at the same time.

3) A shift in depth occurs only under special circumstances and

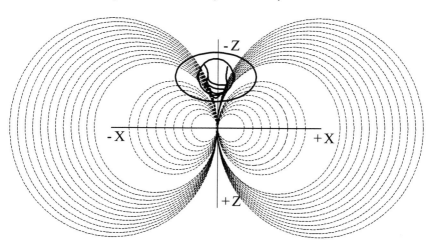

Fig. 7:1. Shifts in depth moves the crux or cross point outwards along the Z axis (view: down from above the head).

the central core of the Assemblage Point energy moves closer to the surface of the chest or even outside the surface of the chest. This is a powerful experience that reinforces and stabilises the Assemblage Point location. The depth of the shift depends on the skill and the available free energy of the person conducting the shift. This type of shift increases the energy potential of the Assemblage Point. The vortex becomes concentrated into a smaller diameter core and becomes brighter in appearance. A shift in depth is a movement of the crux or cross point of the Assemblage Point outwards away from the centre of the body along the Z axis.

Realignment Aids

The average healthy person's Assemblage Point enters just inside the right side of the chest and exits near the right shoulder blade in the centre of the back. A large framed strong healthy centred person with training can shift and centralise anyone's Assemblage Point by slapping or thumping the rear location or pivot point using the palm of the right hand, at the same time, making a clenched fist with the

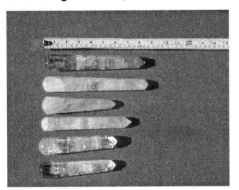
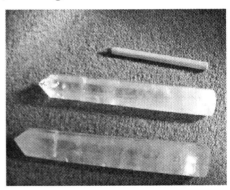

Fig. 7:2 - 3. Quartz crystals with polished domed ends shown against a tape measure and ballpoint pen for size scale.

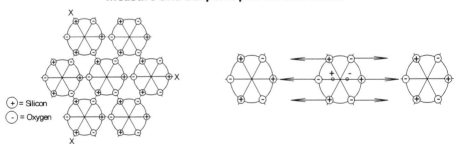

Fig. 7:4 - 5. Negative and positive polarisation of the electrons of quartz. Polarisation = oxygen negative and silicon positive.

left hand, which is placed on the centre of the subject's chest. The technique requires great personal energy, and also the full cooperation of the person receiving the shift.

However it is much easier and requires less personal energy expenditure if a specially designed shifting aid or tool is used. American Indian tribal medicine men use a specially machined and polished quartz crystal to capture the energy lines of the Assemblage Point and drag it to the desired location. As strange as this may appear, (and I know that many of you will doubt the feasibility), it is true and these are the scientific principles why. A number of crystalline materials possess a piezo-electrical property, quartz being employed frequently. Quartz is not the only mineral that can be put to practical use for the purposes stated above but its properties

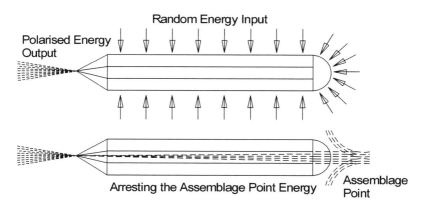

Fig. 7:6. Using a quartz crystal with a polished domed end to arrest the Assemblage Point energy lines.

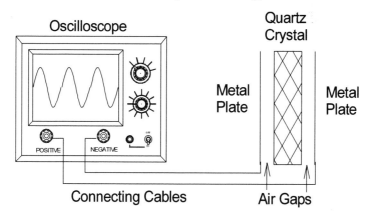

Fig. 7:7. The dielectric resonance properties of crystalline substrates induce a voltage into adjacent metal plates.

permit almost anyone to shift the Assemblage Point.

Piezo electricity relates to the electrical charges in certain crystals when they are subjected to manual pressure (squeezing and tapping etc.) and conversely to the conversion of electrical stress into mechanical strain. Piezo is from a Greek word meaning pressure. The piezo-electrical effect of quartz crystal is a scientific principle. It is used in television, radio and medical equipment; for example, ultra sound and ultra sonic therapies make use of the natural piezo-electrical effect of quartz and other crystalline substrates. For the piezo-electrical effect to function for these purposes, the crystal must be connected into an electronic circuit with wires so that its many properties can be exploited. Liberating the electrical charges when a crystal is stressed is a function of electrical asymmetry within the atomic groups of which the crystal is built. Inside the crystal the constituent atoms are arranged in a definite pattern that is repeated at distances having atomic dimensions. Silicon and oxygen are arranged with respect to each other to produce silicon dioxide (SiO^2). Positive charges are shown carried by silicon atoms (+), negative charges by double oxygen atoms (-).

Not so well known and often denied by the uninformed, is that resonating crystalline substrates dissipate their energy by dielectric transference, inducing it into adjacent objects and the environment. The electrons in adjacent substrates, such as living tissue, will resonate in sympathy when in close proximity to a resonating

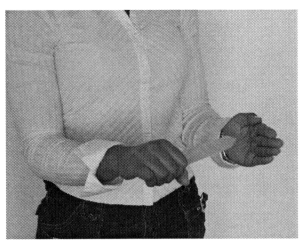

Fig. 7:8. Feeling for the energy breeze emitted from the point of a dynamic or active quartz crystal.

crystalline substrate. The frequency, intensity and quality of the energy induced into adjacent objects and the environment are dictated by the type, size, colour and atomic composition of the crystalline substrate used. Also, the frequency and intensity of the

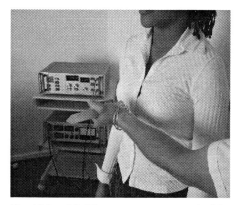 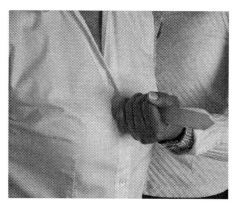

Fig. 7:9 - 10. The correct way to hold a quartz crystal for shifting the Assemblage Point either by using the 'Sliding Shift' or Stage Shifting method, always use your left hand and stand on the left side of your subject.

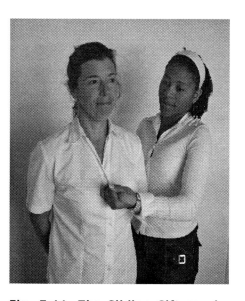 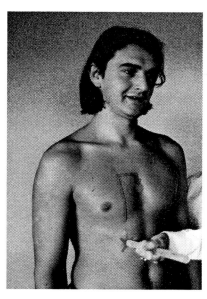

Fig. 7:11. The Sliding Sift can be performed without removing clothes, however only a light cotton vest or shirt should be worn. Synthetic cloths hold static electricity and they along with metal lingerie support stays can interfere with the locating and shifting process.

Fig. 7:12. The Sliding Sift is easily performed without clothes, lubricate the polished dome end of the crystal with one droplet of olive oil so that it does not stick to the subject's skin.

transferred energy can be electronically increased and modulated with medically desirable electromagnetic frequencies.

The natural polarizing properties of quartz are ideally suited for Assemblage Point manipulation. The drawings illustrate the principles of arresting or capturing the Assemblage Point energy. For consistent results observe the following minimum standards for the crystal. The crystal should weigh 200 grammes or more, have a length of a least 18 centimetres and a diameter of 3 centimetres or more. The crystal must have a ground and polished domed end. It should be as clear as possible and must have a well-defined point. The point should have at least three perfect triangles among its six facets and it must be energetic and dynamic. To check this, hold the crystal with your right hand and direct the point at the palm of your left hand. You should feel a breeze of cool, tingling energy penetrating the skin of your left hand where the crystal is pointing.

Most large towns or cities will have shops that support the sale of quartz crystals. Rock, mineral and fossil shops, fancy gift shops and lapidary suppliers are just some outlets where crystals can be

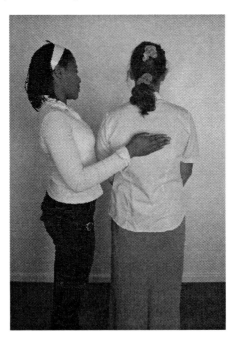

Fig. 7:13. Using the palm of a cupped right hand to slide shift the Assemblage Point rear location upwards. If performing a Stage Shift, use your right hand (flat inside finger parts only) to tap or slap the rear location.

purchased. Polished and finished massage wands that would be suitable for shifting Assemblage Points are readily available. Depending on the size, clarity and weight, the cost can vary from £30 to £100 or more. This is not so bad as only one is required and, if it is not dropped on to a hard floor, should last indefinitely.

Correcting the Assemblage Point takes about five minutes and procedures are painless. The experience can be exhilarating and stabilising. For some people with health problems, the experience can produce a profound relief. Frequent correction to the centre can significantly improve mental and physical efficiency. For personal and group development purposes it can be shifted monthly. It can also be centralised before important meetings or after stressful events. Sports and other team activities can benefit if all members are given the same alignment, in particular if they have experienced a series of defeats.

Realignment Using The Sliding Shift

The following procedures have been developed over many years and when acquiring the skills they should be rigidly adhered to so as not to develop any bad habits. Shifting Assemblage Points is a developed skill and requires practice. Shifting the Assemblage Point by sliding it from one location to another is the easiest and most straightforward method. It is the preferred method for training purposes and best practised with friends and colleagues or in a group workshop situation. The subject or patient must cooperate. This method has some disadvantages. The subject must remove the clothing from the chest area. Using it on female patients whose Assemblage Point location has dropped below their breast can be difficult, sliding or manipulating a dropped Assemblage Point up across a female breast is tricky, but achievable.

1. Find the subject's Assemblage Point location and entry angle by using the instructions in the previous chapter. Mark the locations on the chest and back with a marking pen or small self adhesive labels.

2. Instruct the subject to stand upright looking straight ahead.

3. Stand facing the left-hand side of the subject's body. Holding the quartz crystal in your left hand, place the polished, domed end on the precise location of the subject's Assemblage Point where it enters the chest.

4. Use the palm of your right hand to cover and slide the rear location around the shoulder blade area.

5. Instruct your subject to take three deep breaths, slowly in through the nose and out of the mouth. Make sure that they are really deep, if not get them to take three more or, as many that are necessary to achieve full expansion of their lungs and chest cavity. Between each inhalation and exhalation the subject should pause for one second to allow biological energy to accumulate inside their chest and torso. Inhale to the count of seven, pause one count, exhale to the

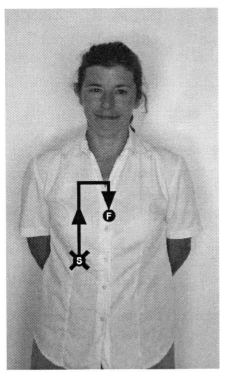 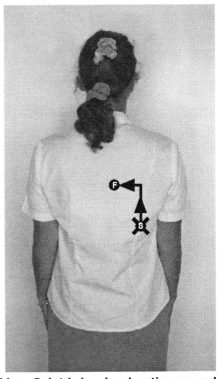

Fig. 7:14 - 15. A) For example: If the Assemblage Point is in a low location around position 'S', Start by placing the domed end of the quartz crystal directly on the exact location 'S'. (Note. The overlaid direction indicators are enlarged for clarity).

B) While the subject is still holding their breath with their throat and sphincter muscles closed, deliberately and firmly slide the crystal up and then over to the centre line and then down to finish at the centre of the chest at 'F', at the same time, using your right hand placed firmly on the rear location, slide it up and over to the centre of their back.

C) When at the centre 'F', twist the crystal half a turn clockwise and remove it from the subject's chest, at the same time using your right hand (flat inside finger parts only), gently but firmly tap you subject on the crown of their head and instruct them to breath freely. The tap on the head anchors or sets the new position.

count of seven, pause for one count, inhale to the count of seven, and so on for three full deep breath cycles (refer to the drawings and photographs provided).

6. On the third breath, when the chest is expanded and the lungs are full with air, instruct your subject to hold their breath in. Next instruct them to contract his sphincter and other muscles in the anus and genital area, and keep them

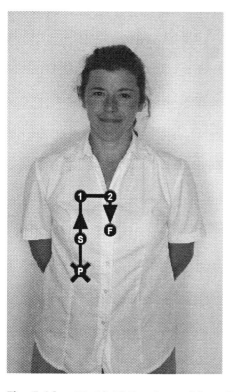

Fig. 7:16 - 17. A) If the Assemblage Point is in a low location around position marked 'P', place the quartz crystal at the front around point 'S' (start), use your right hand to knock or slap the rear location at '1'. (Note. The overlaid direction indicators are enlarged for clarity).

B) The Assemblage Point will jump upwards from the low location and latch onto the crystal at position 'S'. Quickly move the crystal up to Stage '1' at the front and thump the back location at '2'. The Assemblage Point will jump up to Stage '1'.

C) Rapidly move the crystal across to Stage '2' and thump the back location at '3'.

D) Without any hesitation and while the subject is still holding their breath with the throat and sphincter muscles closed, move the crystal down to the centre to finish at 'F' and twice swiftly thump the rear location at '4' then twist the crystal half a turn and remove it from subjects' chest, at the same time using your right hand (flat inside finger parts only), gently but firmly tap you subject on the crown of their head and instruct them to breath freely. The tap on the head anchors or sets the new position.

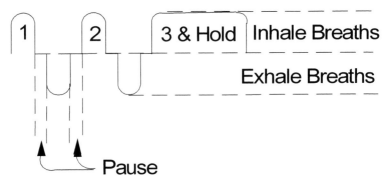

Fig. 7:18. Schematic illustrating the 3 breath cycles with pauses between breaths to the retention phase that enables the Assemblage Point to be shifted.

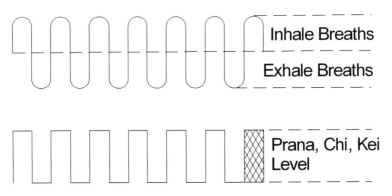

Fig. 7:19. Schematic illustrating how repeated breath cycles without pauses between breaths does not accumulate biological energy.

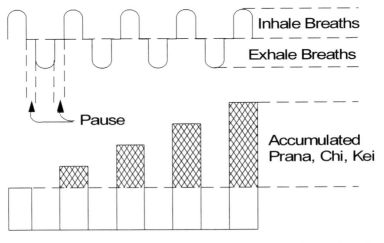

Fig. 7:20. Two Schematics illustrating how repeated breath cycles with pauses between breaths accumulate biological energy.

146

contracted. Then at the same time instruct them to half swallow and close the throat (head upright and the chin tucked back).

7. This effectively closes the upper and lower exit and entry gateways to the body. With the retained breath and closed gateways, energy pressure builds up and loosens the subject's energy field from his physical body. This situation will allow you to slide the Assemblage Point to the central location using a quartz crystal. Most subjects can hold their breath for five or ten seconds and this is sufficient time.

8. Using the quartz crystal, slide your subject's Assemblage Point to the centre of the chest. Simultaneously use the palm of your right hand to drag the rear location into the centre between the shoulder blades. Twist the crystal half a turn and remove it from his chest. Simultaneously, tap the subject lightly on the top of his head with the palm of your right hand, then tell him to breathe normally.

The shift should be in the directions shown in the drawings. It helps to lubricate the domed end of the crystal with a fine vegetable oil so that it slides easily over the skin without sticking.

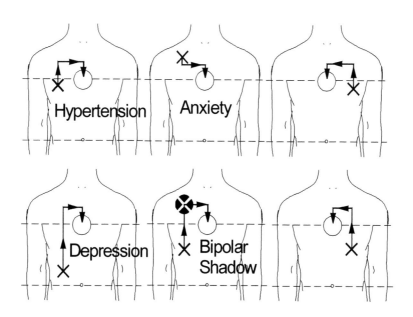

Fig. 7:21. Schematic illustrating the correct direction to shift the Assemblage Point from various detrimental locations.

147

Sometimes, when shifting the Assemblage Point, some subjects may not be able to maintain holding the throat or the sphincter muscles closed. Or they will fail to retain their breath. If this occurs, the Assemblage Point may be lost at any point along the shifting path. This can happen, especially with undisciplined or nervous people. In such cases, the Assemblage Point location and entry angle must be found again and the shifting procedure repeated.

How To Instruct Your Subject

Instruct your subject beforehand as follows, so that they understand and expect what you are going to ask them to do.

"I need your cooperation and assistance in order for you to accumulate the biological energy needed so that I can move your Assemblage Point. I am going to instruct you to take three deep breaths, through your nose, pausing between each breath. When you have taken your third breath, I will ask you to hold your breath and at the same time you must squeeze or hold tightly the muscles in your anus and genitals, as if you are anxious to use the toilet. This will prevent the accumulated energy from escaping from your body. I will then ask you to half-swallow and keep your throat closed and hold on to your breath and I will shift your Assemblage Point".

Once the patient or subject has understood this, proceed to shift their Assemblage Point instructing them, by reading to them the following:

"Please stand upright, arms relaxed by your sides, with your back and shoulders straight and chest pushed out. Relax, place your feet slightly apart. Now relax more and feel and be aware of the weight of your body standing on the floor. Breathe normally and look straight ahead."

"Slowly take a deep breath through your nose, and fill your lungs as much as you can. Now pause. Breathe out as slowly through your mouth as much as you can to completely empty your lungs. Now pause". (One completed breath cycle)

"Inhale slowly and deeply. Now pause. Exhale slowly and deeply. Now pause". (Two completed breath cycles.)

"Inhale slowly and deeply. Now pause. Exhale slowly and deeply. Now pause. (Three completed breath cycles.) Inhale, now hold your breath and squeeze the muscles tight in your anus and genitals.

Now half-swallow and keep your throat closed and hold on to your breath, do not release your breath until I tell you to".

At this point you can then shift the Assemblage Point to a new location by the sliding or stage shifting methods described below.

Realignment Using Stage Shifting

With the following method, the subject can keep his vest on. Instead of sliding the Assemblage Point towards the centre, shifting is done in one or several stages or short steps depending on the distance of misalignment. The rear location or pivot point is dislodged with a firm push or slap to the subjects's back using the palm of your right hand. Shifts of a short distance require only one stage and two pushes. Large distances may require three stages and four pushes to shift it to the centre. The rest of the procedure is the same as for the sliding method above. This method of shifting has another advantage over the previous method. The Assemblage Point can be also shifted in depth. The depth is determined by the force of the shift and the amount of biological energy that is accumulated with the breathing.

1. Use two small adhesive labels or a pen to mark the front and rear Assemblage Point locations. Plan the number of stages you will use to move the Assemblage Point to the centre normally not more than four.

2. Use your left hand to position the crystal on the first stage. Firmly instruct the subject through Steps 2 to 6 as in the sliding shift above and by reading aloud to them the notes in: "How to Instruct Your Subject", above. When the subject is holding his breath and the sphincter muscles and throat are closed, give a firm push or slap to the Assemblage Point rear location with the heel or palm of your right hand. The Assemblage Point will jump and relocate at the crystal. Large framed, recalcitrant or strong-willed subjects often require a firm shove or slap or thump with the palm of your right hand on the rear pivot point to dislodge it.

3. Rapidly move the crystal to stage 2 and again shove or slap the rear location. Long shifts may require a third stage, so push the rear location again to shift the Assemblage Point to the third stage. The subject must continue to hold his breath throughout. You only have a few seconds before he will need

to breathe again, therefore you must be practised and swift.

4. When you arrive with the crystal at the centre give a final firm push between the shoulder blades and remove the crystal from the subject's chest with a half clockwise twist. Simultaneously, using the palm and four fingers of your now free right hand, tap the subject lightly on the head and instruct him to breathe normally.

Allow the subject a few moments to rest. Always re-check the Assemblage Point location, making sure that it has not been left behind at one of the stages. If necessary, repeat the procedure. After the shift, get the subject to lie down, breathe freely and relax for about fifteen minutes. This helps to stabilise and embed the new location.

Confirming The New Location

It is helpful to familiarise the subject with his original Assemblage Point location and the new position after the shift. Touching or pushing the spot with your finger will cause the skin to redden more than skin elsewhere on the chest. The spot is often tender, sore or uncomfortable. Pushing it causes the subject a feeling of slight unease that can pass deep into the chest, often right through to their back. Once the Assemblage Point has been moved to a central position, these sensations will vanish from the original position and migrate to the new location. Helping subjects to take conscious note of the new position will allow them to keep track of their Assemblage Point, and arrange to have it corrected in the future, should it move too far from the centre.

Patients' Considerations

Patients with low locations will often react physically when their Assemblage Point is found. For example, they may start to tremble or shake as you move your right hand across their Assemblage Point. Sometimes they complain of a long-standing pain in their back or associated pains elsewhere when you move your hands into and across the energy lines of their Assemblage Point. Therefore, do not practice on patients - learn the methods with your friends and colleagues first. When you are confident that you can find the Assemblage Point location and entry angle efficiently, then progress to work with patients.

Clinical corrections associated with health problems are best achieved with two experienced professionals. It should be backed up with professional patient management care and generally only be carried out by medically qualified personnel. One practitioner is required to locate the Assemblage Point and the second to do the shifting and each will double check the other's work. However, if one is very confident that the location of a patient's Assemblage Point is in a detrimental location, then one should not be discouraged from attempting to correct it.

As mentioned previously, psychiatric patients suffering from schizophrenia or manic depression can often have an "energy shadow" and "split" Assemblage Point locations. The dominant Assemblage Point must be located and shifted to the secondary split or shadow location. Both are then picked up with the crystal and shifted to the centre. Splits and shadows are not easy to deal with and considerable experience in locating and shifting Assemblage Points is required to be effective. Patients should be reassessed and their Assemblage Point corrected within ten to fourteen days of their first shift. It should then be corrected monthly until their location stabilises. Patients taking antidepressants, tranquillisers or other types of drugs, may require lower dosages or modified drug management following realignment.

Patients withdrawing from non-prescribed drugs or substances may require daily shifting for one week or more until their biological and nervous systems adjust and stabilise. With old or frail patients and young children, shifting their Assemblage Point manually is neither practical nor advisable. In any event very infirm patients may not be able to cooperate or breathe properly, therefore the above outlined procedures cannot be applied and other methods must be used as outlined below.

Youngsters And Juveniles

The Assemblage Point in babies and young children has no fixed location. It is unstable and can move freely. As a child's personality and internal dialogue develop, the Assemblage Point begins to be fixed. Ideally, adolescents and juveniles should be allowed to develop and fix their own location, without interference other than the normal family and educational procedures. As with adults, children with serious misalignment of their Assemblage Point do not find it easy

151

to integrate with their peers. Some youngsters who have experienced accidents, intimidation, bullying, drug abuse, illness, or psychological problems are likely to have misalignment problems. In such cases, any educational or therapeutic methods that will stabilise and centralise their Assemblage Point will help their development. Children over 10 years of age with health problems or symptoms caused by misalignment can gain substantial benefits from the shifting and realignment procedures coupled with other supportive therapy.

Future Rewarding Applications

Other people, from differing backgrounds and having other expertise and goals, can now utilise these methods in pursuit of their personal growth, professional development and areas of research.

For example, education, professional sports, labour and team management, politics, prisoner reform and rehabilitation, social services, armed combat personnel rehabilitation, substance abuse, national security, psychology, psychiatry, counselling, marriage guidance, relationships, yoga, mystical disciplines, martial arts, the arts, rapid learning, the list of applications is exhaustive.

Not only does the discovery of the Assemblage point prove to the sceptics and agnostics that there is more to us humans than mere chemicals, blood, flesh and bones, but, it also has profound benefits for our wellbeing and development.

As a stable and correctly located Assemblage Point increases health and efficiency, aside from the spiritual, medical and psychological benefits, the wider professional application of the Assemblage Point techniques into other areas will greatly benefit humanity. It will save and generate more money than can currently be estimated.

Bibliography, References And Follow-Up Reading

Notes: For more information on correcting the Assemblage Point location using more advanced and up-to date methods refer to Appendix II.

Locating and shifting photographs: Appreciation to therapist Ms. Sharon Bridgman and assistant Ms. Patience Matekesa.

Whale, Jon, Ph.D. *Core Energy - Surgery For The Electromagnetic Body.* Series of 3 articles prepared for Positive Health magazine. 1996. Website addresses:

http://www.positivehealth.com/permit/Articles/Energy%20Medicine/whale15.htm

http://www.positivehealth.com/permit/Articles/Energy%20Medicine/whale16.htm

http://www.positivehealth.com/permit/Articles/Energy%20Medicine/whale17.htm

Whale, Jon, Ph.D. *The Catalyst of Power the Assemblage Point of Man.* Second Edition. Dragon Rising Publishing. ISBN1 873483 05 8

Bauer, Jaroslav, *Minerals, Rocks and Precious Gem Stones.* Aventinum Publishing House, Prague.

Hall, Cally, *Gemstones.* Dorling Kindersley.

Brocardo, G., *Minerals & Gemstones Of The World.* David and Charles, Devon.

Bruton, Eric, F.G.A., *Diamonds.* N.A.G. Press Ltd. London.

Renton. R. N., *Telecommunications Principles.* Pitman.

Fig. 7:22. Charles Robert Darwin FRS (12 February 1809 – 19 April 1882). Portrait by Julia Margaret Cameron. The British naturalist who achieved enduring distinction by producing significant evidence that species originated through evolutionary change. He proposed the scientific theory that natural selection is the mechanism by which such change occurs. This theory is now considered a foundation of biology, It has significantly affected other disciplines such as philosophy, psychology and anthropology.

Chapter 8

SUPERNATURAL MAN AND WOMEN

Contentions between Fundamentalists and Evolutionists are growing and serve a wide audience. Evolutionists support the theory that modern man (homo sapiens) are descended from apes. Alongside humans, Neanderthal man lived across Europe and parts of west and central Asia from approximately 230,000 to 29,000 years ago. It is unclear what factors led to their demise, but climate change and competition from modern humans may have played a role

According to the BBC's Internet web site, in 1967 the Zoologist Desmond Morris stunned the world by publishing a book entitled 'The Naked Ape'. Out of the 193 known types of monkeys and apes only man is not entirely covered with hair. The title and its content intentionally identify man with the apes and compares human behaviour with that of animals. At the time critics of his book labelled

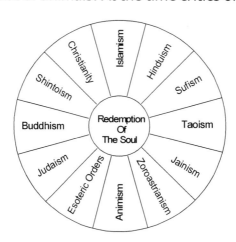

Fig. 8:1. The World's twelve major religions all embrace redemption and resurrection of the soul at the centre of their faith.

him "an inadequately informed amateur" who oversimplified and distorted the way we behave by creating a zoological characterisation of the human being.

Nevertheless, despite his critics, Desmond Morris's work was of sufficient interest to the public that it was translated into 23 languages and was a world best seller.

Recently, Geneticist Svante Paabo and his team isolated long segments of genetic material from a 45,000-year-old Neanderthal fossil from Croatia. Preliminary analysis shows the bundle of DNA responsible for maleness (Y chromosome) in Neanderthal man is very different from human and chimpanzee DNA. Humans have 23 pairs of chromosomes and apes have 24 pairs. This Neanderthal DNA test supports that so far there is no conclusive evidence that we are the descendants of apes. Only time will tell if modern scientific DNA analysis techniques will support the Creationist's and Fundamentalist's opposition to Darwin's theory of evolution.

Aside from being the most dangerous species on this planet, man has unique abilities and potential not embodied in any other species. Mostly for territorial, material, financial and political gain, today there are many groups and individuals who are preoccupied with the assassination of man's aboriginal and contemporary distinctiveness and psychic abilities.

Death and resurrection are the essential principles taught in almost every religion. Through empowered saviours and teachers, it is taught that the mystery of salvation is based on the death of the physical body and the salvation of the soul and ascendance into heaven. Whilst this may or may not be true, the devotions, disciplines, rituals, prayers and philosophies of all religions produce profound benefit for psychological and physical health and also local social order. Believers assert that by projection of His will, the Creator's thoughts are turned into the form of the manifest universe.

The mystical doctrines and practices, the esoteric side of religion provide more than faith. The practice of mystical disciplines provides access to higher states of consciousness and existence. Many gifted individuals are born possessing extraordinary or psychic abilities. Most people who ardently practise religious, ascetic or mystical disciplines, over time and as they approach the 'source' will spontaneously acquire metaphysical powers.

Throughout my childhood and teen years I had numerous spontaneous experiences of higher states of consciousness without understanding, or rather having no point of reference, as to what they were.

I have always been a night-hawk and loan wolf enjoying many pursuits, including in my youth, instinctive boys' activities such as night time fishing, hunting and camping. Around the age of eighteen I was living alone in a rented high attic room of a large boarding house owned by a miserly lady. It was winter time and the house had no heating system. There was a communal pay-as-you-go electric coin slot meter, the only form of power. Within minutes of putting money in the meter, it was gone, used up by the numerous tenants. Everyone was too cold, too contentious and short of money to afford the exorbitant price of electricity cherished by the landlady's slot meter. Most evenings there was no electricity. At the time like many other students, I survived largely on packets of cornflakes and milk obtained from the milk roundsman on credit. I was slim and undernourished almost to the point that could be described as fasting. With little money for alcohol, tobacco or girlfriends my existence then could definitely be described as ascetic. Humour prevailed. I would wait until everyone went to bed, then I would creep down-stairs and feed the meter with coins so that I could use my soldering iron and pursue my electronic experimental construction projects until daybreak.

The room was too small for any furniture permitting only a narrow bed, two wooden chairs, and a low tiny table. Stacked up on and under one chair was my audio and radio frequency signal generators, electrical test meters, power supplies, wave meters and a cathode ray oscilloscope. Used in all computer chips today, silicon transistors, a product of quantum mechanics, had become abundantly available, they had power and I wanted to explore their limitations and possibilities. I would sit cross-legged on the floor concentrating and totally preoccupied working on my electronic projects that where spread out like a ragged bird's nest on the tiny coffee table.

I would work away, in the quiet of the night, with the atmosphere of a clear frosty sky and the frequent screech of owls penetrating the loose roof slates and the gaps in the rough wooden planks lining the walls of the room.

On many occasions I would spontaneously enter an extraordinary state of consciousness, engulfed in brilliant bluish white light invading all of my being. This state would always commence with a bluish beam of white light descending into my consciousness as if there were an aperture in the top of my head. Compulsively, I would close my eyes and direct my attention upwards towards the source of the light. The source was almost too engulfing for me to withstand, yet it would draw me upwards and through an aperture to a plateau where I would be permeated and overwhelmed with an ecstatic energy. This was a timeless infinite reality, but not the final or ultimate reality. I could feel the presence of higher domains and higher greater plateaus but was inept to achieve them. Always I did not want to return and face the glass of water frozen solid by the side of my bunk, or the realities of postwar Britain.

I could find no one in England to assist in the explanation of these experiences. I felt that I had navigated into domains that are available but were not explored or experienced by my contemporaries. Some years later I was fortunate enough to get a posting to south east Asia as the regional electronic engineer. Within weeks of being there I met with people who were educated in eastern philosophies and mystical disciplines, including Buddhism. These topics were common discussions around the restaurant table and part of everyday life.

Eventually I was welcomed into the homes of a group of people

Fig. 8:2. A graphic drawing of the light experienced through the crown aperture when in special states of consciousness such as 'close to death' experiences or during meditation.

that held regular meetings and discussion groups. Enjoying their company, they introduced me to eastern esoteric knowledge and sciences and the reasons for their belief in reincarnation. They explained that in the hours before dawn, I had been unconsciously practising a form of concentrated meditation. They further stated that I had achieved a state where I abandoned my ego and gained access to high states of spiritual consciousness that they defined as 'Nirvana' or 'Satori'. They authenticated my experiences as natural special states that are ardently pursued by the ascetic monks of the region using fasting and meditation. They confirmed that the best time to achieve these states was in the hours before sunrise and that my dedication to my projects was an essential part of the discipline process required for this attainment.

The clarity and reality of those experiences and the desire to return for further exploration became an appointment that has been with me all of my life. In Asia I realised that logic, thinking or rationalisation could never transcend itself. That it could not by itself manage and manipulate the unmanifest vital cosmic energy they referred to as 'Prana, Chi or Kei'. That numerous psychic and spiritual powers are a product of, or can be gained through, the adept's masteries over prime unmanifest pranic energy. The spectrum of mystical disciplines taught internationally in esoteric schools train students to see, hear, feel, decode, accumulate, polarise, modulate and manipulate pranic energy. Initial training is centred on the student's personal energy, but inevitably, as the

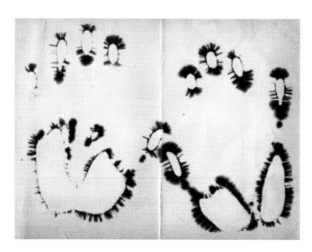

Fig. 8:3. A Kirlian photograph of the author's hands illustrating the polarised pranic energy emissions from the extremities.

159

adept becomes competent, he is able to influence the energies of others. I knew beyond any doubt that if I were to advance I would have to embark on a mystical discipline that would provide me with the skills to accumulate and control pranic cosmic energy.

The nobility of asceticism and becoming a monk was not for me. I wanted to retain and enjoy my professional scientific and family responsibilities and continue to earn an income. My following years were taken up with the fervent practice of numerous esoteric mystical disciplines and studies that I rigidly adhered to. They included Zen,

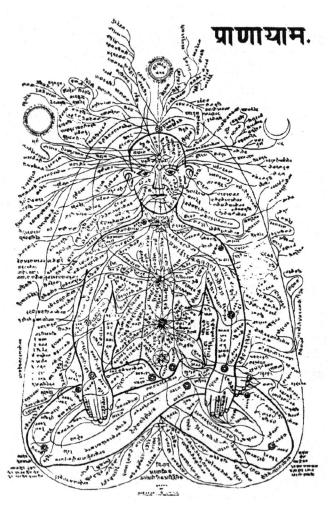

Fig. 8:4. An ancient Tibetan schematic illustrating the seven major and ten minor Chakras. Also shown are the seven major planets and the psychic channels (Nadis) connecting to them.

Raja, Kundalini, Krya, Mantra, Japa, Dharana and Tantra yoga and meditation. These disciplines are a combination of physical, mental, and spiritual exercises specifically designed to gain mastery over unmanifest pranic energy for the purpose of evolving one's physical, emotional, mental and psychic aspects to their full potential. I would get up before dawn and at set times in the night to practise exercises such as pranayama, meditation, concentrated visualisation, chakra development, mantra chanting and so on. I also set aside time at my work space to continue with them throughout the day and evening. Gradually I read and assembled a small library of books and papers about philosophy, world religions, mystical disciplines and all kinds of esoteric subjects.

Later, I built a sensory isolation flotation tank. I spent many thousands of hours floating in minimal gravity, in total darkness with all of my senses cut off from the external world. The sensory isolation tank was a most useful tool. In those days, I would often use the tank when my family had retired for the night. Two hours of profound relaxation floating on high density Epsom salt water allowed sufficient energy to be accumulated equivalent to a good nights sleep. Used in conjunction with some physical exercise and a reasonable diet, I was able to make deep explorations into areas of consciousness way beyond the possibilities of the five senses of this material world. Also, importantly I did not need to take time out from my employment or family life. Furthermore, the isolation tank is a modern unblemished scientific tool; results did not depend on undertaking the limiting belief systems or propaganda associated with many spiritual and mystical disciplines.

Here I do not want to renounce the value and benefits of the mystical disciplines that I had previously pursued as they had in fact prepared me for the tank explorations. In the isolation tank I developed the ability of three dimensional visualisation and a photographic memory. Some years later when I had designed and developed the electronic gem therapy apparatus, I discovered that sapphire gem stones electronically stimulated at Theta brainwave frequencies produced even more profound levels of relaxation and trance states of consciousness. Unlike the floatation tank, gem therapy lamps are much more user friendly producing rapid results in comfortable room environments.

Mystical Disciplines And The Assemblage Point

The abstract core of most spiritual and mystical disciplines, whether they are European, American, Indian, Chinese, Japanese or aboriginal is that the adept deliberately sets out to accumulate and store excesses of cosmic vital energy within himself by absorbing it perhaps from the sun, earth, herbs or power plants, animals or the atmosphere. Virtually all schools of mystical disciplines employ special deep breathing exercises and breath retention to build up reserves of prana or chi energy that is generally stored in the solar plexus area in the first instance. When sufficient energy is accumulated, it can, by using 'intent' be directed to different parts of the body or even projected outside into other people or material or psychic entities.

There are vast numbers of disciplined exercises designed to develop a wide range of psychic abilities which necessitate secrecy and regulated initiation rituals and ceremonies. Although there are countless books, web sites, teachers and esoteric schools worldwide describing and teaching mystical disciplines and esoteric knowledge, virtually all of them have never heard of the Assemblage Point and do not take into account or incorporate the knowledge and its effects into their curricula. With the discovery and the publication of the medical and psychological effects of different Assemblage Point locations it is necessary to provide a general updated overview of the abstract core that these teachings base their work on.

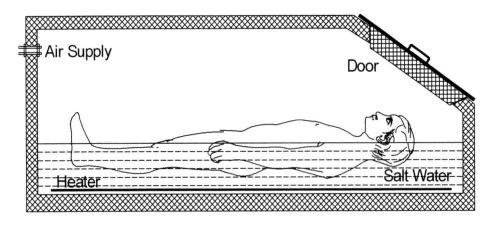

Fig. 8:5. Sensory Isolation Floatation Tank: contains high density salt water 25 cm deep, heated to 34.5 degrees Celsius. Air conditioned, sound and light proofed. The user floats at virtual zero gravity in total isolation from the outside world.

"Up from Earth's Centre through the Seventh Gate I rose, And on the throne of Saturn sate, And many a Knot unravelled by the Road, But not the Master Knot of Human Fate." Omar Khayyam.

Omar Khayyam, an Islamic Sufi, was familiar with esoteric Muslim, Tibetan and Indian mystical disciplines. His rhyme refers to leaving the physical body by the seventh gate or crown chakra, the gate of Brahma, an aperture situated at the top of the head, through which the self may leave the body. He was probably predisposed with an active kundalini energy and a centralised Assemblage Point location.

Zeus, Apollo And Hermes

When Apollo discovered his herd of cattle missing Hermes was in bed sound asleep. Even so, Apollo woke him with accusations of theft. Although Hermes adamantly denied his involvement, Apollo hauled him before Zeus the King of the Gods to account for himself.

At the throne of Zeus the denials continued and after giving Zeus a wicked wink, Hermes produced his famous Lyre. As Hermes played all of the Gods in Olympus held their breath with delight. Even Zeus's fierce Eagle approved. Apollo was so impressed that he admitted that Hermes's music was well worth fifty cattle. So pleased was Hermes with Apollo that he gave him his Lyre. Apollo in return gave Hermes a golden staff called the Caduceus which had the power over sleep and dreams, wealth, health and happiness.

Excesses of vital pranic energy properly controlled and directed can be used to accelerate the development of the seven attributes of: wisdom, intuition, expression, compassion, intent, passion and instinct.

The Tibetan, Indian and far Eastern mystics have developed techniques of concentration and visualisation that create seven energy plexuses within the quantum energy body, called chakras. These chakras are located at specific points in the body and the accumulated energy is directed at them by numerous methods combining concentration, physical exercise, visualisation and sound. In the average person, the chakras probably do not exist or are very weak, and they may have to be created or awakened by conscious effort. Each chakra is assigned numerous attributes or benefactions. It is claimed that the chakras distribute energy throughout the physical body by means of a network of invisible psychic conduits or channels called nadis, estimated to be 72,000 in number. These nadis are hollow fibres, or channels or ducts woven throughout our physical but are in fact said to be components of our energy body. They convey streams of polarised pranic energy throughout our entire being.

Located at junction points of the nadis network are minor chakras or meridians. Acupuncture is a system of medical treatment that sets out to deliberately manipulate and redirect the vital energy that is distributed along these nadis to manage or cure disease. Some sensitive types of people claim to be able to see, or feel the energy radiating from another person's chakras and their physical body.

The conception of chakras as understood in Eastern philosophy does not exist in western medical science. Yet medical science acknowledges that everything we encounter is experienced entirely in the domain of the mind (brain). Therefore, western science cannot dismiss their existence. The primary importance and level of existence of chakras therefore, is hypothesized to be in the psyche and in the spirit. In Eastern metaphysics, the chakras are thought to be levels of consciousness, and states of the spirit, and 'proving' the existence of chakras is asking to 'prove' the existence of a soul.

However, there is evidence that chakras have a physical manifestation as well. Adepts deliberately accumulated biological (pranic) energy and by using concentrated meditation, they can direct it to any particular chakra or part of the body. These techniques increase localised hyperthermia, hyperperfusion, hypermetabolism and vasodilation. As mentioned in Chapter 4, the higher energy emissions of intuitive types and feeling personality types can be scientifically measured using radiometric scanners.

Chakras are associated with the glands in the endocrine system, and also with the positions of the spinal nerve ganglia (also known as "plexuses"). The various hormones secreted by these glands do have a dramatic effect on human psychology, and any imbalance in one or more can cause a psychological or physical disturbance in a person.

People that have active, or energised chakras, may have physical manifestations in the body at these glands. This will undoubtedly stimulate the production of related hormones and other biological chemicals. This may be the reason why certain individuals experience subjective emergence of psychological and spiritual experiences.

Perhaps the most psychologically dramatic and potent secretion of these glands are similar in structure to the psychedelic drug Dimethyltryptamine (DMT). This is similar to the hormone 5-Hydoxytryptamine (Serotonin) and is possibly the precursor for the hormone Melatonin. These are thought to be synthesized by the pineal gland, corresponding to the brow chakra or 'Third Eye'. Many individuals have sought spiritual breakthroughs through using analogous chemical and hallucinogenic plant aids.

The Chakras are spinning vortices of radiating pranic or chi energy that nourish the organs and glands in the body. Each of the seven chakras has a number of segments or ducts that correlate to its rotational or vibrating frequency. According to Tibetan, Sanskrit, Ayurvedic and Tantra testimony, the chakras derive their energy

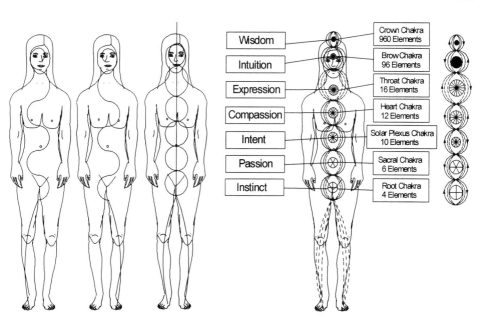

Fig. 8:6. Like entwined strands of DNA, the human caduceus of the three great Nadis: a) 'Ida' extending from the left nostril to the right large toe. b) 'Pingala' extending from the right nostril to the left large toe. c) both superimposed on the central channel called 'Sushumna.

Fig. 8:7. Sympathetic with our breathing and emotions, the polarised Pranic energy oscillates up and down the three great Nadis energising the Chakras. The higher the levels of Pranic energy flowing, the more powerful and effective our chakras perform.

from three principal nadis or subtle etheric conduits or channels inside the energy body, they are named ida, pingala and sushumna.

- The ida nadis channel is associated with the left nostril terminating at the right large toe.

- The pingala nadis channel is associated the right nostril and terminates at the left great toe.

- The sushumna nadis channel extends from the base of the spine to the aperture at the top of the head.

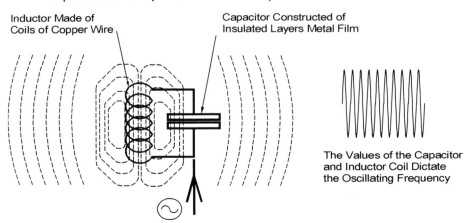

Fig. 8:8. Resonating mechanical tuned circuits such as musical instruments transmit energy as pressure waves. Resonating electronic circuits transmit electromagnetic waves.

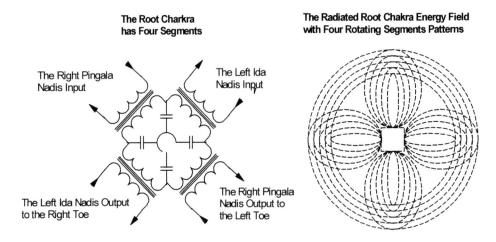

Fig. 8:9 & 10. The Nadis and Chakras are etheric vortex structures resonating with polarised pranic energy similar to electronic tuned circuits.

The Caduceus

The Caduceus of Hermes has two snakes entwined around the central staff, at the head of the staff are two wings. It was carried by Heralds and Ambassadors in times of war and was later adopted by the medical profession as their emblem. Today, the World Health Organisation has chopped the caduceus in half, only using a single snake and staff as their emblem!

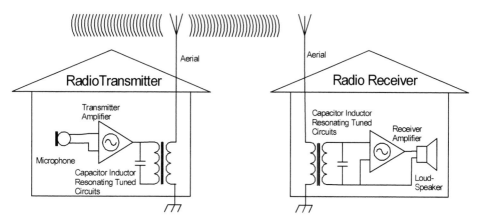

Fig. 8:11. The energy generated by oscillating tuned circuits can be transmitted and received over vast distances.

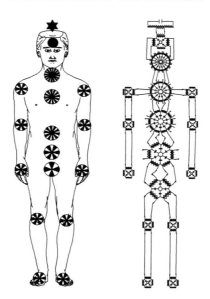

Fig. 8:12 & 13. The human quantum energy system of the Nadis and Chakras can be represented as a series of resonating and transmitting interconnected electronic tuned circuits.

The Hindu name for the Caduceus is called Meru Danda and it represents the entwined left and right great nadis, ida and pingala. The wings represent the flight to immortality through the rising kundalini energy in the great sushumna channel (symbolised by the central staff) as the vital force exits the body by means of the crown aperture.

In the average person, pranic energy oscillates up and down the ida and pingala channels and is in phase or sympathy with our physical breathing. These two channels, like the snakes of the caduceus, are woven around six lower chakras and, as we inhale and exhale, the oscillating energy up and down them is induced into each of the chakras. The chakras distribute vital pranic energy to their associated organs and glands of the physical body via the thousands of minor nadis that radiate outwards. The function of the chakras not only affect the vitality and health of the physical body, but they also have a profound effect on our personality and personal power.

The meeting place of ida, pingala and sushumna is at the root chakra. The pranic energy oscillating up and down the ida and pingala can cause stirring in the movement of the dormant energy called kundalini. For the average person, this energy when active is usually released sexually, or in some cases in creative projects. The mystic can, by deliberate and controlled breathing and other types of esoteric disciplines, (including refraining from sexual activity), increase the vital pranic energy that normally oscillates up and down the ida and pingala channels.

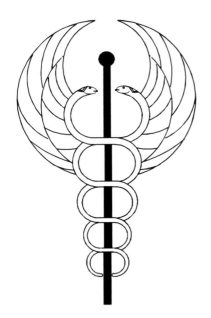

Fig. 8:14. The Caduceus Staff represents the left, right and central channels of the mystical human energy structure.

Pranic energy is accumulated in the solar plexus region and when there is sufficient it is mentally and physically guided or pushed downwards by the adept to strike and charge their root chakra. From there it is directed upwards along the central sushumna nadis penetrating all of the six higher chakras to exit through the crown chakra aperture, the gateway of Brahma. As the kundalini energy penetrates the higher chakras it can energise them, improving the health of the body and causing the energy field or aura to expand. It can also pass straight through to and out of the crown aperture. Examples of breathing techniques used to accumulate energy can be found in the previous chapter.

Persons with an active kundalini are more effective in their daily lives, possessing psychic and other spiritual powers. The Laya Yoga Sanskrit text states that the adept by meditating on the kundalini energy in the root chakra that shines with the lustre of ten million suns, becomes a master of speech and all types of learning, free from all disease and full of great gladness. In order for the kundalini energy to rise up through the central spinal channel sushumna, to and through the crown chakra, the location of the assemblage point is critical. Its location must be in or close to the centre of the heart chakra. This is the only location possible for the assemblage point, if all of the chakras are to remain charged and functioning correctly at their optimum efficiency.

It is essential for all schools and students of any type of religious, mystical or esoteric discipline to understand the relationship of the practitioner's Assemblage Point location to the work. Should the assemblage point be located too far from the centre of the heart chakra, then it is possible for the kundalini energy, if deliberately, spontaneously or accidentally stimulated, for example by the unwitting use of drugs or anaesthetics, to rise up either the

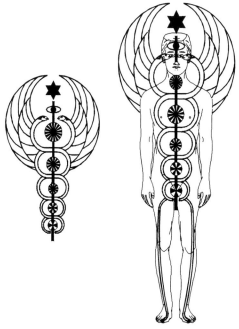

Fig. 8:15. The Caduceus Staff in man is seven active chakras and a rising kundalini.

ida or the pingala channel, instead of sushumna. This will cause numerous types of undesirable psychological and physiological consequences including possible psychosis.

One aspect of the kundalini experience is that although the practitioner proceeds to guide or raise his energy upwards, at the point of exiting through the crown aperture, the kundalini experience is perceived as descending from domains above. Little or no sensation is experienced in the spine or physical body as it rises towards the crown aperture.

Another aspect is that an individual with an active kundalini energy will, by quantum field transfer and modulation, cause the

Fig. 8:16. 17th century representation of the 'third eye' connection to the 'higher worlds' by alchemist Robert Fludd.

energy of other individuals in close proximity to rise. This is one aspect of the power that some oriental mystics hold over their followers.

Like the Assemblage Point and the nadis, the seven chakras are part of our invisible anatomy; they are components of our quantum energy body. There is a mutual influence between the physical body and the energy body. The seven chakras are minor epicentres of pranic energy that exert a primary influence on the major organs and glands of the body. The vital currents of life force flow most vigorously when the organs and glands of our physical body and

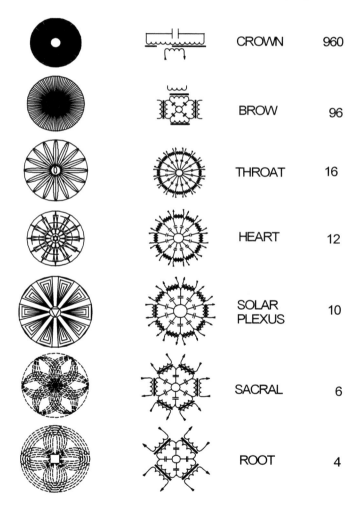

		CROWN	960
		BROW	96
		THROAT	16
		HEART	12
		SOLAR PLEXUS	10
		SACRAL	6
		ROOT	4

Fig. 8:17. A graphical illustration of the seven major Chakras, their electronic circuit model with their corresponding vibrational rate ratios.

the mystical components of our energy body are in harmony. The efficiency and health of our physical body and our material environment can be improved by the practice of mental and physical exercises that works directly to strengthen our chakras.

Even if the chakras do not exist, merely proceeding with the practice of the mystical disciplines and teachings associated with them, will on the mental and quantum energy plane bring them into existence.

The Assemblage Point definitely does exist, it proves that we have an energy body as well as a physical body. Its existence has been confirmed by thousands of individuals including medical doctors and has been used by them to cure disease. Here is the fundamental difference between Homo Sapiens and other primates. Whilst apes and all other species are entirely at the mercy of the Darwinian forces of evolution and natural selection, all of us possess the possibility to accelerate our physical and psychical development by the practice of religious and mystical disciplines and the study of esoteric and spiritual knowledge. We are the only species on this planet endowed with the power to affect and improve our quantum

CHAKRA COLOURS, SYMBOLS & VIBRATIONAL RATES						
CHAKRA	COLOUR	ELEMENTS	ESOTERIC VISUALISATION SYMBOL		RADIATING ELEMENTS	
CROWN	VIOLET	SOURCE	VIOLET STAR ABOVE CROWN	✦	960	1344
BROW	INDIGO	PRANA	INDIGO BEAM FROM ABOVE	⇒	96	134
THROAT	BLUE	ETHER	BLUE OVAL	◗	16	22.8
HEART	GREEN	AIR	GREEN SIX POINTED STAR	✶	12	16.8
SOLAR PLEXUS	YELLOW	FIRE	YELLOW TRIANGLE	▼	10	14.0
SACRAL	ORANGE	WATER	ORANGE CRESCENT MOON	︶	6	8.4
ROOT	RED	EARTH	RED SQUARE	■	4	5.6
AVERAGE CHAKRA FREQUENCY IN CYCLES PER SECOND (Hz) 2 x RMS (.707) x The Number of Elements e.g. Base = 2 x .707 x 4 = 5.6 Hz						

Fig. 8:18. Schematic of the attribute of the seven major Chakras.

or morphogenic energy fields that influence our physical and mental form together with our environment. It could definitely be said that the Gods (quantum consciousness) through the 'Word' has bestowed us with the unique ability to change our fate and form and reach out towards immortality.

While some humans may behave like apes, there is one essential distinction: humans have comprehensive language skills.

Knowledge is the true path to freedom. Simply reading about mystical and spiritual disciplines and studying the related philosophies will activate the dormant powers within us. There is a vast amount of literature available containing very detailed instruction, description and philosophies relating to the chakras.

The belief systems, descriptions and philosophies vary between different schools and ethnic cultures. The chakras are incorporated into a very broad spectrum of professional knowledge and coveted in one form or another by the major religions, acupuncturists, therapists, yoga schools, astrologers. Here once again is a short overview that will I hope will provide a map that harmonise, corroborate and tie together the other foregoing maps and information in this book:

Crown Chakra

Other Name(s):	Sahasrara (Sanskrit); the Gate of Brahma; the Throne of Saturn.
Position:	Crown of head.
Controls:	Pineal gland, The six lower chakras, Every aspect of Mind and Body.
Site of:	Primary pranic energy. Meeting place of Ida, Pingala and Sushumna, the three major nadis of the subtle body.
Seat of:	spiritual desires and aspirations.
Attributes:	knowledge, wisdom and guiding principles. Point of access for the seven higher chakras. Point of access to this and the other seven true planes of existence; other domains, matrices and Universes. Point of union of all opposite

polarities.

To Activate: Visualise a star –shaped aperture (the Star of David) through which a Violet light can be perceived.

Meditation: By directing ones attention above the crown in meditation a bright blue light can be found. Here, the adept acquires strange powers and conquers our twin enemies: time and death.

Structure: Nine hundred and sixty radiant segments.

Energising colour: Violet.

Fortifying Gem: Dark blue Sapphire.

Associated planet: Saturn.

Brow Chakra

Other Names: Ajna; Third Eye;

Position: Centre of the forehead.

Controls: Pituitary gland.

Site of: Interface between the primary pranic energy of the spiritual and the physical world via the crown chakra, and the secondary pranic energies of the physical world of the lower chakras. Direct connection to the root chakra via the Ida and Pingala, these extend from the nostrils, cross at the brow chakra then descend down to the root chakra. The ida and pingala channels also connect to each of the five lower chakras.

Seat of: The centre of command.

Attributes: Reason, intuition, precognition, clairvoyance, clairaudience and other psychic abilities.

To Activate: Visualise a descending ray of blue light entering the head vertically via Crown chakra, then seeing it turn forwards to exit the forehead through the Third Eye.

Meditation: On this chakra results in the adept being released from the consequences of his actions in previous incarnations.

Structure: Ninety six radiant segments.

Energising colour: Indigo.

Fortifying Gem: White diamond.

Associated planet: Venus.

Throat Chakra

Other names: Vishuddha

Position: Throat

Controls: Thyroid gland; Respiratory organs.

Site of: Expression of our higher states consciousness, (a function of the brow and crown chakras); also all the attributes (or lack of them) generated by the four lower chakras, provided they are active or open.

Seat of: Expression of our self in all of our creative activities.

Attributes: Expression and Creativity.

To Activate: Visualise a Blue Oval Shape in the well of your throat centre of your chest. When this image is firmly established, then mentally expand its size until everyone and everything you know, this planet, even the universe is contained within it.

Meditation: the adept becomes a sage in sacred and esoteric knowledge.

Structure: sixteen radiant segments.

Energising Colour:	Blue.
Fortifying Gem:	Light Blue and Yellow Sapphire.
Associated Planet:	Jupiter.
Alchemic element:	Ether.

NB. The tone of our voice is modulated directly by the frequency and intensity of the energy contained, or available in, our other chakras. By listening to another's voice and analysing their articulation it is entirely possible to decode the efficiency and development of their chakras.

The four lower chakras modulate our voice with the quality of:

- Earth, as the steadfastness of the root chakra,
- Water, as the amorous qualities of the spleen chakra,
- Fire, as the consuming functions of the navel chakra,
- Air, as the compassionate characteristic of the heart chakra.

None, some, or all of these aspects are expressed via the throat chakra, depending on which of the respective chakras are energised and functioning. Concentrating and decoding the frequencies and numerous modulated signals present in everyone's voice (and also our handwriting) permits an understanding of both the individual's abilities and limitations.

By gaining mastery over the frequencies and modulations of our voice, what we say, how and when we say it and what we refrain from saying, it is possible to modulate and energise the lower and higher chakras to a greater efficiency.

Heart Chakra

Other Name(s):	Anahata.
Position:	In the centre of the chest, midway between throat and navel.
Controls:	Thymus gland.
Site of:	Our feelings and emotions.
Seat of:	The noble qualities, Love, Compassion, Charity, Gentleness, Loyalty, Honesty, Ethics.

Attributes:	Transmutes the element Air, Regulates the sense of touch and emotional feelings.
To Activate:	Visualise a six-pointed Green Star, known as the Seal of Solomon in the centre of your chest. When this image is firmly established, then mentally expand its size until everyone and everything you know, this planet, even the universe is contained within it.
Meditation:	The adept develops paranormal powers e.g. The ability to see and hear over great distances; to merge into and sense another persons feelings or body; Precognition.
Structure:	Twelve radiant segments.
Energising Colour:	Green.
Fortifying Gem:	Emerald.
Associated Planet:	Mercury.
Alchemic Element:	Air.

NB. This chakra is *not* the same as the Assemblage Point, although in some rare individuals the location of their Assemblage Point maybe in the centre of their heart chakra,

Solar Plexus Chakra

Other Names:	Manipura.
Position:	At the Navel.
Controls:	The Adrenal glands; The Heat generated in our body; Digestion.
Site of:	Accumulation of Pranic energy; Psychic Heat or Mystic Fire.
Seat of:	Willpower and Intent.
Attributes:	When the energy in this chakra is high: our Intent and Will operate in the physical world unimpeded; our desires

materialise without effort, (as long as these are in line with the Crown and Brow chakra energies and therefore with Universal consciousness); When the energy is low, the reverse happens and we seem to trudge through life. Associated with the sense of Sight.

To activate: Visualise a Yellow Inverted Triangle in your umbilical region. When this image is firmly established, then mentally expand its size until everyone and everything you know, this planet, even the universe is contained within it.

Meditation: The adept can accumulate and discharge vast amounts of pranic energy, (as used for psychic purposes and in the martial arts); mastery over this chakra: frees the adept from all disease: fulfils secret desires; confers the ability to penetrate the deepest layers of consciousness of others.

Structure: Ten radiant segments.

Energising colour: Yellow.

Fortifying Gem: Citrine.

Associated Planet: Mars.

Alchemic Element: Fire.

NB. The energy levels of this chakra must be retained and protected. It is of paramount importance. The umbilical gap left from birth creates a natural weakness at this chakra, and through it energy is easily robbed by individuals low on the scale of emotional health.

Sacral Chakra

Other Name(s): Svadisthana.

Position: Five centimetres below the navel.

Controls: The sex glands and hormones. The sense of taste.

Site of: Our sexual centre.

Seat of: Sexual function.

Attributes: Passion and Avidity.

It contributes to the distribution of fluids throughout the body. Saliva, semen, vaginal fluids, blood and urine are all in good order when this chakra is functioning normally.

To Activate: Visualise an Orange Crescent Moon below your umbilical region. When this image is firmly established, then mentally expand its size until everyone and everything you know, this planet, even the universe is contained within it.

Meditation: The adept acquires the ability communicate with spirit entities in the astral worlds.

Structure: This chakra has six radiant segments.

Energising Colour: Orange.

Fortifying Gem; Carnelian.

Associated planet: The Moon.

Alchemic element: Water.

NB. Two days before menstruation the energy levels of this chakra in women are drained and reversed. This continues for about 3 - 5 days up until the middle of the menstruation, (and can contribute to their premenstrual tension), after which it starts to revert and re-energise normally.

Root Chakra

Other Name(s): Muladhara; Base chakra.

Position: Around the Coccyx, at the base of the spine.

Controls: Adrenals; Kidneys; Bladder; Spinal Column; our sense of Smell; Bones; Teeth; Nails; Solids.

Site of:	Our connection to Earth.
	Meeting point of Ida, Pingala, Sushumna
Seat of:	Power, the mystical Kundalini. Our Survival Instincts.
Attributes:	Survival and Foundation.
To Activate:	Visualise a Red Square down below you. When this image is firmly established, then expand its size until everyone and everything you know, this planet, even the universe is contained on and above it.
Meditation:	The adept gains mastery of desire, envy, anger and passion.
Structure:	Four radiant segments.
Energising Colour:	Red.
Fortifying Gem:	Ruby.
Associated Planet:	The Sun.
Alchemic Element:	Earth.

NB. When this chakra is working or open, we are: automatically grounded; we know how to survive; we feel good in whatever situation that we are in; our feet are firmly on the ground and we are secure. When the root chakra is not functioning, then the reverse of the above is true: we are dependent on someone else for our survival; we feel insecure and nervous; We can be easily manipulated by other people. The general feeling of insecurity and mental noise is partly because the energy in the Solar Plexus chakra is dependent on the correct function of the Root chakra. Generally, the solar plexus chakra and its polarisation of the attribute 'intent' cannot function properly without the root chakra operating. An efficient solar plexus requires the stabilising and grounding elements of the root chakra, and also for the kundalini energy to be active.

Persons With All Chakras Functioning Are Extraordinary

The tone of an individual's voice gives the listener an opportunity to quickly discriminate the predominant and weak chakra energy levels of whoever is speaking.

A person with an active or energised:

1) Root chakra: has a solid, official, unbending authoritarian tone of voice.

2) Sacral chakra: a seductive sexual watery tone.

3) Solar plexus chakra: possesses a warm, persuasive, penetrating voice.

4) Heart chakra: is sympathetic and consoling in tone.

When the Throat chakra is not modulated by the energy of the four lower or two upper chakras the voice tone is duplicitous.

Persons with all chakras open at the same time are rare and extraordinary. Their voice is modulated with the attributes of all of the chakras. They are wise and ethical, intuitive, expressive, compassionate, persuasive, passionate and authoritative.

The Intrinsic Human Quest

The range of beatific and horrific experience available to human consciousness in these times is enormous. All of us have our personal accounts of positive and negative experiences to narrate. Daily the media provides us with wretched accounts of accidents, murders, suicide, terrorism and catastrophes, all accounts of human experiences in the negative domains.

All Sporting activities bring people together and raise our physical and emotional levels of health. Motor car racing, sailing, mountain climbing, potholing, sky diving, flying, space exploration, scuba diving, horse riding, shooting, skiing, and many other extrovert pursuits can be, and often are, mortally dangerous. The risks are high. Every year many accidents occur and the participants recover to get up and have another go.

Firefighters, paramedics, police, search and rescue personnel, military personnel are all professionals whose duties incur high risks of accident, trauma or mortality.

What is it about these pursuits and professions that is so attractive and why do people engage in them?

By contrast, the use of hallucinogenic, recreational, prescribed drugs and other consciousness-altering substances in these times, has developed into a major social problem for societies worldwide. Today young people use hallucinogenic and all types of other substances for recreation, hedonistic, socialistic and escapist purposes. They often use them in conjunction with alcohol in bars, night clubs and discotheques or in squalid environments. Many have become addicted or dependant on one chemical supplement or another. Others less fortunate have experienced tragedy, disease, psychosis, crime, or imprisonment. The risks are very high. What do they get out of it and why do they do it?

Aborigines employ power plants and herbs containing poisons, hallucinogenic and stimulating alkaloids for dignified spiritual reasons in conjunction with the strict disciplines of tribal ceremonies and customs. They approach their use with awe and extreme caution and most often fast for several days beforehand. Why do they use these powerful and dangerous plants?

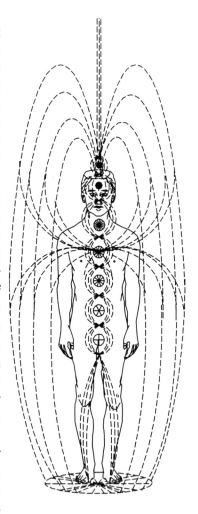

One answer is that these and many other activities provide us with peak intense experiences and exhilaration where our ego dissolves. Intense challenging experiences change and alter our perception and state of consciousness. We are spiritual beings and the reality of today's planet-side economic robotic survival routines is too boring for many people's conscious awareness to tolerate for any lengthy period. The entertainment benefits for awareness far surpass the dangers and risks to the individual or the cosmos. When we engage in these activities fear and pain are attenuated, kundalini can rise and we can feel timeless, touching our immortality. Cosmic conscious awareness does not want peace, it wants something novel, something new,

Fig. 8:19. Kundalini: energy entering and exiting the crown Chakra.

something dangerous, something exhilarating, anything to occupy the cosmic void.

Positive Levels Of Conscious Being

Chronic negative experiences are detrimental to health and prosperity, whereas positive states are beneficial. With good personal management of our Assemblage Point location together with control of our brain frequencies, we can avoid the negative states and at the same time advance our personal and professional achievements, or provide access to the higher states of consciousness.

The numerous possible negative and positive conscious states of existence that can be experienced, together with the brain frequencies and the Assemblage Point locations, are combined and mapped as follows:

Trans Universal Consciousness. 99:1 % Essence v. Ego Ratio.

The self is in complete fusion or union with Universal Consciousness. An eternal infinite state of existence outside of the human body, a fully conscious state where the self is absorbed in a vast and timeless space sustained by intense currents of pranic energy.

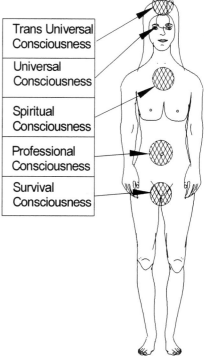

The self is dissolved in timeless consciousness and is conciliatory to universal law and cosmic energy. It is a thin film of consciousness, linked to all of the other entities existing at this level. These all have their backs to the void, enclosing all of the known universes, converting the void, creating the energy to sustain the universe.

The self is only 1% ego and 99% essence.

The brain frequency range is

Fig. 8:20. The energy locations for the higher states of human consciousness.

Trans Universal Consciousness

Universal Consciousness

Spiritual Consciousness

Professional Consciousness

Survival Consciousness

Delta & Theta, between 0.1 and 7.8 Hz. Consciousness functions: Automatic, self operating, instinctive, involuntary. The energy, vital force or kundalini energy is positioned in the Maha, the spiritual centre above the head, the crown chakra.

Abnormal energy levels will be present and the location of the crux of the Assemblage Point may be some distance away from the surface of the body.

Universal Consciousness. 90:10 % Essence v. Ego Ratio.

- The self is engaged in astral or time-travel to or in other domains, realities, matrixes or universes.
- The self is a point-source of consciousness, energy, light and love.
- It is interacting with, or witnessing, other spiritual entities in time- travelling, clairaudience, clairvoyance, channelling or lucid dreaming.
- The self is only 10% ego and 90% essence.
- The brain frequency range is Theta, between 3.2 and 7.8 Hz.
- Consciousness functions: Dreaming, trance, rapid learning, self hypnosis, and other altered states.
- The kundalini energy is positioned in the Path, the mental centre in the head, the brow chakra.
- The Assemblage Point crux may be off or away from the surface of the body and the location may drift to the left side of the chest.

Spiritual Consciousness. 85:15% Essence v. Ego Ratio.

- The self experiences a very high blissful state in the body and down on the Earth.
- A state where one's body receives current or waves of cosmic energy and the self is in tune with the universal transmission of cosmic love, cosmic energy, divine grace, chi, prana, wisdom, knowledge and power.
- There is heightened bodily awareness where the self is

connected with nature, earth spirits, and the reception and transmission of Nirvana and Baraka.

- It represents the highest function of bodily and Earth-side functioning and consciousness.
- The self is only 15% ego and 85% essence.
- The brain frequencies is in the Alpha range, between 7.8 and 14 Hz. Consciousness functions: Relaxing, meditation, balancing, healing and feeling. The kundalini energy is positioned in the emotional centre in the chest or the heart chakra.
- The Assemblage Point location will be in the centre of the chest or heart chakra and may be just a few centimetres in front of the heart chakra.

Professional Consciousness. 75:25% Essence v. Ego Ratio.

- The self is absorbed and preoccupied with pleasurable activities to do with one's profession, work, relationships, sports, hobbies and other physical, mental, intellectual or metaphysical interests.
- The self is doing what it knows how to do and likes to do best.
- A high state of humour and ethical principles is operating.
- The self is 25 % ego and 75% essence.
- The brain frequency range used is Beta, between 14 and 21 Hz.
- Consciousness functions: Invigorating, exhilarating, thrilling, stimulating and rewarding.
- The kundalini energy is positioned in the belly, the navel chakra.
- The Assemblage Point location will be slightly on the right side close to, or in the centre of the chest.

Survival Consciousness. 50:50% Essence v. Ego Ratio.

- Here the self is engaged in learning, absorbing and or

transmitting data, skills and information.

- It may be working on a demanding task or project requiring the acquisition of new data and skills, or teaching and training others in new skills.

- The self is sensitive about maintaining good ethics, self discipline, principles and craftsmanship.

- The self is 50% ego and 50% essence.

- The brain frequency range used is Beta, between 21 and 25 Hz.

- Consciousness functions: Conceptualising, assimilating, integrating, concentrating.

- The kundalini energy is positioned in the base chakra, on the earth.

- The Assemblage Point will be in the average male or female position.

Negative Levels Of Consciousness

Unlike the positive levels above, the following negative levels do not have any physical location in the body. For a fuller description of the medical effects of the negative levels refer to Chapter 4.

Negative Levels: Aggravated Conformity. 25:75% Essence v. Ego Ratio.

- The self is functioning in a negative depressive state, doing routine chores, working, existing, but in a state of emotional distress, fear, pain, guilt, anger, anxiety, fatigue or distress.

- If a person is habitually in this state, then the Assemblage Point location and entry angle may be incorrectly positioned and misaligned, and inclined to be in a low right side location.

Negative Levels: Overwhelming Distress. 15: 85% Essence v. Ego Ratio.

- The self is in an extreme negative state.

- It is locked into the body that is overwhelmed with emotional or physical pain, fatigue and malaise. The distress is at such a high level that it is impossible to work or concentrate on any external affairs or attend to normal duties or daily tasks.

- Here again, should this state be sustained for a lengthy time, the Assemblage Point may be in a detrimental low location.

Negative Levels: Concentrated Persecution. 10:90% Essence v. Ego Ratio.

- The self is in a desperate negative state.

- The self is compressed to a small point. Everything is meaningless and life is pointless. It is a state of ultimate fear, paranoia, neurosis, where suicide seems to be the only option for escape.

- Any length of time spent in this state may cause the Assemblage Point to drop to a low location. Also, low locations of the Assemblage Point caused by any previous traumatic incident can precipitate this state of consciousness.

Negative Levels: Eternal Inferno. 1:99% Essence v. Ego Ratio.

- The self is trapped in a universe of the quintessence of evil and the deepest of hell from which there is no escape.

- The self is completely meaningless and is fused with other malevolent entities in the universe that are sinister or diabolically satanical. One is incarcerated there for eternity.

- Here again, any length of time spent in this state may precipitate a very low Assemblage Point location and low locations can precipitate this state of consciousness.

Increasing Positive States And Reducing Negative States

Man becomes what he dreams. Negative experiences appear to be a necessary inconvenience, yet without them, the attributes that sustain the positive levels would not exist. There would be no need for instinct, passion, compassion, expression, intuition or wisdom and we could all float around in the stagnant waters of complacency and pseudo-contentment. Sir Isaac Newton combined 'Holy Scriptures' with his scientific professional duties (see chapter 4). Experiencing diversified consciousness of the higher levels endows 'genius'. All 'Holy Scriptures, believe them or not and regardless of their religious culture, when read, heard or contemplated, grant access to the highest states of consciousness. Additionally, they provide safeguards against participating in the lowest levels. Understanding the maps of the positive and negative levels of consciousness by recapitulating one's life experiences can lead to unique and stable states of being and freedom.

Exercise: Sitting in full sunlight and absorbing the seven rainbow colours from the sun, directing the colours to the appropriate parts of the body as the breath is retained can improve the activity and attributes of the seven chakras. These simple breathing techniques accumulate prana, as outlined in the previous chapter.

Day 1: Sunday. Preparatory phase: Sitting in morning sunlight with an upright spine, establish deep rhythmic breathing through both nostrils for a minimum of twelve full breaths, using the seven one seven one count as in the previous chapter. Always pause for one count between inhaling and exhaling.

Practise this with the eyes closed and at the same time visualising radiant cosmic energy entering the thousands of filaments or channels of your energy body.

Secondary phase: Once a deep breathing rhythm has been established on the thirteenth breath hold the breath inside for a count of seven. At the same time strongly visualise the colour Red. Direct the colour red to the root chakra area. After retaining the breath for a count of seven, breathe out slowly through both nostrils to the count of seven. Complete three full breaths for the colour red, always retaining the breath to a count of seven and pause for one count before inhaling again.

Day 2: Monday. Proceed with the preparatory phase outlined in day one. On the thirteenth breath, retain the breath for a count of seven and visualise the colour Orange, directing it to the sacral chakra, midway between the base of the spine and the umbilical region. Complete three retention breaths using the colour orange.

Day 3: Tuesday. Proceed with the preparatory phase. On the thirteenth breath, retain the breath for a count of seven and visualise the colour Yellow, directing it to the solar plexus chakra, at the umbilical region. Complete three retention breaths with colour yellow.

Day 4: Wednesday. Proceed with the preparatory phase. On the thirteenth breath, retain the breath for a count of seven and visualise the colour Green, directing it to the heart chakra. Complete three retention breaths with colour green.

Day 5: Thursday. Proceed with the preparatory phase. On the thirteenth breath, retain the breath for a count of seven and visualise the colour Blue, directing it to the throat chakra area. Complete three retention breaths with colour blue.

Day 6: Friday. Proceed with the preparatory phase. On the thirteenth breath, retain the breath for a count of seven and visualise the colour Indigo. Draw this colour down from above the top of your head, visualise it turning at right angles and exiting through the brow chakra at the centre of the forehead. Complete three retention breaths with this technique.

Day 7: Saturday. Proceed with the preparatory phase. On the thirteenth breath, retain the breath for a count of seven and visualise the colour Violet. Draw this colour down from above the top of your head, directing it around your crown. As before, complete three retention breaths.

The recommended duration is two weeks and is best practised during a waxing moon phase. The environment must be clean, relaxed and free of chemical and electromagnetic pollution.

A central located Assemblage Point is essential. Both nostrils must be clear and open so that the accumulated prana, chi or kei is balanced in the left and right psychic channels (ida and pingala). It is common for one nostril to be restricted or closed, this can be unblocked by massaging the opposite large toe or by applying pressure using a clenched fist under the opposite arm pit.

For steadfast personality types, the secondary retention phase can be extended from three breaths to a maximum of twelve breaths.

This exercise should be restricted to the hours between sunrise and noon and should be practised at the same time each day, preferably before breakfast. It should be done in a relaxed smooth and easy manner, since force or exertion just add tension.

This discipline should not be practised by pregnant women. Women should not practise this exercise for the 2 days before the onset of menstruation or during menstruation, making 7 days in any given month that are prohibited. The reason for this is that there is a reverse flow of energy in these days, and if practised during this time, the menstrual period could be cut short from the normal 5 days to 3 days. Commence the exercise on the first Sunday following cessation of the menstrual flow.

Do not practise this if you are ill, taking drugs or medication or if you are receiving psychiatric medications or therapy.

This is a pro-active exercise. One of the many benefits of this exercise will be to increase the awareness of colours in general. Dreams will become more colourful, vivid, memorable and meaningful. The desires to buy bright coloured clothes, or decorate the house in brighter decor, at this time should be disregarded until one has become accustomed to the increased energy and consciousness levels.

Fig. 8:21. Dr John C. Lilly. MD. (January 6, 1915 – September 30, 2001) was an American physician, psychoanalyst and writer. He is best remembered as a pioneer researcher into the nature of consciousness using as his principal tools the isolation tank, dolphin communication and psychedelic drugs. He was an iconoclast and prominent member of the Californian counter-culture of scientists, mystics and thinkers that arose in the late 1960's and early 70's. Albert Hofmann, Gregory Bateson, Ram Dass, Timothy Leary, Werner Erhard, and Richard Feynman were all frequent visitors to his home.

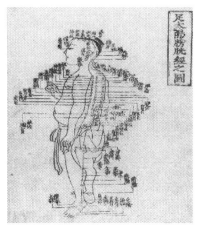

Fig. 8:22. Acupuncture chart from Hua Shou (AD 1340s, China Ming dynasty). This image from Shi si jing fa hui (Expression of the Fourteen Meridians). ([Tokyo] : Suharaya Heisuke kanko, Kyoho gan [1716]).

Fig. 8:23. Baron Dr. Carl (Karl) Ludwig von Reichenbach (February 12, 1788 - January 19, 1869) was a notable chemist, geologist, metallurgist, naturalist, industrialist and philosopher, a member of the prestigious Prussian Academy of Sciences, and considered one of the top 1,000 scientists of all times.

He dedicated himself in his last years to research an unproved field of energy combining electricity, magnetism and heat, emanating from all living things, which he called the Odic force (Prana, Chi or Kei).

Bibliography, References And Follow-Up Reading

Avalon, Arthur, (Sir John Woodroffe). *The Serpent Power - the Secrets of Tantric and Shakti Yoga (1928)*. Dover Publications Inc.

Brunton, Paul, Dr. *The Wisdom Of the Overself*. Rider.

Brunton, Paul, Dr. *The Inner Reality*. Rider.

Brunton, Paul, Dr. *The Spiritual Crisis of Man*. Rider.

Brunton, Paul, Dr. *A Search in Secret India*. Rider.

Brunton, Paul, Dr. *The Secret Path*. Rider.

Brunton, Paul, Dr. *A Search in Secret Egypt*. Rider.

Brunton, Paul, Dr. *The Hidden Teachings Beyond Yoga*. Rider.

Brunton, Paul, Dr. *The Quest for the Overself*. Rider.

Castaneda, Carlos, PhD. *The Art of Dreaming*. Harper Collins.

Castaneda, Carlos, PhD. *A Separate Reality*. Penguin Books.

Evens-Wentz, W.V., *The Tibetan Book of the Dead*. Oxford University Press.

Fludd, Robert. *17th century representation of the 'third eye' connection to the 'higher worlds'*. Ref: http://en.wikipedia.org/wiki/Third_eye.

Gabriel, Stux, MD and Bruce Pomeranz, Prof. MD. PhD, *Basics of Acupuncture*. Springer-Verlag.

Garrison, Omar. *Tantra*. Academy Editions.

Harner, Michael, *The Way Of The Shaman*. Bantam Books.

Heffern, Richard. *Secrets of the Mind Altering Plants of Mexico*. Pyramid Books.

Hunt, Rowland, *The Seven Keys to Colour Healing*. Lowe and Brydone.

Huxley, Aldous. *The Doors Of Perception & Heaven And Hell*. Penguin Books.

Johari, Harish, *The Healing Power Of Gem Stones In Tantra, Ayurveda, Astrology*. Destiny Books.

Krishna, Gopi, *The Awakening of Kundalini*. E. P. Dutton & Company.

Leadbeater, C. W., *The Chakras*. The Theosophical Publishing House.

Lad, Vasant, Dr. Ayurveda, *The Science Of Self Healing*. Lotus Press, Sante Fa, New Mexico.

Leary, Tomthy. *The Politics of Ecstacy*. Paladin.

Lilly, John, C. Lilly MD. *The Deep Self, Profound Relaxation and The Tank Isolation Technique*. Simon and Schuster, New York.

Lilly, John, C. Lilly MD. *The Centre of the Cyclone*. Calder and Boyars.

Lilly, John, C. Lilly MD. *The Human Biocomputer*. Abacus.

McGillion, Frank. *The Opening Eye*. Coventure Ltd.

Merrell-Wolf, Franklin. *Pathways Through To Space - An Experiential Journal*. Julian Press.

Morris, Desmond, *The Naked Ape*. Triad Grafton Books. Also see BBC's web page: http://news.bbc.co.uk/onthisday/hi/dates/stories/october/12/newsid_3116000/3116329.stm

Mantak Chia, Michael Win. *Taoist Secrets of Love - Cultivating Male Sexual Energy*. Aurora Press.

Mantak Chia & Maneewan Chia. *Healing Through The Tao - Cultivating Female Sexual Energy*. Huntington.

Motoyama. Hiroshi, *Theories of the Chakras: Bridges to Higher Consciousness*. Quest Books. The Theosophical Publishing House.

Reichenbach, Baron, Karl, Von, *The Mysterious Odic Force*. The Aquarian Press.

Prakash, Satya, Swami. *Pantanjala Raja Yoga*. S. Chand & Company Ltd.

Sannella, Lee, MD. *Kundalini - Psychosis Or Transcendence?* H. S. Dakin Company.

Scuts, Richard Evans. *Hofmann, Albert. Plants of the Gods. Origins of Hallucinogenic Use*. Hutchinson.

Scot-Mumby, Keith, MB, ChB. *Virtual Medicine*. Thorsons.

Stafford, Peter. *Psychedelics Encyclopedia*. Tarcher.

Swiftdeer Reagan, Harley, Ph.D. *Training Manual for Aura Perceptual Analysis*. Gold Horse Unlimited., USA.

Watts, Alan. *The Way of Zen*. Pelican Books.

Wilson, Robert, Anton. *Promethus Rising*. Falcon Press, USA.

Chapter 9

Journeys Out Of The Body

The accumulated experiences of my life and those of thousands of friends and acquaintances around this planet have concluded that individual consciousness is not restricted to the physical body or the five senses. This is not a question of 'belief', but is the accountability of 'knowing' as a result of direct interaction with universal quantum consciousness for sustained periods.

Countless individuals have published accounts of their experiences and journeys into other states of consciousness. Extra sensory perception, out–of-the-body experiences, astral travel, travelling, clairvoyance, astral projection, are just some of the terms used. The fact is that the 'locals or realms' experienced by individuals exploring the supernatural are as real, unique, comprehensive and engulfing as our own world.

Searching the Internet using the keywords 'journey out of the body', one search engine pulled up over eight million listings. Other keywords are: Astral elevation, disembodiment, dream time, ESP projection, etheric projection, flight of the soul, mind projection, mind travelling, mystic death, psychic travel, shamanic journey, soul travel, spirit walking. I was surprised by the extensive Internet listings supporting thousands of books for sale, accounts of personal experience, web sites providing courses and training and discussion forums. I concluded the interest in high states of consciousness was much greater than I had previously imagined. It is a vast global networking community.

Out of the body experiences can also occur while under surgery, anaesthetics, close to death encounters such as car accidents, substance abuse and drug overdose. Additionally being very sick with infections or disease and extreme hunger and thirst can elicit similar experiences. There are many personal accounts listed on the Internet.

In 1972 Robert A. Monroe a businessman published a book entitled: 'Journeys Out Of The Body'. This is an extraordinary book containing graphic diary accounts of his and the supernatural experiences of others. This book also contains specific instructions and methods that the reader can practise to experience astral travel.

Robert Monroe's work also makes a number of significant disclosures that are relative to the Assemblage Point.

In 1958 Monroe found himself leaving his physical body to travel via a 'second body' to other locales far removed from our consensus physical and spiritual realities. He conducted a series of experiments that conclusively affirmed the existence of a 'second body' that could be projected from his physical body. Using disciplined mental techniques, he could shift his conscious awareness into his 'second body' and travel to distant locales while his physical body remained behind in a trance state.

While on one of his frequent out of the body excursions, he discovered that his second body was attached to his physical body via a cord consisting of hundreds of tendon - like strands packed neatly together. This cord was attached to the centre of his back and the hundreds of strands or filaments spread and fanned out to form his second body. This suggests that his projected 'second body' had an Assemblage Point entering at the centre of the shoulder blades.

Another intriguing disclosure of his was that when he occupied his second body, his body image was reversed, his left leg and left arm was on his right side and vice versa. The transposition of his consciousness from his physical to his projected second body somehow produced a 'mirror image' effect. Monroe assumes that he is not unique and that every human retains the possibility to project or possess a 'second body'.

He is not alone. Dr. Carlos Castaneda undertook specific shamanistic instructions to gain mastery over his dreaming double or 'second body'. His books contain many graphic accounts of the journeys that he and his companions made into supernatural realms via their dreaming doubles.

The Assemblage Point is intrinsic in the shamanic teachings of Don Juan Matus as recorded in Castaneda's books both in relation

194

to the physical body and the second body or dreaming double. Don Juan discusses the importance of the Assemblage Point of the physical body with regard to health and disease and this is recorded in Castaneda's book: 'The Fire From Within' published in 1985. Robert Monroe's book 'Journey Out Of The Body' suggests that there is also an Assemblage Point attached to the back of the 'second body' or dreaming double as do the later books of Carlos Castaneda.

To avoid any confusion between this work and my previous publications, the Assemblage Point information that I have presented here is entirely to do with the Assemblage Point of our physical body and emotional level of health as it is on this planet, and not the Assemblage Point of the 'second body' or dreaming double existing in some distant supernatural realm or parallel universe.

The Science Of The Death Process

The law of energy conservation states that energy can neither be created nor destroyed. It can only be changed in form.

When we are alive, we have "life energy" in our body. When we are dead that energy is gone. Physics says it does not cease to be; it can only change form. Therefore, there is a part of us, the energy part, which exists beyond the body, and continues after the body ceases to be.

The following notes were given to me by a medic who attended the final weeks of the life of a famous Indian Guru. They reveal some amazing details concerning the process of his death.

"_. . . . .Interestingly, a few weeks before he left his body, he told me he could see the "vibrating blue light" over his forehead. He asked me to feel its powerful pulsation. He told me that if it moved over his navel it meant death. Two days later he told me_

Fig. 9:1. The Buddhist Exit From Labyrinths of the Human Assemblage Point Series.

195

it had moved to his hara or navel area. He left his body a short while later."

This important disclosure illustrates how the energy body unshackles itself from the human physical body envelope and in many ways corroborates the teachings of the shaman, Don Juan.

'The Tibetan Book of The Dead' by Evans Wentz is ostensibly a translation of sacred Tibetan scripture of the science of the death process. Within it is detailed information concerning the manipulation of an energy referred to as the "Vital Force". This Vital Force is the life force or energy that leaves the body at the moment of death.

The Tibetan text states that the process of death is the same for all sentient beings and that the dying person will come face to face with the 'clear light of the void'. This is an ecstatic state of consciousness that western saints and mystics call illumination. The process of a natural death as apposed to an accidental or violent death takes about three and half days. During this period the dying person will be in a state of swoon. Accompanying symptoms are many and variable such as:

1) Heavy pressure on the body as if the body is sinking into the earth.

2) Clammy coldness as if the body is sinking into water.

3) Bodily disintegration as if it is being blown apart into atoms or sinking into fire.

Each of these symptoms is accompanied by unmistakable external changes to the physical body. These can be loss of sight, loss of hearing, loss of consciousness, erratic or gasping breathing. Tibetan lamas or priests trained in the science of the death process are able to recognise the various psychic symptoms to determine the precise time that the energy body releases its bonds to the physical body. This science of

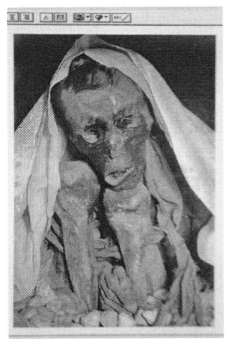

Fig. 9:2. Sangha Tenzin a mummified Buddhist Monk. His Hymalayan tomb was exposed in 1975 by an earthquake.

the death process has been arrived at by dying lamas explaining the process of death itself to their students in elaborate discriminating detail.

During the critical moment of the death process when the dying person's breathing ceases but before the heart stops beating, the 'vital force' is located in the area of the heart centre within the central psychic channel called the sushumna nadi. There it remains so long as the heart is beating. At this point momentary confrontation with the 'clear light of the void' (illumination) occurs. When the heart stops beating, then the vital force is thrown backwards and downwards and rushes into the left and right psychic nerves (the ida and pingala nadis) and exits via the navel gap.

The Vital Force is manipulated by a priest, medicine man or shaman assisting the dying person before the dying person's breathing is arrested. Pressure is applied to arteries around the neck, each side of the throat to maintain the dying person in full consciousness. These death rights are performed as the person is dying to prevent the vital energy from traversing the navel nerve centre and exiting through the gap just below the navel. With the priest's assistance and under these circumstances, the only other exit for the 'vital force' is though the crown aperture (Brahmanic aperture), and full consciousness through the death process is maintained.

The Tibetans believe that enlightenment occurs and reincarnation is prevented when the vital force passes out through the crown aperture.

The Mystery Of The Two Apertures

The energy of the human body is finite. Regardless of the best of medicine, at the end of the day, we all die.

As a person approaches death, their Assemblage Point descends down towards the navel area. The Assemblage Point locations of old infirm patients who are close to death, will generally always be very close to the navel line. The navel aperture is a natural weakness in the human energy field that relates to the aperture of the umbilical cord. For the developing foetus, the navel aperture is the source of energy and vitality. This aperture is closed shortly after birth, but there remains a weak point that stays with us for life. When death occurs, the person's vital energy returns to the universe. It leaves their body by the same route that it entered in the beginning, that is, out through the navel aperture.

In India's northern Himalayan State of Himachal Pradesh which is about 6000 metres above sea level, there is a tomb that was exposed in 1975 by an earthquake. Inside the catacomb was a mummified Tibetan monk believed to have been there for at least five hundred years. The full details of the discovery where reported in a television documentary program. The mummy was identified as Sangha Tenzin, a Buddhist monk.

The heroic priestly human was discovered sitting in a cross legged meditating position, shrouded with a shawl over his head and shoulders. It is fabled that he sacrificed his life to save the inhabitants of a local village from starvation. He was well preserved, skin was unbroken and there was hair on the head. He had induced self mummification by a special ascetic diet and starvation to reduce his body fat, shrink parts of his body and reduce body fluids to prevent putrefaction.

One very interesting point that bewildered the TV reporters was that he was using a meditation belt which was wrapped around his thorax and then down around his knees. Tibetan monks from a Tibetan Monastery were interviewed by the TV reporters and they stated that the monk had sacrificed himself by using a secret Tibetan meditation ritual and that his meditation belt was part of the Tibetan monastic ritual, but they would not comment on the strange way it was wrapped around the monk's neck.

The reason for the single turn of the meditation belt around the neck was so that the monk when in his final moments of death could apply pressure to his thorax via the weight of his legs pressing on the belt. This practice is arranged so that pressure is applied to the neck as a self induced method to prevent the vital force from progressing downwards to the gap at the umbilical region, thus preventing his vital force from exiting his body via the navel portal. This guarantees that he succeeds in his spiritual life on earth and exits via his crown aperture and eliminates the assistance of a second person's presence at the time of death.

For this reason, I personally am not interested in euthanasia. Whilst I cannot possibly predict the circumstances of my death, I would prefer to retain courage and pass through the experience consciously.

Not only in life, but even in death, it would seem that we are given a choice. The Tibetan Book of The Dead and many other books, including the self sacrifice of the monk, makes it clear that there is a second aperture at the top of our head. The possibilities look exciting. We have the choice to leave the body by the normal route of the average man, that is, when our Assemblage Point traverses the navel. Or we can, by using special techniques, die another type of death, perhaps the "hero's death", with the Assemblage Point or vital force exiting through the crown aperture at the top of the head and retain full consciousness throughout our death process.

Fig. 9:3. The 14th Dalai Lama, Tenzin Gyatso, born (Reincarnated) on July 6, 1935, in conversation with President George W. Bush in the White House on May 23, 2001, the year of the 9-11 attacks on the Twin Towers of the World Trade Centre, New York. The Dalai Lama was awarded the Nobel Peace Prize in 1989.

Tenzin Gyatso was recognised as the rebirth of the 13th Dalai Lama and renamed *Jetsun Jamphel Ngawang Lobsang Yeshe Tenzin Gyatso* (seven words- see Chapter 10). His name translates as "Holy Lord, Gentle Glory, Compassionate, Defender of the Faith, Ocean of Wisdom". Tibetan Buddhists normally refer to him as Yeshe Norbu or in English "Wish Fulfilling Gem".

Bibliography, References And Follow-Up Reading

Brunton, Paul, Dr. *Hermits in The Himalayas.* Rider.

Brunton, Paul, Dr. *The Inner Reality.* Rider.

Brunton, Paul, Dr. *The Spiritual Crisis of Man.* Rider.

Evens-Wentz, W.V., *The Tibetan Book of the Dead.* Oxford University Press.

Lilly, John C. MD. *The Scientist.* Lippincott.

Lilly, John, C. Lilly MD. *The Centre of the Cyclone.* Calder and Boyars.

Monroe. Robert, *Journey Out of the Body.* Corgi Books.

Stapledon, Olaf, *Star Maker.* First Published by Methuen 1937. Penguin Books.

Tenzin, Sangha Buddhist monk. See: http://www.phayul.com/news/article.aspx?id=6214 and http://www.cyberindian.com/india/index.php?action=showdetail&id=3053

Wallis Budge,E. A. *The Egyptian Book Of The Dead - The Papyrus Of Ani.* Dover Press..

Whale, J. The *Buddhist Exit. From Labyrinths of the Human Assemblage Point.* Oil on Canvas: Size 28 x 22 inches, framed.

Merrell-Wolf, Franklin. *Pathways Through To Space - An Experiential Journal.* Julian Press.

Chapter 10

THE AFTERLIFE

An early integrated account of journeying though the extreme lower and very high states of consciousness is recorded by the Italian poet Dante (1265-1321 AD). Completed just before his death, 'The Divine Comedy' records his journeys through hell and the seven steps of purgatory. Later he journeys through the seven circling spheres towards the abode of God and heaven. This great mystical work has often been rationalised as a long progress of understanding and has inspired many great artists.

On completing the final draft of this book and having printed a copy, due to many months of intense concentration and then abruptly with nothing on my mind, I was left with the feeling of a great vacuum. With this feeling I retired to bed and that night I journeyed out of my body. Although I prefer a good night's sleep, sometimes 'otherworldly' excursions are unavoidable. For me the main factors that distinguish 'out of the body' experiences from those of ordinary dreams and lucid dreams is: unfamiliar landscape, strange fauna and flora, unearth-like architecture, strange languages and unaccountable time differences and time travel. Besides these, the other fundamental distinction is that I can traverse large distances without any effort.

Fig. 10:1. Dante shown holding a copy of The Divine Comedy, next to the entrance to Hell, the seven terraces of Mount Purgatory and the city of Florence, with the spheres of Heaven above, in Michelino's fresco.

I do not need to walk, climb or swim. Without the need to use arms, legs or feet, I can propel myself at great speed in any direction and through any medium just by an act of will alone.

Seven Heavens And Seven Hells

On this particular occasion I was confronted by a huge pair of ornamental gates guarded on the inside by a large creature with long glistening fur, a lion's mane and large claws and teeth. This gatekeeper let me pass into a curious celestial world. I travelled on, levitating high across the country at great speed. Eventually I arrived at a hamlet and from the door of one of the dwellings came out a beautiful woman with long blond hair. She invited me in to stay with her. I declined, saying that it was not my home and I had to find my own house.

Fig. 10:2. Dante is lost in Canto 1. Gustave Doré engravings illustrated The Divine Comedy (1861 1868).

Days went past and I visited many towns and villages looking for my road and house without success. Everyone I confronted had no idea how to assist. I simply could not remember my address. I became quite concerned and eventually I was approached by a voice, a formless entity on my left side. He suggested that I follow him to a place he knew that had some paper upon which I could write down my address. Guiding me through the streets, we entered a large, columned building into a vaulted hall and approached a counter. I stared at the three pieces of parchment scattered on the counter, drawn on each was a hieroglyph similar to the ancient Egyptian style. I was looking for an unused piece to write on, while at the same time trying to remember my address. Floundering with this and not finding a pen I

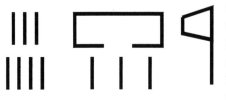

Fig. 10:3. Egyptian Hieroglyphs for a) Number Seven b) Hall or House c) God.

realised I had no arms or hands to write with. Suddenly I remembered my PO Box number and blurted out loud 'PO Box 31'.

Instantly I was back with my body in my bed, heart pounding and gasping for air. My pulse rate was close to 200 beats per minute and I had been sweating profusely. It occurred to me that had I not remembered my post office box number, I may well have been trapped in that domain not to return to earth, my deceased body being discovered in the morning by the housekeeper.

Seven Heavens Of Egypt

All of the following day I was puzzled by the significance of this excursion and could not get the hieroglyphs out of my mind. Still perplexed a day or so passed before I remembered that I had a copy of the Egyptian Book of the Dead (The Papyrus of Ani) in my library. I quickly located it and it fell open at the following text:

"Hall of the seventh, The name of the doorkeeper is Sekhmet-em-tsu-sen...."

Reading backwards from this, I discovered that the ancient Egyptian mythology spoke of seven Halls or Chambers of the journey of the afterlife. Sekhet-Aaru, the land of the blessed, was divided into seven sections, each of which was entered through a Gate having a 'doorkeeper', a 'watcher' and a 'herald' in attendance. Examining the hieroglyphic text, so far as I am capable to decipher, the three glyphs on the pieces of parchment that I witnessed out there had the meaning of 'seven', 'God' and 'hall or house'.

I had attempted to read this book in 1974, but at that time I couldn't make much sense of it. Reading from it thirty two years on triggered poignant synchronicities.

Fig. 10:4. Illustration of the Seven Chakras above the Crown Chakra.

203

Seven Heavens Of Hindu And Buddhist Religions

According to Buddhism and Hindu belief systems, there are three sets of seven chakras. The lower set of chakras belong to the instinctive, or animal body or under-worlds, and they exist below the root or base chakra discussed in previous chapters. They are called:

1) Atal, 2) Vital, 3) Sutal, 4) Rasatal, 5) Dharatal, 6) Mahatal, and 7) Patal.

As human incarnates, we have transcended these seven lower chakras, and in our realities and personal evolution we deal with the seven chakras relating to our physical form. These have been discussed in earlier chapters and they are:

1) Muladhara, 2) Svadhisthana, 3) Manipura, 4) Anahata, 5) Vishuddhi, 6) Ajna, 7) Sahasrara.

Above this set of chakras is said to be the third set. This third set is the lokas (chambers or halls), the higher domains or dimensions of existence. When we cease to be human beings, and transcend our individuality or ego, then the third set of chakras begins to function within us. We move up higher and expand. The seven higher chakras are called:

1) Bhu Loka, 2) Bhuvar Loka, 3) Swaiia Laka, 4) Maha Loka, 5) Janaha Taka, 6) Tapaha Laka and 7) Satya Laka.

These are the seven higher dimensions, heavens, or planes of consciousness that are held in awe by the Tibetan, Indian and Southeast Asian religions. Exploring and connecting with the higher domains while living on earth is the sacred quest, it provides the initiates with special powers together with high levels of emotional and physical health.

Fig. 10:5. The Angel Gabriel (Jibril) cleansing Mohammed's heart of impurities in preparation for his ascent to heaven, while the other angels watch. From the 16th century manuscript The Progress of the Prophet, from Turkey.

The point that I had missed in 1974 was that the ancient

Egyptian religion also proclaimed the existence seven heavens each with a Doorkeeper, Watcher and Herald (The Seven Arits or Halls).

1) The First Arit. Hall the First. The name of the Doorkeeper is Sekhet-her-asht-aru.

2) The Second Arit. Hall the Second. The name of the Doorkeeper is Unhat.

3) The Third Arit. Hall the Third. The name of the Doorkeeper is Unem-hauatu-ent-pehui.

4) The Fourth Arit. Hall the Fourth. The name of the Doorkeeper is Khesef-her-asht-kheru.

5) The Fifth Arit. Hall the Fifth. The name of the Doorkeeper is Ankhf-em-fent.

6) The Sixth Arit. Hall the Sixth. The name of the Doorkeeper is Atek-tau-kehaq-kheru.

7) The Seventh Arit: Hall the Seventh. The name of the Doorkeeper is Sekhmet-em-tsu-sen.

Seven Heavens Of Islam

The Islamic religion also has seven heavens and the Holy Koran states:

067.003 (Al Mulk [The Sovereignty, Control, Dominion]) He Who created the seven heavens one above another: No want of proportion wilt thou see in the Creation of (Allah) Most Gracious. So turn thy vision again: seest thou any flaw?

017.044 (Al Isra [Isra, The Night Journey, Children of Israel]) The seven heavens and the earth, and all beings therein, declare His glory: there is not a thing but celebrates His praise; And yet ye understand not how they declare His glory! Verily He is Oft Forbear, Most Forgiving!

Fig. 10:6. The Christian Exit of Compassion (Male) From Labyrinths of the Human Assemblage Point Series.

Seven Heavens Of The Early Christians

The early Christian writings titled the 'Ascension of Isaiah' compiled around 150 200 C.E. also refer to seven heavens. Isaiah's otherworldly journey begins as he ascends with the angel guide to "the firmament" above the world, but below the heavens. He then proceeds through each of the heavens to the dwelling place of the Most High (God) and his "Beloved" (Christ) in the seventh heaven:

'Chapter 10: 7. And I heard the voice of the Most High, the Father of my Lord, saying to my Lord Christ who will be called Jesus: 8. "Go forth and descend through all the heavens, and thou wilt descend to the firmament and that world: to the angel in Sheol thou wilt descend, but to Haguel thou wilt not go. 9. And thou wilt become like unto the likeness of all who are in the five heavens. 10. And thou wilt be careful to become like the form of the angels of the firmament [and the angels also who are in Sheol]. 11. And none of the angels of that world shall know that Thou art with Me of the seven heavens and of their angels. 12. And they shall not know that Thou art with Me, till with a loud voice I have called (to) the heavens, and their angels and their lights, (even) unto the sixth heaven, in order that you mayest judge and destroy the princes and angels and gods of that world, and the world that is dominated by them: 13. For they have denied Me and said: "We alone are and there is none beside us." 14. And afterwards from the angels of death Thou wilt ascend to Thy place. And Thou wilt not be transformed in each heaven, but in glory wilt Thou ascend and sit on My right hand.'

Fig. 10:7. The Christian Exit of Devotion (Female) From Labyrinths of the Human Assemblage Point Series.

Descent And Ascent Of Christ Through The Seven Heavens

Isaiah hears the voice of God calling on his Beloved (Lord Christ) to descend, to trace the steps that Isaiah had just traversed. Isaiah then witnesses the descent of the Christ to the womb of the Virgin Mary.

Chapter 10: 17. *And so I saw my Lord (Christ) go forth from the seventh heaven into the sixth heaven...................... 19. And I saw, and when the angels saw Him (Christ), thereupon those in the sixth heaven praised and lauded Him; for He had not been transformed after the shape of the angels there, and they praised Him and I also praised with them. 20. And I saw when He descended into the fifth heaven, that in the fifth heaven He made Himself like unto the form of the angels there, and they did not praise Him (nor worship Him); for His form was like unto theirs. 21. And then He descended into the forth heaven, and made Himself like unto the form of the angels there. 22. And when they saw Him, they did not praise or laud Him; for His form was like unto their form. 23. And again I saw when He descended into the third heaven, and He made Himself like unto the form of the angels in the third heaven. 24. And those who kept the gate of the (third) heaven demanded the password, and the Lord gave (it) to them in order that He should not be recognized. And when they saw Him, they did not praise or laud Him; for His form was like unto their form. 25. And again I saw when He descended into the second heaven, and again He gave the password there; those who kept the gate proceeded to demand and the Lord to give. 26. And I saw when He made Himself like unto the form of the angels in the second heaven, and they saw Him and they did not praise Him; for His form was like unto their form. 27. And again I saw when He*

Fig. 10:8. Seven Branch Candlestick (Manorah). Illustration: Sack of Jerusalem on inside wall of Arch of Titus in Italy.

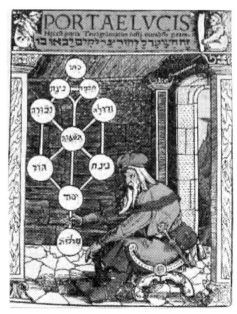

Fig. 10:9. Medieval painting of the Kabbalistic Tree of Life.

descended into the first heaven, and there also He gave the password to those who kept the gate, and He made Himself like unto the form of the angels who were on the left of that throne, and they neither praised nor lauded Him; for His form was like unto their form. 28. But as for me no one asked me on account of the angel who conducted me. 29. And again He descended into the firmament where dwelleth the ruler of this world, and He gave the password to those on the left, and His form was like theirs, and they did not praise Him there; but they were envying one another and fighting; for here there is a power of evil and envying about trifles. 30. And I saw when He descended and made Himself like unto the angels of the air, and He was like one of them. 31. And He gave no password; for one was plundering and doing violence to another. Chapter 11: 2. And I indeed saw a woman of the family of David the prophet, named Mary, and Virgin, and she was espoused to a man named Joseph, a carpenter, and he also was of the seed and family of the righteous David of Bethlehem Judah.

Isaiah then witnesses the birth, life and crucifixion of Jesus. He then witnesses the resurrection and ascension of Jesus up through to the seventh heavens and take his place next to God.

Fig. 10:10. The Exit of Zion From Labyrinths of the Human Assemblage Point Series.

20. In Jerusalem indeed I was Him being crucified on a tree. 21. And likewise after the third day rise again and remain days. 22. And the angel who conducted me said: "Understand, Isaiah": and I saw when He sent out the Twelve Apostles and ascended.................25. And He ascended into the second heaven, and He did not transform Himself, but all the angels who were on the right and on the left and the throne in the midst. 26. Both worshipped Him and praised Him and said: "How did our Lord escape us whilst descending, and we perceived not?" 27. And in like manner He ascended into the third heaven, and they praised and said in like manner. 28.

And in the fourth heaven and in the fifth also they said precisely after the same manner. 29. But there was one glory, and from it He did not change Himself. 30. And I saw when He ascended into the sixth heaven, and they worshipped and glorified Him. 31. But in all the heavens the praise increased (in volume). 32. And I saw how He ascended into the seventh heaven, and all the righteous and all the angels praised Him. And then I saw Him sit down on the right hand of that Great Glory whose glory I told you that I could not behold. 33. And also the angel of the Holy Spirit I saw sitting on the left hand. 34. And this angel said unto me: "Isaiah, son of Amoz, it is enough for thee;... for thou hast seen what no child of flesh has seen. 35. And thou wilt return into thy garment (of the flesh) until thy days are completed. Then thou wilt come hither."

Jewish Seven Halls

A writing titled 'The Hierarchy of the Blessed Angels' mentions a different list of the seven archangels. They list them as following: Raphael, Gabriel, Chamuel, Michael, Adabiel, Haniel, Zaphiel. The first obvious teaching diagram of the Jewish esoteric tradition is the seven branched Manorah candlestick specified by God to Moses on Mount Sinai (Exodus 25). The seven branches represent the seven Halls:

1) Hod, 2) Gevurah, 3) Binah, 4) Keter, 5) Hokhmah, 6) Hesed, 7) Nezah.

The Kabbalah is a teaching tradition of hidden knowledge, the inner and mystical aspects of Judaism. The earliest documents associated with the Kabbalah come from the period 100 to 1000 A.D. They describe the attempts of "Merkabah" mystics to penetrate the seven upper halls (Hekaloth) of creation in order to reach the Merkabah the throne of God. These mystics appear to have used fasting, repetitious chanting, prayer and posture to induce trance states in which they contested their way though the seven gates and

Fig. 10:11. St Michael Fighting the Seven-Headed Dragon. Painting by Jehan Fouguet. 1420-1481, France.

209

guards to reach an ecstatic state in which they "saw God".

Mysterious Number Seven

The popularity of seven seems impressive and subjective.

In the Holy Bible, the New Testament has seventy-six verses containing the word 'seven'. The Old Testament has four hundred and eighty-six verses containing 'seven'. In the book of Revelation there are no less than forty-one verses containing 'seven' or 'seventh'.

> **Revelations 1:20:** *The mystery of the seven stars which thou sawest in my right hand, and the seven golden candlesticks. The seven stars are the angels of the seven churches: and the seven candlesticks which thou sawest are the seven churches.*

> **Revelations 8:2:** *And I saw the seven angels which stood before God; and to them were given seven trumpets.*

> **Revelations 8:6:** *And the seven angels which had the seven trumpets prepared themselves to sound.*

Continuing with seven: Seven ages of man; seven ancient wonders of the world; seven heavens; seven hells; seven pillars of wisdom; seven rays of the sun; seven musical notes; seven octaves on a piano; seven steps of Buddha; seven sisters of Australian Aborigines and Greek mythology; seven sacraments; seven councils of the early church; seven altars of Baalam; seven trumpets; seven seals; seven bowls; seven chakras of the body; seven riders of the Apocalypse; seven lost Golden Cities of El Dorado. The Dance of the Seven Veils; seven levels of the Chinese Taoist deities; Rome, was built on seven hills; seven deadly sins; seven beatitudes; seven virtues.....

Fig. 10:12. The Gates of Hell, Musée Rodin.

Seven Egyptian Hathors as Fates and the priestesses of Hathor have seven jars in their seven tunics. Ra has seven hawks representing the seven Wise Ones. There are seven houses of the underworld. Seven is the sacred number of Osiris; seven strings to Apollo's lyre; Pan's seven pipes; seven Wise Men of Greece; seven Great Holy Days in the Jewish year; seven branches to the Menorah; seven Jewels of the Brahmanas; seven gods before the floods and seven Wise Men saved from it.

In Islam the perfect number is seven with seven heavens; seven climates; seven earths and seven seas; seven colours; seven prophets; seven states or stations of the heart; seven attributes of God. The cave of Mithras has seven doors, seven altars, and a ladder with seven rungs symbolising the seven grades of initiation. There are seven branches to the Tree of Life each having seven leaves. The seven classical 'planets' : Sun, Moon, Mars, Mercury, Jupiter, Venus and Saturn lend their names to the seven days of the week. Both Celtic religion and shamanism have a world tree. In shamanism, the shaman climbs the world tree to go into the seven heavens. In Celtic religion, the Gods descend on the tree to mortal realms.

The Japanese people like the rest of the world, appear bewitched by the number seven. In Japanese folklore, there are seven treasures and seven

Fig. 10:13. Dante's guide rebuffs Malacoda and his fiends between ditches five and six in the eighth circle of Inferno, Canto 21.

Fig. 10:14. The Inferno Exit Eternal Drama Triangle: Persecutor, Victim & Rescuer From Labyrinths of the Human Assemblage Point Series.

deities of good luck. Japanese Buddhists believe people are reincarnated only seven times. The Japanese Zen Way to the Martial Arts called Bushido and is the way of the Samurai. The 'Way' is imperative and absolute and is bound by seven essential principles:

1) *Gi: The right decision, taken with equanimity, the right attitude, the truth. When we must die, we must die.*

2) *Yu: Bravery tinged with heroism.*

3) *Jin: Universal love, benevolence toward mankind; compassion.*

4) *Rei: Right action, a most essential quality, courtesy.*

5) *Makoto: Utter sincerity; truthfulness.*

6) *Melyo: Honor and glory.*

7) *Chugo: Devotion, loyalty.*

Seven-Headed Serpent

The seven headed dragon or serpent appear in the Holy Bible, throughout myths of the Middle East, India, Persia, the Far East, Cambodia, South America, Celtic lands and Mediterranean.

Revelations 12:3: *And there appeared another wonder in heaven; and behold a great red dragon, having seven heads and ten horns, and seven crowns upon his heads. (KJV)*

Fig. 10:15. Dante see the Divine Light. Gustave Doré engravings illustrating The Divine Comedy (1861 1868).

Revelations 12:7: *And there was a great battle in heaven. Michael and his Angels fought with the dragon.*

Revelations 12:8: *And prevailed not; neither was their place found anymore in heaven.*

Revelations 12:9: *And the great dragon was cast out, that old serpent,* *called the Devil and Satan, which deceiveth the whole world; he was cast out into earth and his angels were cast out with him.*

Seven Hells

Almost all religions believe in the hell, because most of them say that hell is a punishment for people who did wrong when they were alive. The Holy Koran states:

Al Qur'an, 015.043. *(Al Hijr [Al Hijr, Stoneland, Rocky City]) And verily, Hell is the promised abode for them all!*

Al Qur'an, 015.044. *To it are seven gates: for each of those gates is a (special) class (of sinners) assigned.*

Ancient Hindus believe that hell is a place for people who had been evil before dying. The Hindu Rig Veda speaks of " a deep abyss of lowest darkness." Some explain that there are no less than seven different hells. Classical Buddhism recognizes no less than seven 'fiery hells' superimposed on the general Land of No Return (avichi). Each hell is flanked on either side by four torture chambers (ustadas). These include a fiery pit and a quagmire. These are their hells:

1) *Revival (sanjiva), where the damned are eventually reanimated by winds;*

2) *The Black String (kalasutra), where damned are cut to pieces;*

3) *Concussion (sanghata), where damned are dashed between two mountains;*

4) *Weeping (raurava);*

5) *Great Weeping (maharaurava);*

6) *Heating (tapana);*

7) *Excessive Heating (pratatapana).*

The Zoroastrians said that there is a hell of "unending darkness" and also spoke of a "lake of fire to which the wicked will be ultimately consigned for their whole life.

The Spiritual Crisis Of Man

If we persevere and live our life to the highest ethical and moral standards, train ourselves and practise steadfastness and fortitude, what would be the purpose if our 'End' is exactly as that of a person that lived his entire life in intoxicated malevolency and corruption? The answer is common sense. If our consciousness passes through the death phase, we will encounter the full force of universal consciousness and the vast matrix of realities that comprise it.

People of dissimilar genetic origins have their customs and religions. All religions have their sanctioned heavens and their dreaded hells. Through their saviours and prophets, they maintain sanctuaries, prayers, scriptures, ethics and disciplines that fortify the faithful towards attainment and illumination. At the quantum level, the universe is large enough to accommodate all.

The ultimate human drama triangle is war, a persecutor/victim/ rescuer game. It is executed to kill and introvert the enemy into chronic apathy and propitiation. War also shifts the Assemblage Points location of masses on all sides into a detrimental position. Agnostics, Atheists, Darwinians and evolutionists often suggest that religions are responsible for the torment, contention and wars between humans. It seems to me that all of the religions of the human species have a common meta-program laid down in their scriptures intended to provide a passageway into their seven heavens and means to avoid falling into their seven hells. This meta-program has operated over thousands of generations regardless of continental geographical locations.

I am not a scholar of religious scripture, neither am I privileged with access to their esoteric documents and disciplines, but appears to me to have a universal unknown source.

All of the religions teach us the ethical standards of acceptable behaviour to discourage anarchy and permit us entry into their promised lands of heavenly paradise. Further, the numerous religions have inspired former generations to provide this planet with priceless works of art, music, architecture, mythology and science. Without the inspiration of their faith, humanity today would certainly be impoverished.

For many, the theory of evolution by natural selection has displaced our former religious beliefs and conscientious standards of social behaviour. Darwinist philosophy has lead to the 'survival of the fittest mentality' that has dominated scientific, industrial and social behaviour for the last two centuries. It has resulted in reckless exploitation, wasteful misuse and depletion of earth's natural resources, the daily extinction of plant and animal species along with the myriad of pervading environmental pollution and social behaviour problems. A recent opinion poll determined that over seventy percent of people living in the United Kingdom thought that standards of social behaviour or propriety had seriously deteriorated. Our prisons are overcrowded. The current Labour government is beside itself, it has generated three thousand new laws. That is one for every day that it has been in power. It is building more prisons in a vain attempt to temper the escalating negative and dangerous aspects of current international, national, social and domestic behaviour.

Our social deterioration is not caused by religious beliefs. All religions appear to stem from the same source and have much the same objectives. They have in the past provided teachings that have enabled adherents to moderate and transcend the negative aspects of human behaviour and the negative levels of emotional health. Thus they improve the stability of the Assemblage Point location.

So far as there is any contention between different religions and races, there is only so much room for discussion as the objectives of all of the main religions, belonging to the numerous races, have remained much the same for thousands of years. The accountability can be squarely attributed to an erosion of those principles and standards that propagate the highest levels of emotional health.

At all levels of human affairs from governments downwards, the 'survival of the fittest mentality' spawns bad behaviour by indulgence in the 'seven deadly sins': pride, envy, anger, sloth, greed, gluttony and lust with the inevitable consequences of whole communities falling into the chronic negative levels of emotional health, a hell on earth impoverished by the seven-headed serpent of seven vices.

Aside from the secret shamanic body of knowledge held and practised by the South West American Yaqui Indians and the Himalayan Tibetan Buddhist monks, I have not discovered any other religious or ethnic source that embraces the Assemblage Point in their culture. Yet every living man of every religion, agnostics and atheists alike, all endure their Assemblage Point locations and their emotional level of health.

Without including the human Assemblage Point in their science, atheists and evolutionists low on the scale of emotional health, those who uphold the 'survival of the fittest' mentality, use their science to introvert and invalidate those who try to preserve their faith. Accordingly anyone who holds religious tenets is deemed to be irrational.

The contrasting drama triangle is that radical and subversive righteous wrathful individuals and groups low on the scale of emotional health resort to the holy scriptures to justify and conceal the wrath they discharge, when attempting to introvert others high on the scale down into chronic appeasement and apathy.

The zoologist, Prof. Richard Dawkins is Oxford's Professor of the department of Public Understanding of Science. In one of his many published articles entitled 'The Improbability of God' he claims that there is no reason to believe that any sort of gods exist but there is good reason for believing that they do not exist and never have. He says that it has all been a gigantic waste of time and a waste of life and would be a joke of cosmic proportions if it was not so tragic.

Religious believers uphold that creationism is the truth about science so that all the facts of science and all scientific discoveries fit the creation model of origins. God has revealed himself to man in scripture, which makes it necessary for men to know, understand and obey the Word of God. They contend that it is the evolutionist that possesses an unreasonable faith in a theory that has not yet proven how life originated in the first place.

Prof. Dawkin's articles and books have provoked numerous responses, some vitriolic. In Dr. Brad Harrub's article entitled: 'Nature Attacks Religion', he quotes Prof. Richard Dawkins further as saying: *"I cannot see how this could be good for science, supernaturalism is fundamentally anti-scientific. Scientists work hard at trying to understand. Supernaturalism is an evasion of this responsibility. It's a shrug of the shoulders."* Dr. Harrub commentary on this is: *"Thus, Dawkins reduces belief in God to simply an act of shrugging one's shoulders."*

The Province Of The Mind Has No Limits

The late scientist, Dr John C. Lilly was the originator of the sensory isolation flotation tank. He spent a large part of his life researching the human mind and recording its countless states of consciousness together with its varied belief systems. I meet John for the first time in Berlin, in the summer of the year before the Iron Curtain was lifted. John cautioned me that in the province of the mind, what I believed to be true either is true or becomes true within certain limits and that these limits are further beliefs to be transcended. In the province of the mind there are no limits.

Professor Albert Einstein once said: "*Imagination is more important than knowledge. For knowledge is limited to all we now know and understand, while imagination embraces the entire world, and all there ever will be to know and understand.*"

Our true abode is in the 'mind', the science of evolution by natural selection is the study of life 'out there' in the material world and is conducted from inside the mind of the scientist. The Gods and Faith endure in the province of the mind and the mind has no limits. In the vast quantum domains of consciousness there is every good reason to believe in deities, prophets or spirit guides for example, as well as wrathful entities. By letting go of our limiting beliefs our consciousness expands. Anyone who takes a journey into the higher states of consciousness will discover boundless landscapes inhabited by spirits, entities both divine and malevolent.

Had Darwin, Freud or Jung discovered that the entry angle and location of our Assemblage Point has a direct influence on 'how we think, how we feel and how we behave', they would have also discovered the human energy field, the key to the supernatural and spiritual aspects of human existence. Had those early Victorian scientists and physicians known about their Assemblage Points and alongside their work, developed the blueprints contained in this book and in my earlier publications, then this planet and life as we know it today would be different. It would have evolved to a higher state of being.

The disciplines of true science lead man to a union with the universe out there, as it 'is' and not as he wishes it to be. The disciplines of the ascetic and spiritual life lead man to union with higher states of consciousness such as compassion, divine or saintly illumination, samadhi, satori, nirvana and so forth. Experiencing high states of consciousness not only lead us to the knowledge that we are not alone, but provides us with a level of fulfilment unobtainable by science and materialism alone. There is no choice between the two; both are necessary for a full and satisfactory life and compassionate coexistence on this planet.

The discovery of the Assemblage Point proves that there is more to man other than flesh and bones and death as the 'End'. With the publication of these blueprints, political, military, legal, financial, scientific, medical, educational and religious organizations throughout the world have the unique opportunity for an unprecedented way forward.

Incorporating this knowledge into their professional agendas will not only improve the quality of their life and their physical and emotional level of health, but also through their offices, for all of the millions living on this planet who endure positions low on the scale of emotional health and have lost faith.

Fig. 10:16. Dante and Beatrice gaze upon the highest Heaven; from Gustave Doré's illustrations to the Divine Comedy Paradiso Canto 31.

The highest positive and lowest negative levels of consciousness that we can experience on earth are indicators of what we maybe exposed to after the death of our physical body. In the domain of quantum consciousness there are no limits. We may come face to face with holy, wise or wrathful deities. How well we disciplined and trained ourselves when inhabiting and shackled to the relative comfort and safety of our physical body while on this planet may determine our fate in the unimaginable boundless currents of the quantum domains.

At the quantum level, the universe never began and will never end. All of the finite big bangs, the stars and galaxies, the black holes, our births, lives and deaths are only transforming events in the endless amplifications and attenuations of the intensity of the infinite frequencies of its being, an intelligent and creative being forever camouflaging its true form with change.

Bibliography, References And Follow-Up Reading

Alltonnian, H. & More, M. *Journeys into the Bright New World.* Para Press

Brunton, Paul, Dr. *The Wisdom Of the Overself.* Rider.

Brunton, Paul, Dr. *The Inner Reality.* Rider.

Brunton, Paul, Dr. *The Spiritual Crisis of Man.* Rider.

Dante. *The Divine Comedy - III Paradise.* Penguin Classics.

Dawkins, Richard Prof. *The Improbability of God.* http://www.simonyi.ox.ac.uk/dawkins/WorldOfDawkins archive/Dawkins/Work/Articles/1998 sumimprobabilityofgod.shtml

Evens-Wentz, W.V. *The Tibetan Book of the Dead.* Oxford University Press.

Forrest, Lynne. *The Three Faces of Victim - The Three Roles on the Drama Triangle Persecutor, Rescuer and Victim.* http://lynneforrest.com/html/

the_faces_of_victim.html

Harris, Thomas, Anthony. *I'm OK You're OK*. Harpercollins.

Fortune, Dion. *Psychic Self-Defence - A Study in Occult Pathology and Criminality.* Samuel Weiser.

Harrub, Brad, Ph.D. *Nature Attacks Religion*. Apologetics Press, http://www.apologeticspress.org

Harris, Thomas A. MD. *I'm OK - You're OK -Climbing Out Of The Cellar Of Your Mind.* Pan Books

Leadbeater, C. W., *The Chakras.* The Theosophical Publishing House.

Lilly, John C. MD., *Simulations of God - The Science of Beliefs.* Batam Books.

Merrell-Wolf, Franklin. *Pathways Through To Space - An Experiential Journal.* Julian Press.

Monroe. Robert, *Journey Out of the Body.* Corgi Books.

Motoyama. Hiroshi, *Theories of the Chakras: Bridges to Higher Consciousness.* Quest Books. The Theosophical Publishing House.

Stapledon, Olaf, *Star Maker.* First Published by Methuen 1937. Penguin Books.

Fouguet, Jehan. *St Michael Fighting the Seven-Headed Dragon. Painting.* Ref: http://en.wikipedia.org/wiki/Saint-Michael

Wallis Budge,E. A. *The Egyptian Book Of The Dead - The Papyrus Of Ani.* Dover Press..

The Holy Koran.

The Holy Bible. (KJV)

Whale, J. *The Christian Exit of Compassion (Male).* From Labyrinths of the Human Assemblage Point Series. Oil on Canvas: Size 28 x 22 inches, framed.

Whale, J. *The Christian Exit of Devotion (Female).* From Labyrinths of the Human Assemblage Point Series. Oil on Canvas: Size 28 x 22 inches, framed.

Whale, J. *The Exit of Zion.* From Labyrinths of the Human Assemblage Point Series. Oil on Canvas: Size 28 x 22 inches, framed.

Whale, J. *The Inferno Exit-Eternal Drama Triangle: Persecutor, Victim & Rescuer.* From Labyrinths of the Human Assemblage Point. Oil on Canvas: Size 28 x 22 inches, framed.

Wilhelm Schneemelcher, translation by R. McL. Wilson, *New Testament Apocrypha : Writings Relating to the Apostles Apocalypses and Related Subjects* (Louisville: John Knox Press, 1992), pp. 603 620. & C. Detlef G. Müller. *New Testament Apocrypha, vol. 2, pp. 604 605. (See* http://www.earlychristianwritings.com/text/ascension.html)

Epilogue

When first planning the structure of this work at the end of 2003, I had not envisaged chapter ten. In a way this book has turned out to be a scientific autobiography. I have revealed more about myself than intended. The insertion of chapter ten was the consequence of the 'intervention' of forces or powers beyond my control. The high energy 'out of the body' experience that transported me to the domain where I witnessed the three Egyptian hieroglyphs stopped me dead in my tracks and delayed the completion of this book by a further six months.

Originally titled: *'Naked Spirit - Including The Assemblage Point Blue Prints'*, the intervention of the information from the higher state of consciousness mentioned in chapter ten was the trigger that enabled me to subtitle this work: *'The Physical, Psychological, Emotional And Spiritual Maps For Health And Disease Including The Assemblage Point Blueprints'*.

My intent was that this work would appeal to a large audience. Throughout its preparation, I have witnessed an exacerbation in global anxieties. Perhaps chapter ten was necessary and will help to petition a wider cross-section of interested readers. I hope I have succeeded in providing the information in a clear and concise way that will enable anyone reading it to maintain or aspire to high levels of health and satisfaction.

In the forgoing I have provided the tools to transform some of our current limiting difficulties on earth. Only time will tell if the application of the Assemblage Point blueprints is of sufficient interest to professional and vocational individuals that it becomes global common knowledge and practice. Learning to immediately *'see'* the Assemblage Point location and to *'discern'* the emotional level of health of other people is the easiest way to avoid trouble and the fastest way to get on. In any event, whatever should transpire , it is advisable to stay centred as it provides the highest personal strength and the best chance of survival.

To be continued.   Jon Whale

Seeking Assemblage Point Correction Or Training

Since my first publications in 1996 many clinics and practitioners have embraced the Assemblage Point and electronic gem therapy methods into their practice. Searching the Internet using the keyword 'assemblage point' and electronic gem therapy' will bring up thousands of listing and references.

Amongst these are numerous clinics and practitioners worldwide that provide these therapies. Some of the sites vend training courses and related apparatus as well as unrelated paraphernalia. Most of, if not all use descriptive text, drawings and photographs taken directly from my work. Others modify or paraphrase their presentations to suit their particular agendas and sales pitch occasionally exhibiting it as if they are the originators. The Assemblage Point data is worth more money than can currently be estimated.

Over the years, I have personally trained many doctors and practitioners and several have voiced their concerns for the public pertaining to dilution and misuse of the methods. Anyone seeking training or treatment by any of the methods outlined in this book should seek practitioners and trainers who are qualified and high on the scale of emotional health as outlined in chapter 4.

I receive many e-mails requesting my recommendations for a suitable practitioner or good training programs. Some comment, complain or ask questions about particular practitioners or their web sites. As I am largely unable to verify the quality or effectiveness of the practice of others, I am not in a position to make any public comments or recommendations concerning any particular practitioner or training program listed on the Internet or elsewhere. Although this is certainly no guarantee, what I can say is that professionals high on the scale will demonstrate high ethical standards in their literature or Internet presentations. They will always provide source references and web links back to original work. Therefore, anyone seeking treatment or training would be well advised to carefully inspect their links, references and sources before making an appointment or parting with any money.

For the latest information and blogs, please see:
www.nakedspirit.co.uk

Appendix I

ASSEMBLAGE POINT PROFILES

The following profiles are anecdotal case notes of people who have received manual Assemblage Point correction (circa 1996) using the methods outlined in chapter 6 & 7. They illustrate the versatility of the simple methods for managing a diverse range of conditions and situations. In each case, the manual manipulation and correction methods were employed as outlined in this and my previous books and articles.

1. Clinical Depression Following Concussion

Tony B, aged 13, March 1996. Four years previously, Tony had fallen backwards from a high stone wall at his school. He had lost consciousness and was hospitalised for concussion. He suffered headaches and vomiting after regaining consciousness. Later he developed alopecia and eczema at the site of his head injury (parietal bone left side). Tony's mother reported that he had been a very energetic and extrovert boy before the accident. However, since the accident he had not attended school; he had developed agoraphobia and insomnia, and hardly ever left his bedroom. Over the years he had seen many specialists for various examinations, X rays and scans. He had received extensive treatment from

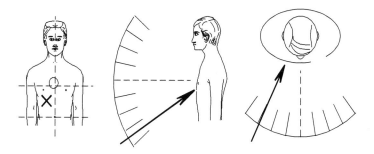

Fig. A1:1. Tony B's Assemblage Point Location.

223

homoeopaths, osteopaths and a physiotherapist, with some slight improvements. More recently, his psychiatrist had voiced the opinion that he was suffering from M.E. and he would have to go into hospital for tests to determine a suitable drug medication.

He was receiving antidepressants and anti-inflammatory analgesics.

On examination, the location of his Assemblage Point was found to be very low down on the right side, just above the critical line at the navel. His depressed attitude, slurred speech, monotone voice and hunched posture were confirmation of the low location. Tony admitted that he was always staring at the ground. He complained of having no energy and extensive pains. Tony was a cooperative patient, so shifting his Assemblage Point up and across to the central location was easy.

Two weeks later, on his second visit, his mother reported he had been cycling and attending local social functions and that he had been sleeping far better. Tony told us that he had experienced much more energy, but over the last few days he complained that it had 'dropped away'. Examination revealed that his Assemblage Point had partially dropped. This is normal with long term misalignment. He received treatment similar to that on his first visit. On his third visit, he arrived on his bicycle, having cycled 12 miles. His complexion, energy, speech and posture were much better. His Assemblage Point had slipped down a little. Tony said that his psychiatrist had noted a significant change in him.

Tony's alignment was corrected five times over a three month period. Each time the correction distance was less, and the interval between visits was greater. Six months later, Tony was free from pain, sleeping normally, off all medication, and was taking up extrovert activities, including archery and fishing. Given the length of time that he had been ill, his recovery was remarkable. He left behind 4 years of negative states of consciousness, which had considerably disrupted his education and personal development.

2. Chronic Panic Attacks

Clare W, aged 18. September 1996. Clare reported that she was experiencing panic attacks that had started years before when she was attending junior school. She had been seeing a clinical psychologist since breaking her leg when having an attack.. Her Assemblage Point was checked and found on the far right side of the chest at an acute angle, passing through the heart. There was also a shadow location 8 cm higher up, in the location for panic. The shadow location and her Assemblage Point were joined and shifted to the centre. Just over a year later, a letter was received from her. She wrote that she had not experienced any attacks since her treatment, and that she had now gained complete control over herself and her life.

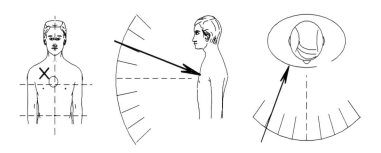

Fig. A1:2. Clare's Assemblage Point Location.

3. Hypertension (Stress)

Ms. R. J., Business Manager. September 1998. *'I had been experiencing a very stressful time at work. I had been working 6 days each week until late at night for many months and had more than my fair share of problems with junior staff. Due to this, I was drinking and smoking too much, and finding it very difficult to relax. Two years previously, I had my Assemblage Point shifted to the centre, so I knew what to expect. However, its location was further on the right this time. The shift made me feel much less stressed and my pulse rate was much slower afterwards. Most noticeable was my breathing; I had a great feeling of relief and I could breathe*

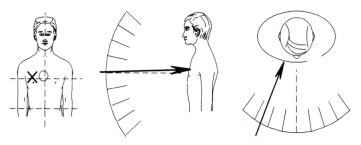

Fig. A1:3. Ms. R. J's Assemblage Point Location.

more deeply and freely; my cigarette and alcohol consumption spontaneously reduced, because I felt completely centred again".

4. Feeling Of Detachment, Anxiety And Depression

Tony S, aged 24, April 1997. Tony had been ill for 8 years. He complained of feeling detached from his body, anxious, depressed and having no energy. This condition had started when he first began work at 15 and he had been unable to work for the past several years. He had attended a psychiatrist, psychologist and hypnotherapist. He had also tried acupuncture, healers and been to see a psychoanalyst, throughout which time he reported that his condition had got worse. It required five attempts to shift his Assemblage Point up successfully, from the low chronic fatigue location just below the liver. Tony required three more corrections over a 2 month period, during which he made steady progress to recovery.

5. Agoraphobia And Clinical Depression

Mr. N. O. aged 32, September 1989. This man, a professional sculptor and artist in the film and television industry, had not attended work for over a year. He had developed agoraphobia after taking LSD at a party. After the effects of the drug had worn off, he became increasingly distressed with work and travelling on the underground railway to London.

He was signed off sick by his doctor and attended psychiatric therapy. His situation continued to deteriorate and he spent most of his days dreaming and making drawings of strange science fiction situations in black ink. He attended for Assemblage Point correction at the suggestion of one of his friends. Examination revealed that

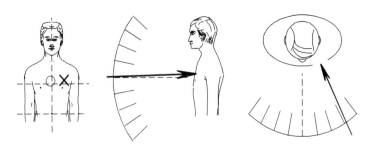

Fig. A1:4. Mr. N. O's Assemblage Point Location.

his Assemblage Point was on the left side of his chest. His Assemblage Point was moved to the right side of his chest and he attended for several more monthly corrections. He eventually made a full recovery back to his former health and activities.

6. Chronic Mental Illness With Depression

Ian B, aged 28. 13 November 1996. Ian was referred via London doctors for assessment and treatment. His situation had become so untenable that he was going to be hospitalised for further psychiatric drug therapy. This sensitive young man presented with a grey complexion, very low biological energy and seriously depressed frontal brain energy.

His mother reported that he was experiencing aggressive, violent, and destructive outbursts, but most of the time was totally depressed. He had periodically vandalised his home, and had thrown furniture, smashing the living room window. Examination revealed that his stationary Assemblage Point was found only 6 cm above the critical line (navel); also, the rear location or pivot point was below the shoulder blades. He also had a number of shadow locations. At some time in the past, possibly when he had become ill in Germany, or perhaps due to the many depressive drugs including chlorpromazine, prescribed by his psychiatrist, Ian's Assemblage Point had dropped to this dangerous location. This would have caused him extreme physical and emotional distress and would have been responsible for his symptoms.

Ian's Assemblage Point was manually shifted up and across to the centre of his chest (thymus area), a total distance of some 30 cm. After treatment, Ian's mother said that he had not looked so well in years. Ian was instructed to return within 14 days, for further correction and treatment.

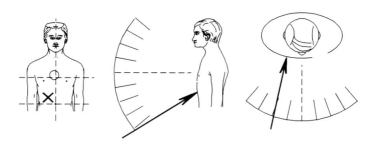

Fig. A1:5. Ian B's Assemblage Point Location.

On Ian's second visit (25 November 1996), his Assemblage Point had dropped somewhat. This was to be expected after such a long illness. His complexion and posture remained improved. He was more talkative, friendly and extrovert. His mother reported that he had been singing and playing his cello. Ian received similar treatment to that on his first visit and his Assemblage Point was shifted to a central position again.

On his third visit (9 December 1996), Ian's condition had clearly continued to improve. His Assemblage Point location had stabilised, slightly to the right of the centre (normal). He was physically and mentally much stronger. His mother said that he had attended an orchestral rehearsal at a local college, playing his cello.

7. Concussion Related Social And Alcohol Problems

Mr. David H, aged 32. October 1994. This strong, hard-working man complained of feeling different from other people. He wanted to know why others avoided his company. He was drinking too much and felt dejected; his behaviour was unpredictable and this was getting him into trouble with the police. He also thought others were afraid of him. He further added that his troubles had started some years back, after someone gave him a bang on his head with a wooden stick.

David's Assemblage Point alignment was low and to the far right, abnormally different to that of the average person, probably due to his head injury. We pointed this out to him and realigned his Assemblage Point to the centre of his chest. This was a turning point for him. As the months passed his behaviour became more socially acceptable, suggesting that the misalignment had been responsible for his antisocial behaviour. He had been projecting his feelings of paranoia onto external situations, thus triggering incidents that involved him with the police.

8. Clinical Depression

Jane W., aged 46. November 1997. Jane had been suffering from clinical depression for the past 10 years. Over the years, her consultants had prescribed drugs, electroconvulsive shock therapy, and long term counselling. She had a variety of symptoms. Her current medication was a cocktail of four different drugs. Her

Assemblage Point was found low on the right side of the body, entering at an acute angle through her liver area (typical M.E./ chronic fatigue location). Jane received three corrections to the alignment of her Assemblage Point over a 6 week period. After her second treatment, she returned to driving her car.

9. Non Specific Central Shift

Mr. N. D., Company Director. October 1998. Mr. N. D. reported that, 'Normally I have trouble with my vision I have to wear glasses or contact lenses. When I had my assemblage point corrected, I was instantly stunned when my vision cleared and I could see without glasses. Although I had thought that I was a healthy, fit and balanced person, I was impressed with the new feeling of being centred. I still do not fully understand what this energy centre is. Being sceptical, I was delighted to discover and become aware of my assemblage point. I can see that it has a definite place in my future'.

10. Periodic Dislocation Of The Hip

Veronica S., aged 16. May 1998. This young lady complained of headaches, lower back pain and a painful left knee. Her main problem was that her right hip joint would periodically dislocate, although she was tall with a sporting body tone. She was scheduled for hip surgery. Veronica was requested to walk slowly back and forth across the room; members of her family were present, and everyone observed that her frame was twisted towards her right side from the hips upwards.

Her Assemblage Point was found on the left side of the chest meridian, entering at an acute angle. Left locations are not common. After her Assemblage Point was corrected, she was left to relax for 20 minutes. As she walked back and forth across the room again,

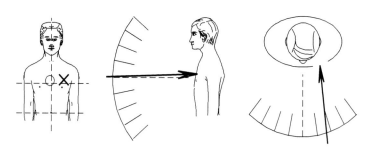

Fig. A1:6. Veronica's Assemblage Point Location.

all present could see that her frame was now aligned properly. On her second visit, 2 weeks later, she reported that her headaches, knee, and back pain had cleared up. Her parents cancelled the hip surgery.

11. Continual Cold, Trauma, Migraines And Lack of Energy

Gladys H., aged 50. May 1998. This introvert, rational lady had been ill for 10 months with a continual cold, trauma, migraines, lack of energy and inability to work. Her Assemblage Point location was entering upwards from low down around her liver area. Gladys received Assemblage Point correction.

On her second visit she reported that she felt 100% better, with more energy, sleeping through the night, dreaming more, and much happier. Her cold and sinus problems had cleared up.

12. Non Specific Central Shift

Ms. V. C., aged 34, Therapist. March 1987. '*Before the shift I felt off the centre, a bit low in my mood, self conscious, and anxious. I also felt separated from many people in the group. After the shift, I saw things much differently; I felt centred and easy with myself. My spirit lifted, and my eyes got much brighter. I seemed to have more energy, and I could feel more empathy with the whole group. I no longer felt anxious and could perceive myself in relation to others differently.*'

13. Anxiety

Mrs. K. B. Therapist. May 1998. This lady reported, '*I am a nervous person, but I can tolerate the underlying feelings quite well. Over the years I have learnt to cope by being careful with what I eat and being sure to get enough sleep and rest. What I was most taken with after the shift was a feeling of solidness and physical strength. It is a feeling that I have never experienced before. My mind was naturally quiet and I felt more aware of the world and less preoccupied with my feelings. I know that this is a subject that I will be investigating. I can think of many my clients that would benefit from this therapy*'.

14. Dropped Assemblage Point Due To Drug Overdose

Mr. David R., aged 62. 1987. This very intelligent and kind man was receiving medication for sleeping problems and severe stress. The emergency services were called to his home in the early hours of the morning. His apartment was flooded and David was discovered unconscious in a cold bath with the taps running. He was taken to the hospital and released the following evening. He telephoned in a distraught state, saying that something was very wrong with him, but he did not know what it was.

On examination the following day, his Assemblage Point was found only 9 cm above his navel. He had very little physical or mental energy. His other symptoms were intense burning and discomfort in his bladder; he would have to visit the bathroom every few minutes. His respiration was laboured.

His Assemblage Point was shifted vertically upwards and across slightly. His treatment was completely successful and he was back at his desk the following day.

15. Substance Abuse

Ms. K. J., aged 22. February 1997. This extrovert young lady had been using ecstasy, cocaine and amphetamines some 3 years previously. She had recently been experiencing panic attacks and pain in her ears, the latter thought by her doctor to be caused by an infection. Her Assemblage Point was found far to the right and entering from a very acute angle on her right side. Some 10 minutes after her Assemblage Point was corrected, she experienced a 'popping' sensation in each ear. Kate's anxiety cleared up with a single correction.

16. Non Specific Central Shift

Mrs. D. B., University Lecturer, retired. November 1995. This lady reported, *'I asked Jon about spiritual matters, especially reincarnation. Handing me two powerful therapeutic magnets, he said, 'The eye cannot see magnetic waves, but we can experience their effects'. Then he instructed me to place one magnet in each hand and to bring my hands slowly together. Suddenly the magnet in my left hand jumped out and across several inches to crash against the second magnet in my right hand. The magnetic power was too strong for me to control physically. He then said, 'Enveloping every living person is a strong energy field that is visible only under special circumstances'. He emphasised that, just as I had experienced the power of the magnets, I could, any time I liked, experience the power of the human energy field.*

As a practising Christian, I felt great doubt, but also curiosity, and took up his challenge. Following instructions, I brought my hands towards his chest and upper back. As my right hand came within 12 inches of his chest, a 'power' took over and I could not control my arms. I felt strong tingling sensations pass up my right arm and across my chest, connecting to my left hand at his back. My hands automatically came into and touched the centre of his chest and back. I admit I was frightened. Something beyond me, a field of energy, took control of my hands and arms.

Over the next 2 weeks, I became very aware of my own Assemblage Point location. I was aware of curved energy lines entering my upper right chest through to my shoulder blade. These energy lines seemed connected to a kindred spirit 'out there'. The next time I saw Jon, I asked him if he would confirm my location. He told me the precise location and angle of entry, then came over to me and touched the exact spot. Becoming aware of my own assemblage point has confirmed my belief that we all have a 'spirit energy' outside or above the physical body that dies. My discovery complements my Christian faith.'

17. Circulation Problems With Heart Palpitations

Ms. E.G., aged 24. March 1998. This young lady had previously been taking amphetamines ('speed') with some friends. Since then, she had been experiencing hot flushes, numb fingers, hands and feet, circulation problems and heart palpitations. Her Assemblage

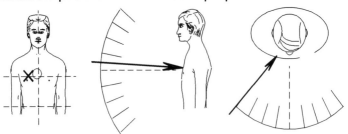

Fig. A1:7. Ms. E. G's Assemblage Point Location.

232

Point location, as expected, was entering at an acute angle on the far right and from the right passing through her heart. Her symptoms cleared after correction. Her pulse was checked before and after correction. Before the shift, her pulse was fast, irregular and jerky. Correction changed it to a slower, steady and strong beat, her hot flushes and circulation symptoms cleared up.

18. Depression And Drug And Alcohol Dependence

Ms. J. S., aged 25. November 1993. This pretty, intelligent and sensitive young lady was 7 months pregnant. For several years previously, she had been taking numerous prescribed and illegal drugs, mainly strong central nervous system depressants. At times, she would also take illegal stimulants. On top of this, she had a problem with alcohol. She had been hospitalised several times, suffering from drug psychoses. J. S. had managed to reduce her intake of drugs and drink over the months of her pregnancy. However, this did nothing to improve the way she felt inside.

J. S. had been persuaded to attend a local self help support group, where members met to talk and share their experiences. There were several people present with diagnosed psychological problems. At this meeting, her Assemblage Point was centralised and raised from a low position beneath her right breast. At the next meeting 2 weeks later, she told the group that she now felt in control of her life again. She had more physical energy and could get on with things that had previously been too much effort. She said that the effects of the Assemblage Point shift were very pronounced for the first 5 days. Her Assemblage Point had slipped to the right and down a little since the previous correction. This was put right again. At a follow up appointment 2 years later, both J. S. and her baby boy were healthy and happy.

Drugs and the Assemblage Point

I first published the information concerning the effects of drugs on the Assemblage Point in 1997. I also included them in my last book entitled: The Catalyst Of Power. Every time I pick up a newspaper, listen to the radio news or turn on the television, there are always reports or documentaries of incidents of crime, violence, injury or tragedy where drugs and alcohol are implicated. Nine years have past since I first published this information, substance abuse related crime and violence has increased to the point that in the UK it is not safe to venture into the city between dusk and dawn. Our prisons are overcrowded and have burst, dangerous prisoners are being released back on the street too early to make way for newly convicted inmates.

Notwithstanding and yet including alcohol and prescribed drugs (legal), the individuals most inclined to use illegal drugs, will often be introverted personality types. As outlined in chapter three; During their early formation, introvert types often negatively or ambivalently identified with one or both parental figures. For these, the predisposition for an unstable or detrimental Assemblage Point location is rather high. Resorting to chemicals to obtain a feeling of wellbeing is dangerous. Dependency on chemical maintenance will be the most likely outcome. The irony is that in such cases, experimenting with drugs will aggravate their Assemblage Point location's instability. This will compound the potentiality for chronic chemical dependency.

Another factor concerning illegal black market drug supplies, are that dealers due to their illegal racketeering, will be low on the scale of emotional health (-3, covert hostility). Even if the original wholesale supplies are of comparative purity, intermediate dealers will do everything they can to maximum their profits. Therefore, they will adulterate the source materials to bulk them out. Cutting with inert bulking substances weakens the end product, consequently, it is more profitable to mix in cheap surplus medical and veterinary drugs. This practice increases potency and dependency. Unpredictable side effects such as psychotic reactions are greatly increased.

Whereas extrovert personality types, in the main are not so vulnerable to relying on chemicals for an internal feeling of wellbeing. Extroverts can take drugs with little chance of becoming addicted. For this reason, extrovert people do not understand why introverted individuals become addicted. They often have little or no sympathy for addicts, and without profound professional insight, will not be in any position to assist.

Despite spending much time and money promoting and communicating the connection between substance abuse and the Assemblage Point, to my knowledge, not a single journalist, professional body, government agency, charity, television or radio program has ever picked up and reported the importance of the Assemblage Point location with respect to addiction.

Prescribed Drugs

Central nervous system depressants, such as morphine, heroin, chlorpromazine, lithium salts, lorazepam, barbiturates etc., can cause the Assemblage Point to move downwards. These types of drugs suppress the biological energy in the nervous system, therefore the patient's vibrational rate is much slower and, correspondingly, the Assemblage Point location will move to a lower location to reflect this. When the Assemblage Point is close to the critical line, the use of central nervous system depressants (and general anaesthetics) can be dangerous, as they can move the Assemblage Point down towards the critical line. With low locations, the patient's biological energy levels are depleted and death could result.

Fig. A1:8. The opium poppy, Papaver Somniferum, is the type of poppy from which opium and all refined opiates such as morphine are extracted.

Tobacco

Normally, smoking tobacco has very little or no effect on the Assemblage Point location. If it does anything, it increases the heart rate and tends to bend the Assemblage Point towards the right side (hypertension). There are many millions of people who enjoy, regret and repent of smoking and their Assemblage Point locations are generally normal and typical. For some people with an Assemblage Point location high on the right, tobacco can trigger heart palpitations and induce feelings of anxiety, panic and feelings of losing control. When anxiety or panic is present (hypertension), smoking levels can increase and exacerbate the tension. Maintaining a central location reduces the craving for nicotine.

Alcohol

Alcohol causes a small misalignment or bending of the Stationary Assemblage Point to the right side and downwards. Excessive consumption causes gross misalignment to the right and can induce psychotic behaviour. Addiction can occur if the Assemblage Point is seriously misaligned. Without alcohol, and the same applies for depressive drugs, the patient feels bad and drinks or takes drugs to reduce the body's nervous activity and accompanying Beta brain frequency activity and related physical symptoms. The violent and destructive behaviour of some alcoholics is partly due to their Assemblage Point location, which is on the extreme right, the location for extrovert psychosis. As younger males, in general, have an Assemblage Point location on the right side; the consumption of large quantities of alcohol in a short period of time dramatically increases the likelihood of violent behaviour and the smallest provocation can trigger an episode.

Alcohol when consumed along with other drugs is dangerous. Alcohol when combined with central nervous system depressive drugs such as barbiturates, will induce narcosis and can be fatal. This combination will cause the Assemblage Point to drop rapidly.

When alcohol is combined with anti depressive drugs or other CNS stimulants, the outcome is dangerously unpredictable. In this case, the stimulating effects of antidepressant drugs combined with the intoxicating effects of alcohol can result in psychotic episodes. The Assemblage Point moves to the right and is high.

Accompanying the dramatic increase in the consumption of prescribed anti depressive drugs, in the last few years there have been a number of tragic homicides. Alcohol combined with depressive drugs is one of the methods of committing suicide, death is self inflicted. But in cases where alcohol has been consumed with antidepressants, causing an extrovert psychotic episode, death and injury has been inflicted on other members of their family.

A person with suicidal tendencies will have a low Assemblage Point location. Correcting the Assemblage Point location will change their mood and make them feel much better within themselves. People who depend on antidepressants in order to feel good can reduce the risks, save themselves money and improve their health by getting their Assemblage Point shifted to the centre. The central location produces a natural feeling of well being and from this location life's problems can be fun; one does not need to escape or use drugs to cope.

Cannabis

Some types of cannabis preparations, such as dark resin, reduce Beta brain frequencies to Alpha and Theta, which reduces the user's "internal dialogue". The effects, at least for some people, are said to increase left and right brain synergy. Unlike alcoholics, cannabis users can display an agreeable nature and their Assemblage Point will be closer to the centre meridian line. Many users claim to be more in touch with their feelings when using the various preparations of this plant.

For the habitual consumers, problems arise when the drug is unavailable because the central nervous system adapts to the influence of cannabis in the body. Withdrawal sends the Assemblage Point to the right and upwards which produces High Beta frequency activity in the brain, with accompanying distressing symptoms. Cannabis users often resort to alcohol or other substitutes when supplies dry up; a better way is to shift the Assemblage Point

Fig. A1:9. Cannabis Sativa (Hemp), the psycho-active agent THC is produced be the 'female' plant gender.

down to the centre while the central nervous system re adapts itself.

Cannabis can produce negative neurosomatic experiences. Some of the more contemporary preparations of cannabis can, in some people, trigger panic and anxiety feelings. For example, special genetic plant strains grown under artificial light often called 'skunk' can be very stimulating. It is probable that the intense ultra violet lamps, used to encourage the plants' growth, modify the tetrahydrocannabinol molecules to a more active isomer.

Cannabis Sativa or hemp is assigned to the Cannabacea plant family. There is only one other plant in this family and it is the hop plant, used to make beer. The hop plant like cannabis can have a calming or sedative effect, and the flowering heads are often placed in pillows and used by people suffering from insomnia. The tradition of making beer form hops has for some years now been dying, and the beers manufactured today do not have the same calming and satisfying effect as beers of the past. Omitting hops from beer preparations will have the effect of increasing alcohol consumption and addiction.

Recreational Drugs

Amyl and butyl nitrite (nicknamed "poppers" and "sniffers") are sometimes used by homosexuals to help induce "total orgasm" during sex. When repeatedly used to excess, this type of drug can seriously deplete biological energy. Resorting to cocaine and amphetamines in an attempt to make a recovery can result in total exhaustion. Consequently, the Assemblage Point could drop to a dangerous location.

Cocaine and amphetamines are two of the many central nervous system stimulants available today. They are mainly used in conjunction with extrovert activities. As such they can shift the Assemblage Point to the far

Fig. A1:10. The Coca plant, Erythroxylum Coca. The stimulant drug Cocaine that is extracted from its new fresh leaf tips.

right side of the chest, the extrovert psychotic location. They can also shift the Assemblage Point to the high right, the location for anxiety and panic. Locations on the far right side are unstable and physical exhaustion from using stimulants can provide the opportunity for the Assemblage Point to drop down towards the critical line. This will result in chronic fatigue or other diagnostic classification in the depressive spectrum.

Hallucinogenic Drugs

The location of the Assemblage Point determines how we "see" and "experience" reality. If we experience hallucinations, our Assemblage Point will be in a position which is a long way from centre. Hallucinations, dreaming and other types of three dimensional spatial thinking activities are associated with right sided brain activity, which corresponds with an Assemblage Point location on the left side of the chest.

Hallucinogenic drugs such as L.S.D., D.M.T., D.E.T., mescaline, psilocybin, methylated amphetamines (for example, ecstasy, S.T.P., M.D.A.) and cocaine can loosen the Assemblage Point and shift it in any direction. Many factors, such as personality, guilt, fear, health and one's environment, will determine the direction and the degree of the shift of the Assemblage Point. However, in users of such drugs, the general direction of the shift is towards the left side. The larger the dose, the greater the shift and the more exaggerated the experience becomes.

When the effects of the drug have worn off, the Assemblage Point can relocate at a detrimental position and angle. Since the Assemblage Point location determines how we behave and how we feel, using these drugs can cause a sudden change in personality with the physical and psychological symptoms associated with the new location manifesting. Shifting the Assemblage Point back to the position before the drug was taken will generally

Fig. A1:11. Peyote Cacti, Lophophra Williamsii. It is one of the many cacti that contains the Psychedelic drug Mescaline.

correct the situation. Patients suffering long term Assemblage Point misalignment caused by drugs may require several shifts over a period of months. They may also require supportive psychological therapy to assist in the stabilisation of their Assemblage Point.

Anyone experimenting with or researching the effects of hallucinogenic drugs should be aware that their Assemblage Point location will be affected. Therefore they should keep detailed records of the Assemblage Point location, before and after drug experiences. Clinicians using these types of drugs for psychological and psychiatric research will accelerate their research programmes by taking into consideration the patient's Assemblage Point location.

Doctors researching L.S.D. or other drug therapy for chronic alcoholic rehabilitation should take a close look at what is happening to their patient's Assemblage Point, they will then discover a new mechanism. The success or failure of drugs when used for psychological therapies, is dependent on the patient's Assemblage Point location before and after the drug has worn off. Once the researchers get to grips with the Assemblage Point mechanism, they will realise that the use of drugs may not be required, since they will have established that drugs such as L.S.D. shifts the patient's Assemblage Point and this can be done manually without exposing the patient to further risk.

Fig. A1:12. Psilocybe Semilanceata (Liberty Cap), one of the psychedelic mushroom that contains the psycho-active compound psilocybin.

Toxins, Poisons And Pollution

Toxins, including heavy metals such as mercury and lead, petroleum products, together with gases such as carbon monoxide/dioxide, cyanide and chlorine, all depress the central nervous system. They drive the Stationary Assemblage Point down towards the critical line. Toxins created by bacteria deplete the patient's biological energy and have much the same effect on the Assemblage Point location and biological vibrational rate. In acute cases, the Assemblage Point will be left fixed close to the critical line. Should it be below on the right side it may take many months or years for the victim to recover and, if it is in the left location, the patient will be comatose. Either way, correction of the Assemblage Point will help recovery.

Bibliography, References And Follow-Up reading

Whale, Jon, Ph.D. *Core Energy - Surgery For The Electromagnetic Body.* Series of 3 articles prepared for Positive Health magazine. 1996. Website addresses:

http://www.positivehealth.com/permit/Articles/Energy%20Medicine/whale15.htm

http://www.positivehealth.com/permit/Articles/Energy%20Medicine/whale16.htm

http://www.positivehealth.com/permit/Articles/Energy%20Medicine/whale17.htm

Whale, Jon, Ph.D. *The Catalyst of Power the Assemblage Point of Man.* Second Edition. Dragon Rising Publishing. ISBN1 873483 05 88

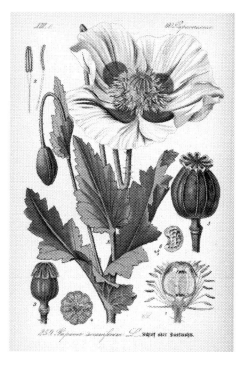

Fig. A1:13. Papaver Somniferum.

Fig. A1:14. Erythroxylum Coca.

Fig. A1:15. Chief Quanah Parker (circa 1840s - February 23, 1911) was a Native American leader, the son of Comanche chief Peta Nocona. He is credited as the founder of the Native American Church Movement. He adopted the peyote religion after reportedly seeing a vision of Jesus Christ while suffering from a near fatal wound following a battle with Federal Troops.

Peyote contains hordenine, tyramine, phenylethylamine alkaloids. They act as potent natural antibiotics when taken in a combined form.

He was given peyote by a Ute medicine man to cure the infections of his wounds. During his treatment, He claimed he heard the voice of Jesus Christ who then appeared to him, and told him in order to atone for his many killings and misdeeds, he must forsake a life of violence and conflict and take the peyote religion to the Indian Peoples.

His words and teachings comprise the core of the Native American Church Doctrine and the "Peyote Road." He taught that the sacred peyote medicine was the sacrament given to the Indian Peoples by the Lord Jesus Christ, and was to be used with water when taking communion in a traditional Native American Church medicine ceremony. The Native American Church was the first truly "American" religion based on Christianity outside of the Latter Day Saints.

His most famous teaching regarding the Spirituality of the Native American Church: The White Man goes into his church and talks about Jesus. The Indian goes into his Tipi and talks with Jesus.

Appendix II

ADVANCED PROCEDURES FOR CORRECTING THE ASSEMBLAGE POINT LOCATION

In the book entitled: *'The Catalyst Of Power - The Assemblage Point Of Man'* chapters 6 and 7 outline the procedures for manual Assemblage Point correction using a quartz crystal for that shift. Since 2001 Lux IV electronic gem therapy lamps can produce the same results.

Manual methods are hardly ever used on patients today. Much simpler and more subtle methods using Transducer Lamps have been developed. These do not require the cooperation of the patient nor the personal time and energy of the practitioner in the same way as manual correction. Furthermore it is not necessary to introduce the patient to any information concerning the Assemblage Point.

Today Assemblage Point procedures have come full-circle regarding the application of the Lux IV for correction of the Assemblage Point. It is no longer truly necessary to locate the Point in the first place, since we know the locations for various conditions.

Using energy medicine alone to address these conditions will generally correct the Assemblage Point location and entry angle to a reasonable position. Although this adjustment may not necessarily be to the coveted central location, it can be to the more typical site for healthy males and females.

The ability to locate or 'see' and record the position of the patient's Assemblage Point is most helpful both in diagnosis and treatment. This is true regardless of the modality of medicine or therapy used. The progress of any patient throughout their treatments and medication is reflected in the movement of their Assemblage Point over time.

The Assemblage Point can move around in meditation, trance and dream states of consciousness when the primary brain frequency is 3.2 - 7.8 Hz. These Theta states of consciousness can be extremely pleasant. Slow brain waves unite both halves of the brain and are especially beneficial for de-stressing and healing.

Electronic gem lamp therapy can modulate high hypertension Beta brain frequencies down to pleasurable Theta states of consciousness and can be used to move the Assemblage Point towards the central location.

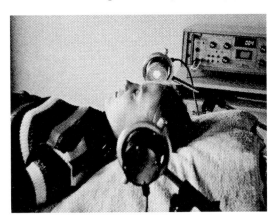

Fig. A2:1. Centralising the Assemblage Point location via profound relaxation treatment using electronic gem therapy lamps containing blue sapphires to each side of the head (3.3 Hz).

Blue sapphires emit a soft, pleasurable, calming energy. These are used to fill two Lux IV Transducer Lamps which are then fitted with violet filters. These lamps are directed at each side of the head. The patient is kept warm, fully relaxed and comfortable in quiet surroundings. The sapphire lamps are electronically vibrated at 3.2 Hz and most people will quickly enter a dreamy, truly relaxed state of consciousness. The heart rate and blood pressure will fall, with pleasurable bodily sensations.

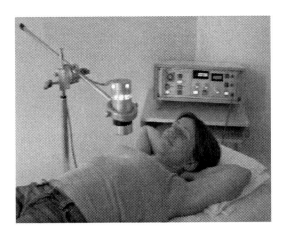

Fig. A2:2. Centralising the Assemblage Point location via an energising treatment to the centre of the chest using lamps containing magenta lamp containing a mixture of seven gems (ruby, carnelian, citrine, emerald, topaz, diamond & sapphire).

The examples given below are for one of the most common pathological Assemblage Point locations. ME, postnatal depression, clinical depression, chronic fatigue syndrome etc.. What these all have in common is that the patient's Assemblage Point will be located in the liver area or lower.

These conditions can be precipitated and sustained due to the patient's Assemblage Point dropping into the liver area or lower. The psychological factors are not important. When the Assemblage Point descends into this area the liver is, or will become, disturbed and not function correctly. If the liver should malfunction then the Assemblage Point can drop down towards the liver. The patient will feel tired, lacking in energy and the body will not respond to his or her mental commands.

The first priority is to raise the patient's Assemblage Point out of the liver area. This is easily achieved by using one or two Transducer Lamps containing diamonds and carnelians at a frequency of 8.5 HZ, targeting the patient's spleen. The treatment's duration should be for a period of about 20 minutes. This will raise the patient's biological energy and the Assemblage Point will move upwards reflecting this higher level of energy (approx.: 5 to 8 centimetres for the first treatment).

Manually check the location of the Assemblage Point to confirm it has moved out of the liver area. The patient's Assemblage Point can be raised further by weekly follow-up treatments.

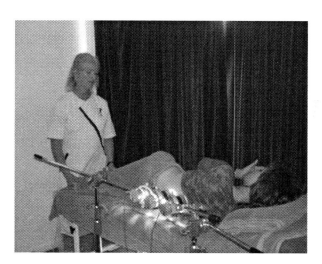

Fig. A2:3. Treatment for a prolapsed disc: Three Lamps, two containing sapphires each side of the prolapse to relax all of the muscles and attenuate pain. A third lamp is set between them containing diamonds and carnelians to energise and stimulate circulation of the injured disc area.

The Assemblage Point can then be moved to the centre of the chest using two Transducer Lamps containing diamonds and carnelians at a frequency of 8.5 HZ. Sitting the patient upright on a chair or stool, use one Transducer Lamp to target the patient's chest centre, just below the thymus gland and use the second Transducer Lamp to target the patient's back exactly in line and opposite the Transducer Lamp at the front.

Ask the patient to sit quietly and breathe in and out steadily and deeply for a minimum of twelve full breaths. Allow them time to relax for about 5 minutes and then ask them to repeat the breathing technique. It will be very beneficial if the patient can pause or hold their breath for a second between inhaling and exhaling. This should be performed in a completely relaxed manner, without deliberation or strain.

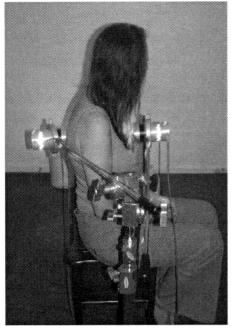

Fig. A2:4. Centralising the Assemblage Point Location Using Electronic Gem Therapy Apparatus. The Lamps Contain A Mixture of Carnelians and Diamonds used for the hypotension spectrum. Emerald and Sapphire are used for the hypertension spectrum.

After 20 minutes, check the patient's Assemblage Point location asking him/her to rest and relax with their eyes closed and without talking for a period of ten minutes. Try not to engage them in conversation. Re-examine their Assemblage Point location. It should move upwards from a low location to perhaps within 1 to 3 centimetres to the right of the chest centre. Make another appointment for the patient to return within 7 to 10 days to repeat the same procedure and again after a period of 2 or 3 weeks. On the first and subsequent visits always attend to the patient's secondary symptoms or complaint as necessary.

For patients with high and far right Assemblage Point Locations, perhaps presenting with anxiety, panic, stressful or hypertension diseases and symptoms, such as hyperactivity or anorexia, the liver will generally require to be cooled and calmed. This is best achieved with treatment direct to the liver itself. Transducer Lamps containing calming, cooling mixtures of gems, normally emeralds and dark blue sapphires, using a green filter and a frequency of 3.3 - 1.5 HZ should be used to lower the Assemblage Point from the high location.

For patients with symptoms and disease relating to an unstable Assemblage Point that moves from one location to another on a daily/weekly basis, such as epilepsy, manic depression or schizophrenia, then a new Assemblage Point location can be created using Transducer Lamps containing dark blue sapphires. In such cases, the unstable or vacillating Assemblage Point is ignored and a new Assemblage Point is created. It is literally drilled through the chest using two Transducer Lamps one each at the front and back of the patient's chest. This seems to have the effect of gathering the patient's random Assemblage Point energies.

Since these types of conditions can involve high Beta brain frequency activity, often greater than 25 HZ, then calming analgesic dark blue sapphires should be employed along with a dark violet filter and a slow calming frequency of 3.3 HZ. As the energy levels or emissions of dark blue sapphires are less than that of diamond and carnelians mixtures then a greater treatment time is required to create a new and stable Assemblage Point. The treatment duration should be around 30 minutes and may need to be repeated on a regular basis of perhaps twice each week or in turbulent cases perhaps daily.

In all of the cases above, scanning the liver and spleen temperature will be helpful for diagnostic and treatment purposes.

Case Studies Of Correcting the Assemblage Point Using The Lux IV

The following case notes are typical of the success of treatment with The Lux IV Transducer Lamps for correcting the Assemblage Point location and related medical problems.

Canadian E-Mail Case Reports

1) One case is of a lady who has environmental sensitivities which would lead to severe asthma. She was on prednisone frequently and missed work often if she had an attack. Episodes of work loss could be up to three weeks. After determining that she had low biological energy and a low Assemblage Point she was given three therapeutic doses of diamond and carnelian, based upon your research, to her chest. After these treatments she was able to come off her medication and so far (over one year ago) has never required the medication. This was a profound change, one I had difficulty in believing myself.

2) The other case deals with a chronic pain patient. This patient is on high doses of blood thinners and has had two strokes of minimal severity about three years ago. This lady, a teacher previously, fell down concrete steps in her school hitting her head twice and damaging her lower back. No operation nor manipulative therapies can be given due to her medical treatment requirements and other medical problems, one of which is diabetes. The patient was in excruciating pain and had great difficulty in manoeuvring, she could not walk without support and could do nothing through the day except find ways to minimise her pain. Her pain ruled her life. Today she can manoeuvre and walk and shop, she has independence enough to drive now. Though still hounded by some pain she has the ability to live a life she would never otherwise have been able. Her greatest gift was being able to stand erect and walk with minimal pain. She now spends her days doing many exquisite crafts.

United kingdom E-mail Case Reports (1)

1) Case Notes for JM a 28 year old gentleman who had an accident

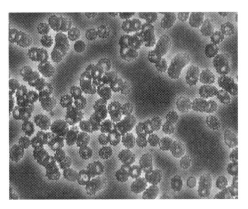 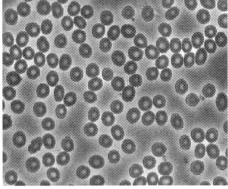

Fig. A2:5 - 6. Mycoplasma Pneumonia. Left photograph illustrates mycoplasmas attached to red blood cells. The right photograph was taken 1 hour later following treatment direct to the spleen using Electronic Gem Therapy Transducer Lamps.

whilst serving in the army during the Bosnian conflict. This gentleman presented at the clinic with chronic back pain directly related to the accident which had occurred some 10 years earlier. He had undergone four operations at the site of the damage to his spine (L3,4,&5) he had steel rods in place and a 'coral cage'. Walking for this gentleman when he was able was with the help of elbow crutches and he was in constant pain which was exacerbated during inclement weather. His Assemblage Point was 9 cm low due to the longevity and seriousness of his condition. Over a period of six weeks he was given a combination of deep relaxation therapy, treatment to the spleen with diamonds and carnelians and an assemblage point move. After this six week period his pain had lowered by 60% and he was able to walk without the aid of crutches and had started to walk around town for periods of up to an hour his first exercise for many years. Maintenance treatment continues.

2) Case Notes for LS a 32 year old lady who suffered from ME (myalgic encephalomyelitis). This Lady presented at the clinic with chronic fatigue symptoms which she had suffered for a period of six years. On checking Her Assemblage Point it was found to be in the liver area. Deep relaxation therapy was given to help her state of depression, along with an assemblage point correction which was continued over a three week period in order to stabilise it's position. After the first treatment this lady reported a feeling of being energised and after the third treatment she reported feeling well enough to start thinking about her future work activities. Her energy levels had increased dramatically and she had started to menstruate again (her periods had been absent for 4 years prior to treatment).

3) Case study of BH a 61 year old gentleman who suffered from Stress and fatigue following the death of his mother. This gentleman presented at the clinic suffering from stress and fatigue which had become progressively worse over a period of two years. His assemblage point was found to be 4 cm low. A combination of deep relaxation therapy using sapphire at Delta brain frequency and carnelians and diamonds to the spleen was used. With this combination, his Assemblage Point location gradually corrected by itself over a period of three weeks. Following this treatment, stress and fatigue levels were much improved. He continues to visit the clinic occasionally for maintenance treatment when he feels the need.

E-mail Case Reports From Holland (EU).

1) *I had a lady with dust contaminated lungs coming over from Denmark. She had worked for years in a dust polluted environment. I have treated her with the lamps containing Diamond and Carnelian at 8,3 Hz and an Orange filter and instantly after half an hour she could breathe like never before!*

2) *Her husband had heart rhythm problems for years. I have treated him with pale blue sapphire and blue sapphire and a violet filter on 1.3 Hz and his problems cleared up. His blood pressure also permanently dropped to a normal rate.*

3) *A man with a very difficult type of rheumatic arthritis could not be helped with the standard medical treatment so I started to put in: Citrine, gold, ruby, diamond and carnelian with a yellow filter on 16.5 Hz and his pains left. This man had pain in every joint and now he has no pain at all.*

4) *We also have quite some experiences with Mycoplasma bacterium. When we watch the blood under a microscope, we can see the Mycoplasma being attached to the erythrocytes. After a treatment with the gem lamp therapy the erythrocytes are clear of Mycoplasma.*

5) *Some cases of Mycoplasma Pneumonia we have treated only the spleen and liver and people felt an instant improvement in their lungs and the pneumonia was gone the next day. I have attached two magnified blood pictures of 'before and after' treatment.*

New Zealand E-mail Case Reports

1) *G.H is a 71 year old gentleman who suffered anxiety and depression made worse by the death of his wife and son. He presented with psoriasis to his forearms and difficulty sleeping. His GP was concerned about his liver with certain enzymes reading well above the normal at 167. His Assemblage Point was 10cm to the right in the anxious location and a shadow was observed in the depressed location on top of the liver. A radiometric scan of his liver revealed it to be 2 degrees hotter than his spleen. He received Bliss treatment and emerald and sapphire to his liver on five separate occasions before having his liver enzymes re-checked at 84. His psoriasis had cleared up and he was feeling relaxed and calm. Renewed energy levels had him returning to his gardening and he wrote to us thrilled with the results.*

2) *C.W. is a 68 year old medical researcher who came to us with a troublesome left ankle that had been damaged in a motorcycle accident when he was 24. Chris received sapphire at 1.6hz for one hour on two separate occasions. He wrote that his ankle had improved substantially and that considering the completely non-invasive and painless nature of the therapy he was sure it was a genuine step forward into a new dimension for medicine of the 21st Century.*

3) *R.T. is a 46 year old tradesman who was suffering from rheumatoid arthritis in his knees. X-rays revealed that most of the cartilage between the bone had disappeared. He was unable to stand up easily after crouching down which made his work painful and difficult. He received emerald, diamond and yellow sapphire at 3.6 Hz with a blue filter to both his knees for 30 minutes every week over a 14 week period. He always noticed less discomfort after every treatment with the effects lasting longer and longer each time. Now one year later we spoke to him and he reports that his knees are still virtually pain free and that he is organising another X-ray to find out just what has changed.*

4) *CD is a 46 year old lady with AIDS. She presented herself with a chronic chest infection that increased medication was no longer able to control and had worsened over the last two years. She was coughing up large amounts of green phlegm and was feeling miserable. We administered diamond and carnelian to energise her blood and chest front and back. After three weekly treatments she started improving substantially and stayed well for six weeks after we stopped. She now continues with fortnightly treatments which keep her lungs functioning normally. She says this is the only thing that works.*

5) *AG is a 48 year old businessman who presented himself as a TM (meditation) teacher who was interested in energy balancing and personal enhancement. We provide him with a weekly energisation of specific biological areas designed to increase consciousness and keep him present with his personal energy field. His partner reports that he has become more loving, productive and organised. She sends him back every week.*

Bulgarian Case Report

'*Two months ago I had my assemblage point centred by a manual shift. Also I had my shadow anxiety locations cleaned up by targeting them with gem lamp therapy. During a period of few days I had the opportunity to experience the blissful therapy (two lamps with blue filter and diamonds, sapphires with a Theta brain frequency - 3.5 Hz applied towards my temples for 30 minutes) that is very pleasant and calming. What I can say about this therapy is that it is supreme for people like me living all my life with an almost constant inconvenience of anxiety. Now I feel very well, I sleep more and better, the chatter in my mind has stopped and my skin got a fresh complexion as if I became younger! The most important thing is that after the centering of my AP I am able to be more comfortable with myself and others. The stressful reactions disappeared from my life as if a magical wand has touched it.*'

UK E-mail Case Reports (2)

1) Case study for a lady with carpal tunnel syndrome, tennis elbow and depression: This 48 year old lady was suffering from carpal tunnel syndrome in both wrists, tennis elbow in the right elbow and also depression following a recent bereavement. Her assemblage point was low in the liver area and was adjusted using diamond and carnelian. Her wrists and right elbow were also treated and at the end of the session she was free of pain. After about one week the pain started to return and she came back for a further treatment. This time her assemblage point was still centred so only the areas of pain were treated. Several weeks later she reported that the pain had not returned and she was now coping with life considerably better. She returned after about one year for a short treatment to the elbow as it was beginning to hurt again. Two years later she remains completely pain-free.

2) Case study for a gentleman with sciatica and arthritis: An 81 year-old gentleman who had been unable to leave his home for several weeks due to acute sciatica was treated at the base of the spine and along his left leg. He was also suffering from arthritis in his right wrist and hand, so this was treated in the same session. During the treatment the pain from the sciatica eased a bit and the arthritic pain disappeared completely. By the following morning the pain from the sciatica had reduced to an occasional twinge and by *the next day it had gone completely. Neither pain has returned after 18 months.*

3) *Case study for a lady with inflammation in the knee and frozen shoulder: A 62 year-old had a very inflamed and painful knee as a result of a fall 3 months previously and had great difficulty walking. She also had had a frozen shoulder for 2 years which restricted movement of her right arm so much that she could raise it in front of her only and then only by about 45 degrees. She was depressed and confused and her assemblage point was low. Initially her assemblage point was centred and then the knee and shoulder were treated directly. The knee responded to treatment immediately, resulting in significantly reduced inflammation and pain, and after two further short treatments is back to normal. The shoulder gradually improved so that after 4 treatments she can swing it backwards and up at the side and can raise it almost completely, albeit with some difficulty. She is now feeling positive and optimistic about the future. Treatment continues on the shoulder.*

Archive Photographs 1995

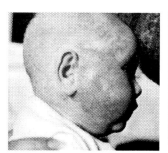

Fig. A2:7 - 9. Chronic contact eczema (covering the entire body), the baby was hospitalised for 3 months with no improvement. Treatment: cooling emeralds and sapphires inside a low power prototype wooden lamp. Following 3 therapy sessions (two to the liver), her condition cleared in 3 weeks.

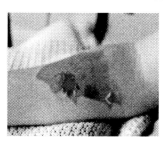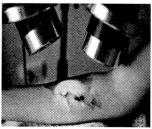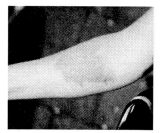

Fig. A2:10 - 12. Arm burn. A single treatment with cooling emeralds and sapphires for 20 minutes. Final picture taken 5 days later.

Ancient And Modern Medical Use Of Gem Stones

As mentioned in chapter six, the energy of certain types of coloured gem stones has an affinity for the chakras. The functional efficiency of the chakras can be increased using electronic gem therapy at the correct frequency and the correct type or mixture and quantity of gemstones. Overactive chakras can be calmed and underactive chakras can be stimulated using the gem lamps and coloured filters.

For thousands of years, balms and tablets containing beryllium aluminium silicate (emerald gem stone powder) and aluminium oxide (blue sapphire powder), have been and are indeed today prescribed by physicians in some countries for pain, contusions, infections, dermatological conditions, digestion and gastric disease, etc. These mineral medicines, like sand, do not dissolve and cannot be absorbed into the body's biochemistry, they therefore function on unconventional justifications compared to today's chemical medications.

The dielectric resonance frequency of emerald substrates is 565 nm and blue sapphire is 400 nm. Gem lamps containing beryllium aluminium silicate and aluminium oxide crystalline substrates are extremely effective for reducing localised hyperthermia, hyperperfusion, hypermetabolism and vasodilation

Fig. A2:13. An example page from King Alfonso's 'lapidary', a 12th century book translated from ancient Arabic scrolls containing medical prescriptions prepared from powdered gem stones.

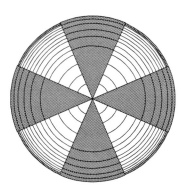

Fig. A2:14. Pattern produced by calcite crystal in convergent polarised light.

as well as dramatically attenuating pain. This type of lamp transducer is electronically modulated at the slow analgesic brainwave frequency of sleep (1.5 HZ). They are employed in perhaps 90% of all presented disease or injury with the exception of geriatric diseases. The patient's experience is always very pleasant, regardless of their presented symptoms or disease, as they receive treatment, over 90% of patients report relief from their pain, irritations, uncomfortable or distressing feelings, emotions and symptoms.

The inverse complementary management equivalent to the above procedure is gem lamps containing aluminium chromium oxide (ruby, 625 nm) or silicon magnesium dioxide (carnelian 610 m) together with carbon (diamond, 470 nm) crystalline substrates and electronically modulated at faster brainwave frequency of alertness (16.5 HZ). This combination can rapidly and effectively reduce hypothermia, vasoconstriction, hypometabolism, increasing local temperature, circulation and biological energy and is most useful for older patients. It is used for management of thrombosis, venus ulcers, phlebitis, chilblains, varicose veins, oedema and related pathology.

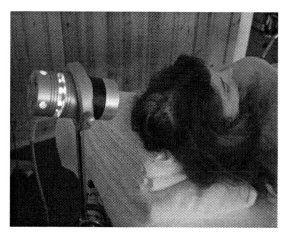

Fig. A23:15. Energising the Crown Chakra with dark blue Sapphire.

Correcting The Energy Of Disease And Injury

Contusions, fractures, burns, carcinomas, lymphomas, melanomas, prostate cancer, dermatological diseases, rheumatoid arthritis, diabetes melitis and associated pathology, liver disease and many other common conditions, including bacterial infections, can be accompanied with localised vasodilation, hyperthermia, hyperperfusion, hypermetabolism and or hypervascularisation: all high energy conditions with higher microwave emission often accompanied with discomfort and pain.

For example, in the case of vasodilated breasts caused by breast cancer, the breast energy emissions are much higher than for a healthy breast, and infrared imaging visibly exposes the areas of malignancy providing the oncologist with additional data not visible or obtainable by X ray mammograms. The hyperthermia can be due to hypervascularisation associated with tumours or increased blood flow through the existing veins. The hyperthermia, a product of malignant tumours, may suppress chemically, the immune response towards malignant cells by inhibiting the neutrophils' phagocytic activity.

Radiometric infrared scanning of the prostate gland area where cancer is suspected or confirmed by blood analysis for prostate specific antigens etc. also reveals high levels of energy emission. Radiometric scanning of malignant melanoma likewise reveals high levels of energy emission, the hyperthermic behaviour of malignant melanoma is more likely to be caused by vasodilation than hypermetabolism. Hyperthermia, hyperperfusion, hypermetabolism and vasodilation, is the white high temperature area which can be seen in the radiometric image of a knee injury in Chapter 1. Radiometric imaging should not be confused with any type of photographic images; infrared microwaves cannot pass through

Fig. A2:16 - 22. From top to bottom: Dark Blue Sapphire, Diamond, Light Blue Sapphire, Emerald, Citrine, Carnelian, Ruby.

glass lenses. It is achieved by using special germanium optics and sensitive semiconductor sensors which scan areas of the body and convert the microwave emissions into voltage values which are stored in a computer memory. The computer mathematically converts the stored voltage data into values of 'degrees centigrade' for each minute part of the scanned area (pixels). The image is created by the computer software assigning a specific colour hue to each of the many designated minute temperature values.

To re-emphasise, Infections, burns, contusions, sprains, pain, all new injuries, inflammation etc. all measure excessive levels of biological energy which require a cooling, calming, analgesic treatment. Correspondingly, problems such as old injuries, old healed bone fractures, leg ulcers, oedema, asthma, allergies, circulation problems, paralysis, numbness, etc. will mostly measure low levels of biological energy, and these problems require a stimulating, invigorating energy treatment. The effects of some common gem stones are listed below.

Dark Blue Sapphire. This gemstone emits the energy, frequency and properties of the colour violet. This colour, according to Sanskrit and Ayurvedic science has healing properties and is said to be the colour of cosmic consciousness with the ability to open the doors of perception and awareness which in turn increases the power of knowledge. Violet is also the colour of the crown chakra. However, dark blue sapphire embraces a wider spectrum of effects over the

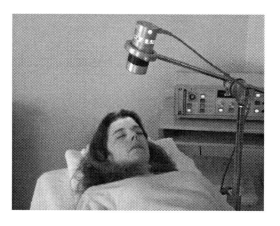

Fig. A2:23. Energising the Brow Chakra with a small diamond and an indigo filter fitted inside the lamp.

Fig. A2:24. Pattern produced by sapphire crystal in convergent polarised light.

colour violet, being cooling, tranquillising, soothing, analgesic, sedative and antispasmodic. Dark Blue sapphire counteracts aggravated vata and pitta and can be used safely for vata and pitta aggravated conditions. The violet energy emissions of sapphire have calming properties and counterbalances the nervous effect of excessive aggravated kapha. Sapphire is also used to open or stimulate the crown chakra when it is underactive or closed. Some Indian documents explain that an overactive heart chakra can be calmed with dark blue sapphire. The frequency or wavelength of violet and dark blue sapphire is around 400 nanometres.

White and Clear Diamond. This gemstone emits the energy, frequency and properties of the colour of indigo. Indigo is a cold colour and according to Sanskrit and Ayurveda is the colour of pure consciousness, it has attributes that relate to the brow chakra and the opening of the 'Third Eye' which increases the power of intuition. When the brow chakra is active, our intuition functions at a high level. The indigo emissions of diamond are very strong, stimulating, invigorating, clarifying, antiseptic, antidepressant. Diamond is helpful in counteracting aggravated kapha. Overuse of diamond may cause aggravation of vata and pitta in some people, it can also interfere with sleep and when correctly used, it can induce lucid dreaming or super alertness and agility. The frequency or wavelength of violet and diamond is 470 nanometres.

Pale Blue, White and Yellow Sapphire. The gemstone emits the energy, frequency and properties of the colour of blue. Pale yellow/white sapphire also emit blue frequencies. This colour has properties of ether and is associated with the throat chakra. The energy emissions of this gemstone are cool, soft, satisfying, antiseptic and balances aggravated kapha. The frequency or wavelength

Fig. A2:25. A Seven Chakra Gem Stone Energiser designed by the author in circa 1982.

258

of blue and pale blue sapphire is 485 nanometres.

Emerald. This gemstone emits the energy, frequency and properties of the colour of green which is associated with the heart chakra. According to Ayurveda and Sanskrit transcripts, this colour has the properties of the element of earth. It is the coldest colour and can be used for any condition where there is excessive heat generated. It is the colour of the heart chakra. However the energy emissions of emerald are many times more effective than the colour green, being cold, unifying, solidifying, analgesic and it also counteracts pitta and vata aggravated conditions. Due to the coldness of the rays emitted by emerald, it can aggravate kapha conditions. Overuse of emerald can aggravate pitta as the pitta dosha will increase by trying to compensate for the emerald's cooling effects. The Indian documents explain that an overactive crown chakra can be calmed with emerald. The frequency or wavelength of green and emerald is 565 nanometres.

Citrine. This gemstone emits the energy, frequency and properties of the colour of yellow which is associated with the navel chakra. Tibetan, Indian and Ayurvedic medicine use powdered red coral for the colour of yellow. However, coral is organic, it does not contain a

GEMS,COLOUR FILTER AND FREQUENCIES USED						
CHAKRA RATES ARE IN CYCLES PER SECOND (HZ)						
CHAKRA	FILTER COLOUR	ENERGISING GEM STONE	GEMS TO USE WHEN OVERACTIVE	RATE FOR BODY SIZE		
				SMALL	MEDIUM	LARGE
CROWN	VIOLET	SAPPHIRE	EMERALD +SAPPHIRE	1440	1344	1248
BROW	INDIGO	DIAMOND	EMERALD +SAPPHIRE	144	134	124
THROAT	BLUE	YELLOW SAPPHIRE	EMERALD +SAPPHIRE	24.0	22.8	20.8
HEART	GREEN	EMERALD	EMERALD +SAPPHIRE	18.0	16.8	15.6
SOLAR PLEXUS	YELLOW	CITRINE	EMERALD +SAPPHIRE	15.0	14.0	13.0
SACRAL	ORANGE	CARNELIAN	EMERALD +SAPPHIRE	9.0	8.4	7.8
ROOT	RED	RUBY	EMERALD +SAPPHIRE	6.0	5.6	5.2

Fig. A2:26. The seven Chakras, their gem stones, colours and frequencies.

crystalline matrix like mineral gems and is unsuitable to use with electronic applications. The substitute citrine emits powerful rays at the frequency of yellow, and is many times more powerful than red coral. The effects of citrine are warming, enlivening, cleansing and can remove the effects of aggravated pitta and kapha. The frequency or wavelength of yellow and citrine is 590 nanometres.

Carnelian. This gemstone emits the energy, frequency and properties of the colour of orange. Tibetan, Indian and Ayurvedic medicine use powdered pearl for the colour of orange. According to Ayurveda, the colour orange and pearl are associated with the spleen chakra. As with red coral above, pearl is organic, therefore the mineral carnelian is substituted for pearl. The effects of carnelian are cooling, moist, harmonising, anti allergic and have anti pitta properties. The frequency or wavelength of orange and carnelian is 610 nanometres.

Ruby. This gemstone emits the energy, frequency and properties of the colour of red and is associated with the base chakra. Rods of ruby are employed in medical surgical lasers. It counterbalances aggravated kapha and vata. Overexposure to ruby may cause excess pitta to accumulate in certain parts of the body. Due to this, ruby is not very often used and carnelian is the preferred choice, being more moderated in its effects. Unlike the colour red, ruby should be

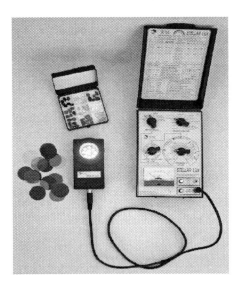
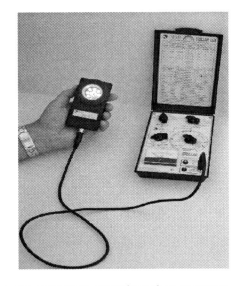

Fig. A2:27 - 28. A prototype electronic gem stone Chakra energiser that operates across a wide band of healing frequencies. Shown with a box of gem stones and colour filters.

used with caution as it is hot, drying, energising and expanding and it can be used for kapha aggravated conditions. The frequency or wavelength of red and ruby is 625 nanometres.

Serendipity plays a large role in scientific discoveries. Many years back I was impeded for an important appointment by a festive hangover from wine. My hypothesis was to energise as much volume of blood as quickly as possible in order to clear my head and other symptoms. I decided to target my spleen with two lamp transducers containing diamond and carnelian substrates at 8.5 Hz. The energised blood passed through the spleen then onto the liver and to every other organ and gland, eventually reaching my body extremities with enjoyable sensual sensations. The treatment worked within 15 minutes. Later, I concluded that this procedure would be helpful for the management of diseases which exhibited hangover type symptoms or worse and this turned out to be the case. Today, many practitioners are successfully using this procedure for the management of asthma, ME, chronic fatigue syndrome, strokes, dementia and many other conditions. Whilst dielectric resonance management of hangovers should be discouraged, however the same and modified procedures are useful for the management of alcoholic disease and related pathology. This procedure is now used for asthma, cerebral thrombosis, embolism or haemorrhage, paralysis, dementia, polymyalgia, vitiligo, muscular/ligamentous strain, adhesive capsulitis, disc prolapse, osteoarthritis, rheumatic disease, allergies and many others.

The rapid and beneficial effects of the above management procedures are scientifically supported for example, by monitoring with radiometric imaging or pathological laboratory analysis.

The discovery of targeting and increasing or decreasing and/or modulating the biological energy of internal organs and glands, improving their efficiency and performance is a quantum leap for medical science. It has become much more than just theoretically possible to adjust the haematology and biochemistry associated with sinister diseases.

A number of prostate cancer patients have been successfully managed by reducing the excessive prostate biological energy and at the same time energising the blood and spleen as outlined above. In each case, subsequent blood tests confirmed very substantial falls in the prostate specific antigen counts (PSA) and other indicators along with a reduction of symptoms. On one occasion, a blind diabetic patient's sight was returned in five minutes by ameliorating optic nerve vasoconstriction. Auto immune disease with hepatitis, jaundice and related symptomatology has been managed using simultaneous liver and spleen 'Push Pull' procedures, achieved by calming and cooling the liver inflammation and raising the biological energy of the blood and cardiovascular system with treatment to the patient's spleen area.

Electronic gem therapy has effective applications for the management of: Acne, Addiction (drug/alcohol), Allergies, Alopecia, Anaemia , Anorexia, Anxiety & Panic, Alzheimer's Disease, Arthritis, Asthma, Bacterium Infections, Backache, Bedsores, Blindness, Blood Pressure, Blood Disorders, Bronchitis, Burns, Candida, Catarrh, Cartilage Problems, Carpal Tunnel Syndrome, Cirrhosis of the Liver, Coma, Conjunctivitis, Cystitis, Depression, Dermatitis, Diabetes, Eczema, Epilepsy, Eye Injuries/Infections, Hay Fever, Heart Disease, Herpes, Hepatitis, Hypertension, Hypotension, Iatrogenic Disease, Influenza, Injuries, Insomnia, I.B.S, Jaundice, Laryngitis, Leg Ulcers, Ligament Injuries, M.E., M.S., Migraine, Neuralgia, Neuritis, Oedema, Pain, Paralysis, Parkinson's Disease, Phlebitis, Pleurisy, P.M.T., Psoriasis, Pressure Ulcers, Prolapse Disc, Repetitive Strain Injury, Rheumatism, Senile Dementia, Scleroderma, Sclerosis, Sciatica, Shingles, Stress, Stroke, Thrombosis, Viral Infections.

DOWSING ENERGY FIELDS

'Real Time' dowsing or divining using a pendulum or two divining rods can be uncannily accurate. I know a number of professional people that employ the ancient art of dowsing in their work. Locating sources of underground water using a 'Y' shaped or split willow branch is just one common example.

A friend who lives in Wales owns a bore hole drilling machine that he uses to drill bore holes into the earth's crust to provide underground water for farmers. Drilling bore holes is an expensive and time consuming task and knowing where and how deep to drill is essential in order to make a livelihood. He uses a method of dowsing using coins, rods and pendulums. His skill is such that he can accurately locate the site of water from a map, then when on the site he can divine the exact spot to drill, the depth of the water supply, the quantity and the quality of the water obtainable.

The ancient dowsers were wise to employ a freshly cut hazel or willow branch. Willow in order to survive and flourish, requires it

Fig. A2:29. Using a forked hazel branch to dowse for underground water.

roots to be near to or in underground water. Willows naturally seek out water courses to inhabit. Disconnecting a willow branch from its supply will empower it, when in the hands of a sensitive ethical person - the ability to locate water. Today, many dowsers use a pair of 'L' iron wire rods.

Dowsers are always spiritual in nature if not in personality. Darwinians uphold the (un)scientific conviction that the mind is contained in the brain and the brain is connected to the universe via the five senses. The ability of dowsers using their skills to locate water proves that there is more to man than the Darwinian view of five senses and the brain encased mind.

Fig. A2:30. Dowsing using a pair of 'L' iron wire rods.

Dowsers when concentrating on their art, quieten their thinking and expand their consciousness into the quantum energy domains. Their tools, the willow branch, pendulum or

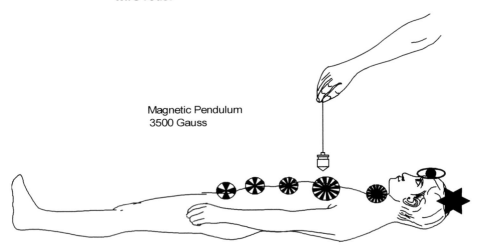

Magnetic Pendulum
3500 Gauss

Fig. A2:31. Using a magnetic pendulum to dowse chakra efficiency.

rods are used like a volt meter to measure the quantum energy fields of the subject matter of their investigation. The dowser quietens his mind by closing his throat chakra (expression), connects with his instinct (root chakra) and directing his intent out through his solar plexus, whilst at the same time concentrating on his intuition via his brow chakra. To be a successful dowser, the required attributes of power are: instinct, intent, compassion and intuition.

Dowsing for water, mineral deposits, lost objects, the best time and

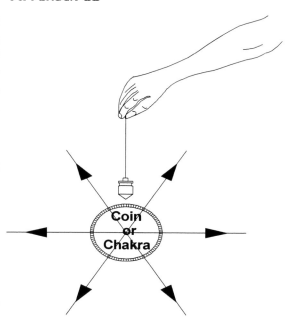

Fig. A2:32. Swinging backwards and forwards is zero efficiency.

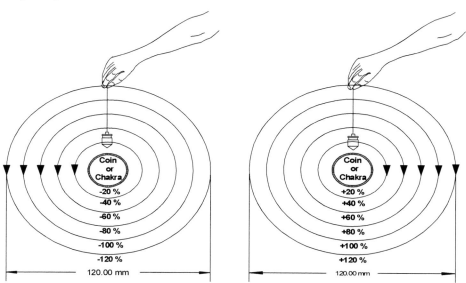

Fig. A2:33 -34. Direction of rotation and diameters for approximate positive and negative percentages of efficiency.

place to plant and sow, the suitability of food or the sex of chickens eggs is 'Real Time' dowsing. This is to say that the person dowsing can directly connect to the quantum energy fields of the matter in hand, therefore the results will often be accurate and repeatable.

On the other hand, forecast dowsing is a method of trying to establish the outcome of future events. Here the dowser cannot connect easily to the energy of the substance of the future, therefore the results will be wrong, variable or sometimes fortuitous.

In the right hands, a magnetic pendulum can easily locate the human Assemblage Point. The same techniques can be employed to measure the energy of the chakras and the seven attributes of power. This is in 'Real Time' dowsing as the person dowsing can directly connect to the energies of a third person. The person under investigation does not need to be present.

The dowsers can sit at a desk and establish the personality type and the emotional level of health of anyone anywhere. It is an easy operation to establish the attributes of family members, neighbours, patients, employees, lawyers, bank managers, employers, directors, councillors, politicians, media personalities. Knowing their attributes will provide not only an indication of their agenda, but also the prospects for the future.

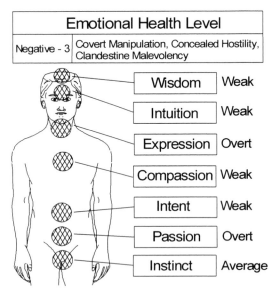

Emotional Health Level	
Negative - 3	Covert Manipulation, Concealed Hostility, Clandestine Malevolency

Wisdom	Weak
Intuition	Weak
Expression	Overt
Compassion	Weak
Intent	Weak
Passion	Overt
Instinct	Average

Fig. A2:35. Compare your dowsing results with the charts in Chapter 4 to determine the level of Emotional Health.

Chakra Dowsing

Holding a magnetic pendulum over the chakras of a person lying relaxed and comfortable on their back will yield surprising results. Standing or siting next to the subject, hold the pendulum over each chakra in turn.

Start at the root chakra and work upwards to the crown chakra. The process can be speeded up by giving the pendulum a gentle swing to start it off. Then hold your arm still and observe the way the pendulum turns or swings.

1) Should it swing backwards and forwards without turning, then the chakra is closed.

2) If it turns clockwise then the chakra has positive energy.

3) Should it turn anticlockwise then the chakra is drawing or draining energy, anticlockwise represents negative energy.

The speed and size of the circumference represents the percentage of positive or negative energy. Refer to the drawings and determine the energy levels of each of your subject's chakras. Record the levels with pen and paper, then compare them to the charts in chapter four. From these you can determine the subject's emotional level of health.

Using the charts also provide the information on the subject's weak and strong attributes. This percentage data for each chakra and attribute provides you and your subject with details of their strengths and weaknesses that need to be worked on. Working on and exercising the underactive chakras and attending to the weak attributes will improve the emotional level of health.

Some General Rules

1) A weak root, solar plexus, throat and brow with a strong heart chakra indicates an introvert emotional feeling type.

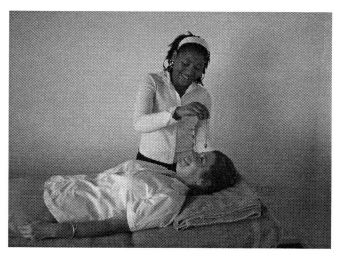

Fig. A2:36. Dowsing the Brow Chakra (Third Eye) with A Magnetic Pendulum. The Third Eye area is very sensitive to magnetism, hence the laughter.

2) Weak root, solar plexus, brow with a strong heart and throat chakra indicates an extrovert emotional feeling type.

3) A weak root, solar plexus, and throat with a strong brow chakra indicates an introvert intuitive type.

4) A weak root and solar plexus with strong brow and throat chakras indicates an extrovert intuitive type.

5) A weak heart, brow and crown with strong base and solar plexus chakras indicates an extrovert practical type.

6) A weak brow and crown with strong base and solar plexus and heart chakras, indicates an introvert practical type.

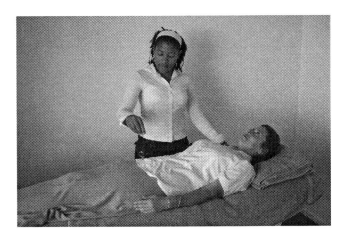

Fig. A2:37. Dowsing the Root Chakra (Instinct and Survival) with a Magnetic Pendulum. Unlike the previous photograph the expressions are spontaneously more pensive.

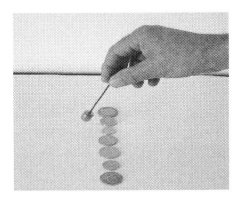

Fig. A2:38. Illustration of employing a Magnetic Pendulum to dowse Chakra energy efficiency using seven nonferrous coins, each representing a Chakra.

7) A weak root, solar plexus and throat with strong heart and brow chakras indicates an introvert rational type.

8) A weak root, solar plexus and heart with strong throat and brow chakras indicates an extrovert rational type.

Using Coins To Dowse Chakra Percentages

Dowsing a person's chakra energy levels in their absence can produce good results. Although it is not as easy as working directly with the

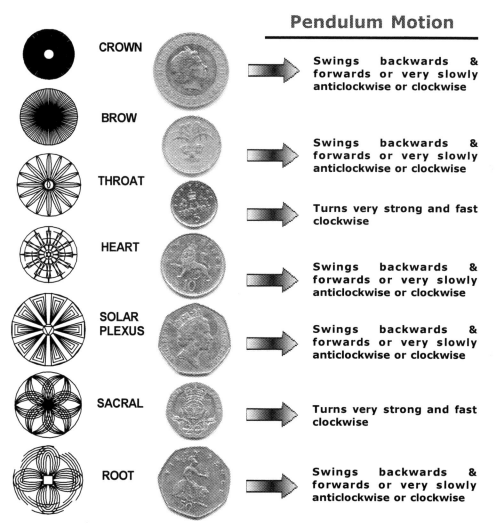

Fig. A2:39. Illustration of Chakra Dowsing using a magnetic pendulum over seven nonferrous coins. The results shown are typical for a covert manipulative person with an emotional level of health of -3.

person's body. Much more concentration and an attitude of indifference as to the results is required. Some dowsers use a 'witness', this can be a sample of the subject's hair, a photograph or their signature.

1) Use exactly the same techniques as above only sitting upright comfortably at a wooden table or desk.

2) Arrange seven coins in an ascending line on a sheet of paper.

3) Write the name of the subject on the top of the sheet of paper.

4) Place a witness sample on the sheet next to their name.

5) You feet should be firmly in contact with the floor. Preferably, do not rest you dowsing elbow on the desk top.

6) Dowse each coin in turn starting with the coin representing the root chakra.

7) Record the percentages on the paper by the side of each chakra coin.

Using The Electronic Dowsing Meter

Electronic dowsing meters are very easy to use. The meter illustrated has ten different scales of subjects relevant to a dowser's work. One of the scales cover from zero to plus 100% and zero to minus 100%. The magnetic pendulum when held over the meter scale automatically starts to swing. All that is necessary is to concentrate on the meter while asking the questions. The pendulum will swing towards and settle on the answer.

Reference: Neal, Alan. *Dowsing in Devon and Cornwall*. Bossiney Books.

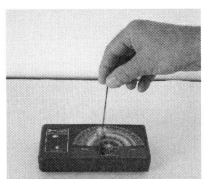
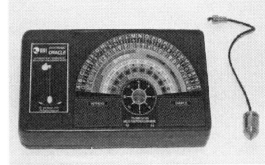

Fig. A2:40 - 41. Automatic Electronic Multifunction Dowsing Meter.

Appendix III

An Introduction to

Dynamic Radiometric Thermal Diagnostics And Dielectric Resonance Management Procedures

First Published By Positive Health Magazine

All objects in the material universe emit energy. The fact that they emit energy is the reason that we can detect them in the first place. Astronomers can determine the temperature and elements of distant stars by measuring the frequencies that they emit. Using a spectroscope, astronomers can split the light emitted from distant stars into individual frequencies displayed as bands of colour (the spectrum). From this they can determine the elements that the heavenly bodies comprise. For example, sodium is yellow at 510 million million oscillations per second or a wavelength 588 nanometres. The overall emitted colour, as seen by the eye, determines the surface temperature of the star. High temperature white dwarf stars emit more energy in the ultraviolet frequency band, whereas cooler yellow and red giant stars emit the bulk of their energy in the infrared frequency band.

Humans are no exception to these universal scientific laws. Humans emit energy away from the body in all directions as electromagnetic waves, at microwave frequencies in the infrared wave band. But this energy is not detectable by the human eye, or indeed by any conventional glass optical photographic or video camera.

The number of oscillations per second for the frequency bands for ultraviolet, visible light and infrared and microwaves are so large as to be too unmanageable on paper, therefore they are always referred to as 'the wavelength'. This is calculated by dividing the number of oscillations per second into the speed of light which is 299,800,000 metres per second (186,284 miles per second). This calculation provides the precise length of each cycle or wave. The values for the very high frequencies instead of being recited in billions of cycles per second are, for convenience, always quoted as the wavelength in micrometers (uM) and nanometres (nM) (See Fig. A3:1).

Amongst certain medical scientists, precision calibrated measurement of the frequencies emitted by the human body is a controversial but useful scientific aid for diagnosis and management of disease. It is scientifically called 'Quantitative Radiometric Measurement' or 'Telethermometry'. This enables medical scientists to gain a greater understanding of some aspects of disease, its progress and management.

The energetic emissions of the human body that are of concern for diagnostic purposes are within a narrow band of infrared microwave frequencies at wavelengths of 8.0 to 12.0 uM. Very sophisticated electronic apparatus is required to detect these emissions.

A useful benefit of radiometric scanning for diagnostics is that there is no physical or intrusive contact with the patient, only the microwave frequencies emitted by the patient's body are recorded and analysed. To avoid error, the environmental conditions must be controlled. The calibration of the radiometric imaging apparatus is critical and the analyst must be ruthless about his interpretations and conclusions drawn from the data provided by the images (See Fig. A3:2, 3 & 4).

For over thirty years this Author has been researching and developing medical management apparatus specifically for the manipulation and/or modulation of biological energies related to disease. He has developed a large number of efficient disease management procedures that implement the scientific laws of dielectric resonance. More recently he has also developed a number of precision calibrated instruments that have provided invaluable data for diagnosis and management (See Fig. A3: 2, 3 & 4).

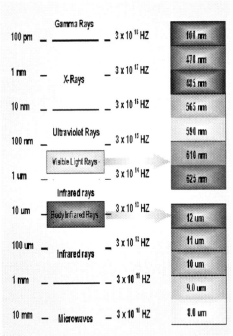

Fig. A3:1. The Body Microwave Infrared Emissions & the Colour Spectrum.

The Domineering Energy Of Disease And Injury

Contusions, fractures, burns, carcinomas, lymphomas, melanomas, prostate cancer, dermatological diseases, rheumatoid arthritis, diabetes mellitus and associated pathology, liver disease and many other common conditions, including bacterial infections, can be accompanied with localised vasodilation, hyperthermia, hyperperfusion, hypermetabolism and or hypervascularisation. These are all high energy conditions producing higher microwave emissions and are often accompanied by discomfort and pain.

For example, in the case of vasodilation in breasts provoked by breast cancer, the breast energy emissions are much higher than a for a healthy breast. Radiometric imaging visibly exposes the areas of malignancy and provides the oncologist with additional data not visible or obtainable by X-ray mammograms. The hyperthermia can be due to hypervascularisation associated with malignancy or increased blood flow through the existing vascular structure. The hyperthermia, a product of malignant tumours, may suppress chemically the immune response towards malignant cells by inhibiting the neutrophils' phagocytic activity.

Radiometric infrared scanning of the prostate gland area where cancer is suspected or confirmed by blood analysis for prostate specific antigens etc. also reveals high levels of energy emission. Radiometric scanning of malignant melanoma likewise reveals high levels of energy emission. The hyperthermic behaviour of malignant melanoma is more likely to be caused by vasodilation than hypermetabolism (See Fig. A3:5).

From Stellar Exploration To Sub-Molecular Energy Medicine

Hyperthermia, hyperperfusion, hypermetabolism and vasodilation produce the red high temperature areas that can be seen in the radiometric image of a knee contusion (Fig. A3:6). Radiometric imaging should not be confused with any type of photographic images. Infrared microwaves cannot pass through glass.

For example, PIP scanning, used by some alternative therapists, is not radiometric as it relies on a normal glass optic video camera to capture the photographic image and computer software to turn up the 'colour hue intensity' to 100% to create the colour distortions seen in the PIP scan images. PIP scan images cannot contain any radiometric information.

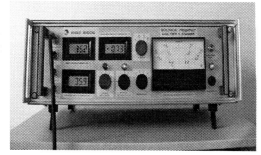

Fig. A3:2. A precision 8.0 - 12.0 uM spectrum Radiometric Scanner Apparatus.

273

Radiometric imaging is truly scientific and is derived from outer space exploration technology. It is achieved by using special germanium optics and sensitive semiconductor sensors that scan areas of the body and convert the microwave emissions into voltage values that are stored in a computer memory. The computer mathematically converts the stored voltage data into values of 'degrees centigrade' for each minute part of the scanned area (pixel). The image is created by the computer software assigning a specific colour hue to each of the many designated temperature values. The hue red is assigned to the hottest temperature value, next orange, then yellow, green, blue indigo and down to violet as the coldest colour. The colour pixels that make up the image represent a precision calibrated map of the temperature mathematics of the radiometric scan that the medical practitioner can use towards diagnosis. It can also be used to monitor disease progress over time.

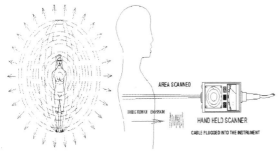

Fig. A3:3. Scanning infrared emissions using an early prototype infrared scanner calibrated against platinum temperature references.

Medical dictionaries quote placebo levels at 30% to 70%. A major problem for alternative therapies is to provide accountable evidence that proves the value of the procedure or products used. Without such evidence and placebo levels running up to 70%, it is almost impossible to reassure the medical institutions and a large percentage of the public of the efficiency of any of the alternative management procedures. Radiometric imaging is quick and cost effective, contemporary radiometric scanners take only a second or so to record and produce an image. These images provide the practitioner with real time data about their patient's condition. Recording 'before and after treatment' radiometric images, provides the practitioner with scientific proof of the competence of his treatment and the progress of

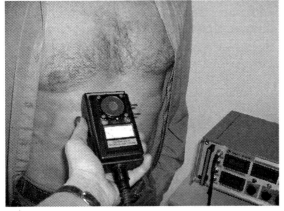

Fig. A3:4. Scanning infrared emissions using an early prototype infrared scanner calibrated against platinum temperature references.

his patient as well as equipping him with substantive scientific proof for further discussion.

The Sinister Intelligence And Power Of Disease

Cancer is capricious cellular behaviour. Psoriasis is unpredictable cellular reproduction of the dermis. Unlike tumours, and fortunately for the patient, the accelerated reproduction of skin cells moves earlier generations of cells (layers of skin) away from their blood supply and they die, dropping off in flakes. Infrared measurement of affected skin in contrasted to adjacent unaffected skin areas can reveal temperature differences of +5.0 ⁰ Celsius (See Fig. A3: 7 and 8). A temperature differential of five degree Celsius is almost implausible and difficult to account for by vasodilation/ hypermetabolism alone. This anomalous differential is more probably due to a combination of vasoconstriction/hypometabolism of unaffected areas together with vasodilation/hypermetabolism of the psoriasis areas. It is as if, by some contrivance, the body or the disease appropriates biological energy from unaffected areas and diverts this energy to propel the psoriasis. This same 'pull-push' energy diversion process appears to occur with malignant tumours and it seems that disease exhibits an intelligence.

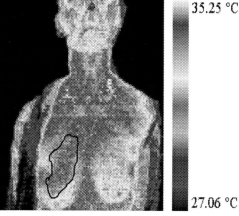

Fig. A3:5. Breast Cancer: Radiometric Image showing hyperthermia on the right breast.

For disease to progress, it requires energy which it

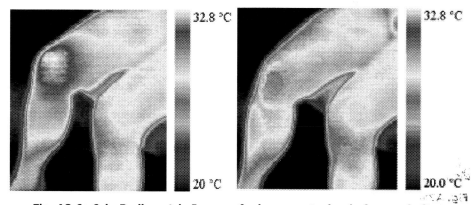

Fig. A3:6a & b. Radiometric Image of a knee contusion before and after treatment with the Lux IV.

expropriates from the healthy body mass. Some insidious diseases apparently are able to create their own supportive positive oscillating energy and chemical feedback system. So, interrupting the energy feedback system and stimulating the aggression of the immune defence system is a conspicuous method of confounding sinister diseases and can be applied alongside orthodox management procedures.

'Push-Pull' Energy Management for Disease and Injury

Modern medical diagnostic procedures are both commendable and indisputably ingenious. Pathological laboratory analysis of the patient's haematology and biochemistry is a fundamental tool supporting disease diagnosis and management. Invariably, abnormalities in the patient's blood and urine samples are found where disease is chronic or terminal. The blood counts for erythrocytes, leukocytes, lymphocytes, platelets, neutrophils etc. are likely to be outside of the normal range, as will other indicators such as the biochemistry constituents. Blood tests for prostate specific antigens, carcinogenic embryonic antigen, erythrocyte sedimentation rate, etc. are indicators for these cancers.

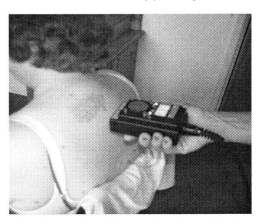

Fig. A3:7. Infrared scanning psoriasis can reveals biological activity of +5.0 ° C. higher than unaffected skin.

If by some means it would be possible to artificially manipulate and re-divert the patient's biological energy away from the disease, or modulate the biological energy of the diseased parts, then such a method would provide excellent management possibilities as well as expeditious palliative care.

Electronic design engineers are brilliant and cunning in their application of strategies to solve problems, e.g. the development of the 'Push-Pull' thermionic vacuum valve power amplifier in

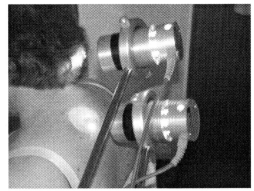

Fig. A3:8. Dielectric Resonance Management of psoriasis lowers biological activity down to only 0.8 ° C. higher than unaffected skin -with just a single 20 minute treatment.

the 1940's. Today almost every manufactured electronic item uses this technique. The application of two power amplifying electronic elements in an inverse complementary mode, one 'pushing' and the other 'pulling' enables awesome amplification of power to be produced, as can be experienced in any discotheque.

Unlike electronic engineering, medicine is not yet a complete science, and when applied to disease management, the electronic 'Push-Pull' strategy can produce outstanding results unavailable elsewhere.

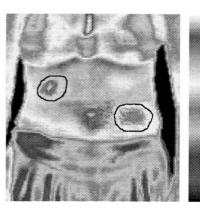

Fig. A3:9. Radiometric Image showing high emissions of the liver area and low for the para-navel area.

Everybody feels better when the sun shines. The universal principle of dielectric resonance is the subatomic transfer of energy between discrete masses. This principle is used to manipulate and/or modulate cellular biological energy via a sub molecular level of valance electron modulation. Modulating electrons in living cells will adjust, increase or decrease the biological energy or life force of the cells. Whale Medical Inc.'s Lux IV is certified EU compliance Class IIA medical apparatus, the special low voltage medical lamps are dielectric resonance transducers that induce, manipulate and/or modulate biological energy for disease management. The Lux IV has been designed and developed to produce rapid and effective results for an ultra wide range of disease management without producing any side effects. A very large percentage of presented injuries and diseases support excessive

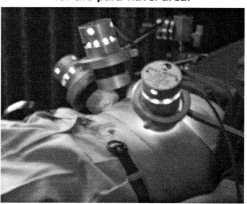

Fig. A3:10. Simultaneous 'Push- Pull' Dielectric Resonance management of the liver and the spleen.

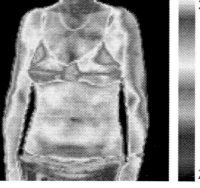

Fig. A3:11. Radiometric Image of the same patient after Dielectric Resonance management.

biological energy, and neutralising the excessive energy and reducing the temperature is a major management consideration as it reduces pain, shock, inflammation, temperature and assists the healing process.

For thousand of years, balms and tablets containing beryllium aluminium silicate (emerald gem stone powder) and aluminium oxide (blue sapphire powder), have been and are indeed today being prescribed by physicians in some countries for pain, contusions, infections, dermatological conditions, digestion and gastric disease, etc.. These mineral medicines, like sand, do not dissolve and cannot be absorbed into the body's biochemistry, they therefore function on unconventional justifications compared to biochemical medications. The dielectric resonance frequency of emerald substrates is around 565 nM and blue sapphire is 400 nM. Lux IV medical lamps containing beryllium aluminium silicate and aluminium oxide crystalline substrates are extremely effective for reducing localised hyperthermia, hyperperfusion, hypermetabolism and vasodilation as well as dramatically attenuating pain. This type of transducer is electronically modulated at the slow analgesic brainwave frequency of sleep (1.5 HZ). They are employed in perhaps 90% of all presented disease or injury. The patient's experience is always very pleasant, regardless of their presented symptoms or disease, as they receive treatment, over 90% of patients report relief from their pain, irritations, uncomfortable or distressing feelings, emotions and symptoms.

The inverse complementary management equivalent to the above procedure is Lux IV lamps containing aluminium chromium oxide (ruby, 625 nM) or silicon magnesium dioxide (carnelian, 610 nM) together with carbon (diamond, 470 nM) crystalline substrates and electronically modulated at faster brainwave frequency of alertness (16.5 HZ). This combination can rapidly and effectively reduce hypothermia, vasoconstriction, hypometabolism, increasing local temperature, circulation and biological energy. It is used for management of thrombosis, venous ulcers, phlebitis, chilblains, varicose veins, oedema and related pathology.

Serendipity plays a large roll in scientific discoveries, many years back this author was impeded for an important appointment by a festive hangover. His hypothesis was to energise as much volume of his blood as quickly as possible in order to clear his head and other symptoms. He decided to target his spleen with two lamp transducers containing diamond and carnelian substrates at 8.5 HZ. The energised blood passed through the spleen then on to the liver and to every other organ and gland, eventually reaching the body extremities. The treatment worked within 15 minutes. Later, he concluded that this procedure would by helpful for management of diseases that exhibited hangover type symptoms or worse and this turned out to be the case. Today, many practitioners are successfully using this procedure for the management of asthma, ME, chronic fatigue syndrome, strokes, dementia and many other conditions.

The dielectric resonance management of hangovers should be discouraged, however the same and modified procedures are useful for the management of alcoholic disease and related pathology. The substitution of ruby with carnelian crystalline substrates produces a softer treatment for conditions midway between the two procedures cited above: examples are asthma, cerebral thrombosis, embolism or haemorrhage, paralysis, dementia, polymyalgia, vitiligo, muscular/ligamentous strain, adhesive capsulitis, disc prolapse, osteoarthritis, rheumatic disease, allergies and many others.

The rapid and beneficial effects of the above management procedures are scientifically supported for example, by monitoring with radiometric imaging or pathological laboratory analysis.

The discovery of targeting and increasing or decreasing and/or modulating the biological energy of internal organs and glands, improving their efficiency and performance was a quantum leap for medical science, it had become much more than just theoretically possible to adjust the haematology and biochemistry associated with sinister diseases and this was later proved with palliative management of a terminal patient with stage three lymphoma and lymphoedema. By targeting appropriately selected organs and glands, practitioners have produced many astounding satisfactory results for patients presenting a wide variety of serious complaints. Understandably, as word got around, patients with powerful terminal diseases began seeking support and in order to accommodate this compromised situation, more complex and powerful procedures were developed incorporating 'Push-Pull' management strategies.

A number of prostate cancer patients have been successfully managed by reducing the excessive prostate biological energy and at the same time energising the blood and spleen as outlined above. In each case, subsequent blood tests confirmed very substantial falls in the prostate specific antigen counts etc. along with a reduction of collateral symptoms. On one occasion, a blind diabetic patient's sight was returned in five minutes by ameliorating optic nerve vasoconstriction. Auto immune disease with hepatitis, jaundice and related symptomatology has been managed using simultaneous liver and spleen 'Push-Pull' procedures, achieved by calming and cooling the liver inflammation and raising the biological energy of the blood and cardiovascular system with treatment to the patient's spleen area.

More recently, a youngish lady had been diagnosed with infiltrating carcinoma lying on the stomach and bowel. Over a few months her health had deteriorated, causing her to loose 22 kilograms, and the prognosis had given her just months to live. Chemotherapy was ineffective for her condition and the hospital, in her case, could not directly assist further. Paradoxically, this patient's haematology and biochemistry were within normal range, from the many pathological tests undertaken, aside from a biopsy, there were no abnormal indicators. Weekly radiometric imaging revealed a hyperthermic area of $+1.8\,^{\circ}$ C. at the liver and $-1.7\,^{\circ}$ C.

hypothermic area at the stomach (zero referenced against the spleen) (see Fig. A3:10). The reasons for this atypical 3.5 ° C. differential are not properly understood, but is was assumed to be hepatitis and stomach vasoconstriction and it was managed as such. Also, the patient's assemblage point location was abnormally low, as is invariably the case for patient's with serious disease.

Due to the proximity of the carcinoma, the stomach could not be given the prescribed stimulating management. This dichotomy was reconciled by giving a thirty minute 'Push-Pull' procedure, calming and cooling the liver and stimulating the blood and spleen instead of the stomach. This was implemented to the liver to slow down her metabolic rate, reduce her blood pressure and to the spleen to raise her biological energy and lift up her low assemblage point location (See Fig. A3:9). The following week, she reported that she had gained weight, was eating, sleeping, working and feeling better. However, the liver/stomach radiometric differential had only marginally improved, nevertheless, this was a turning point from her previously retrogressive predicament and over some four weeks this liver/stomach differential was moderated (see Fig. A3:11).

For the past four months this patient has been receiving weekly or fortnightly palliative care procedures with stimulating treatment to her blood and spleen and occasionally to the thymus area. At the same time calming cooling analgesic treatment is given to the stomach and bowel area, the site of the carcinoma in the hope of slowing down its progress so as to give the immune defences system a chance to gain the upper hand. The hypothesis of raising the biological energy of the blood and the immune defence system via treatment to the spleen (and thymus) and applying calming cooling treatment to the diseased area, at least for the time being for this patient, is paying off. It has decisively improved the patient's health and quality of life. Only time will tell if this patient goes into remission. To be continued in future issues.

Caution. The above management procedures have been in cooperation with the patient's doctors who have provided essential oncology, haematology, biochemistry and other pathology data. This article is for reference, not intended to diagnose, prescribe or treat without medical supervision. The information contained herein is in no way to be considered as a substitute for consultation with a professional physician.

Source Web Site: http://www.whalemedical.com

THE INFRARED BIOSCANNER

Extracts from the Lux IV and Infrared Bioscanner Operating and Training Handbook

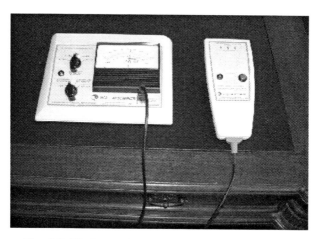

Fig. A3:12. Accurate easy to use Desktop Infrared Differential Scanner.

Advantages In Use

Quantitative real time Infrared Thermal diagnostics combined with real time Lux IV management provide:

* **Rapid calibrated evidence of the biological energy levels accompanying disease or injury.**

* **Indicate the correct type of electronic gem therapy application or other therapy modality required to counteract and heal the problem.**

* **Permit the monitoring of the applied therapy's effects during and throughout treatment.**

* **Provide the clinician and the patient with visual evidence of the effectiveness and progress of the applied therapy.**

* **Increase success rates and shortens the patient's attendance and recovery time as well as save the clinician's time and energy.**

Apparatus Description

This radiometric differential scanner instrument is simple and easy to use. It is battery powered and provides rapid accurate real-time diagnostic assistance. It is extremely sensitive and accurate and provides a very fast response time when scanning the body's natural microwave emissions. The Human Body emits microwaves in the infrared spectrum. Diseased and injured areas emit different levels of energy and frequencies when compared to healthy parts. When the Bioscanner's diagnostic potential is combined with the Lux IV Electronic Gem Therapy lamps, 'Real-Time Medical Diagnostics and Management' is the result.

The temperature of patients can vary; many aspects can affect it, for example: age, weight, height, sex, diet, blood pressure, menstrual cycle, metabolic rate, infection, menopause, state of health, diet, these and many other considerations will affect the individual's temperature. Therefore this, comprehensive thermal maps or models suitable for diagnostic and

Fig. A3:13. The meter showing a positive reading of +2.2 °C.

Fig. A3:14. The meter showing a negative reading of -2.8 °C.

management are almost non existent. Thus there are very few baseline or bench mark values known in relation to the diagnosis of disease and injury. So in the past thermal diagnostics methods have been treated with considerable reservation.

Today all of this has changed. Radiometric differential measurement does not rely on a common baseline or benchmark of calibrated values for different types of injuries or diseases in order to provide rapid accurate assessment and diagnosis. The Infrared Bioscanner does not rely on any of the traditional methods of temperature measurement. The baseline reference temperature value (for a healthy condition) that is scientifically required is taken from the patient rather than from some medically established table of values. The Bioscanner achieves this by taking a reference reading from the patient and this eliminates the problems created by variations of temperature between individuals. Using our ***Infrared Bioscanner***, a 'sample and hold' reading is taken from a corresponding healthy area of the patient. This sample reading is retained in the instrument's memory and the **Infrared Bioscanner** is then used to scan the diseased, injured or affected area and this is compared against the stored value taken from the patient's unaffected or healthy area.

Diseased or injured areas of the patient will emit higher or lower energy levels when compared to unaffected parts. The more serious the presented condition under examination, the higher the deviations of emissions will be and the meter will record these. Using the **Infrared Bioscanner** to scan back and forth across any area, it is a simple matter to pinpoint the exact problem area and the nature of the problem. This greatly assists in determining the correct treatment to improve and correct the patient's energy emissions back towards a normal level.

High Differential Reading

Contusions, fractures, burns, carcinomas, lymphomas, melanomas, prostate cancer, dermatological diseases, rheumatoid arthritis, diabetes melitis and associated pathology, liver disease and many other common conditions, including infections, are usually accompanied with vasodilation, hyperthermia, hyperperfusion, hypermetabolism and or vascularisation: all high energy conditions with higher microwave emission often accompanied with discomfort and pain. The **Infrared Bioscanner** will easily detect and record these to a distinguished difference of 0.05 degree Celsius. The slightest increase in these conditions will cause the Bioscanner's meter reading to increase instantly as it is compared to the healthy stored reference value.

Low Differential Reading

Conversely, conditions involving atrophy, neuropathy, deep vein

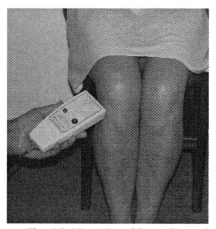 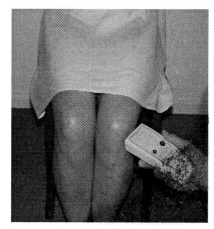

Fig. A3:15 - 16. Taking a 'Sample & Hold' reference from the right knee for comparison scanning of the left knee area.

thromboses, paralysis, ulceration, and so on, exhibit localised hypothermia, hypometabolism, vasoconstriction, low energy conditions with a lower microwave emission. In this case the Bioscanner's meter will decrease towards negative values compared to the healthy reference value.

Fig. A3:17. The meter showing a positive reading.

High And Low Differential Reading

Many conditions will involve tissue areas of both high and low readings. For example disabled patients suffering with spastic, athetoid, dystonic and choreiform muscular problems will present both high an low reading on their limbs depending on the amount of circulation and nerve energy levels in any given muscle group. This is the same for stroke patients with paralysis, some muscles will be under tension with excessive energy and other muscle groups will be with a very low level of energy, possessing no tension or feeling. Using The **Infrared Bioscanner** in conjunction with gem lamp treatment, such differential can be addressed, giving rise to a considerable improvement for the patient's mobility.

Fig. A3:18. Lux IV Lamp Transducer fitted with a violet filter & filled dark sapphire.

One Example Of Use For Back Problems

Set the **Infrared Bioscanner's** meter range switch to +4.0 - Zero -4.0 °C. Target the patient's spine with the scanner's probe and depress the red push-switch. This will store a reference value into the scanner's memory. Scan the spinal area up and down as well as either side. Look for any sudden peaks and dips in the meter reading.

Note that the reading will vary as the spinal column is scanned, normally this variation will be linear showing no peaks or dips by the meter. Any sudden peak

Fig. A3:19. Lux IV Lamp Transducer fitted with a green filter & filled with emeralds and dark sapphire.

or dip in the meter reading will indicate inflammation.

Often with back pain, the pain will extend to one of the hips and down one leg. This is even more likely if a high level of inflammation is measured on the spine around L4 & L5 with the scanner.

Take a reference readings from the unaffected leg and compare the painful hip, knee and leg against it. Although the patient may report feeling pain in their hip or knee joints and general feelings of heat in their leg, the **Infrared Bioscanner** will show a lower energy levels in the affected leg.

Fig. A3:20. The meter showing a negative reading.

This energy imbalance is in part due to the nerve energy that routes down the spine to each leg being blocked in one or more nerve pathways at the site of inflammation. The sciatic pain in the hips and legs is phantom. The pain is generated at the site of the spinal inflammation and may be due to disc pressure and chafing. The nerve pathway is short circuited and the nerve energy to the leg will be lower. The patient will hold their weight on their seemingly good leg and this will require more nervous energy and blood supply which will raise the energy levels accordingly.

Fig. A3:21. Lux IV Lamp Transducer fitted with an orange filter & filled with diamonds and carnelians.

Notes On Skeletal Alignment And Balance

When the sciatic nerve is compromised pain will often be experienced in only one leg. Chronic conditions are self-feeding (refer to the schematic drawing below). The patient naturally attempts to avoid or relieve the leg and back pain by taking their weight on one leg. This over time will cause the pelvic structure to move upwards from the leg that is taking the strain, together with whole body muscle imbalance. The net result is that under examination, the patient's legs appear to

Fig. A3:22. Lux IV Lamp Transducer fitted with a red filter & filled with diamonds and rubies.

be of different lengths when lying on their back with their ankles close together. Also, muscle groups in their back will be under uneven tension. The twisted pelvis applies sideways pressure via the supportive muscle tension to the spine, causing it to curve away in an 'S' Shape, this induces even more disc distortion and pressure, increasing the spinal nerve inflammation and pain.

The rapid way to treat this effectively is by using a Lux IV lamp containing emeralds and dark sapphire at 1.5 Hz. With the patient lying on their side or front, use the lamps to target the spinal inflammation for twenty to thirty minutes. As treatment progresses, the patient's pain will substantially subside and their muscular skeletal frame alignment will relax and correct itself. The leg length if checked after the treatment will be equal.

There are many causes of back pain and their solutions may not involve treatment directly to the back. Abdominal surgery can leave deeply embedded muscle trauma. Hernia operations are very painful and mobility and posture are compromised to get some relief from the post surgery pain. Even years later, the site of surgery can be numb, over sensitive and painful. This can bring about frontal unbalanced transverse muscle tension that ultimately is supported by the spine. Chronic back pain can result. The treatment is not to treat the back, but the site of the surgery.

Not all back pain will show signs of inflammation with high scanner readings. Low scanner readings can be noted. In which case Lux IV lamps containing a red filter, rubies for heat and dark sapphires for the pain are

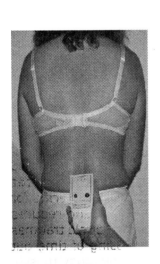

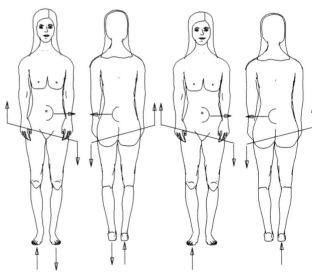

Fig. A3:23. Scanning the Spine and back for inflammation.

Fig. A3:24 - 25. Schematic of the directions of stress and skeletal distortion. Force directions (see text).

included, especially if the pain on-sets with cold weather. Weakness in the back spine and disc problems are treated with an orange filtered lamp containing diamond and carnelians after the inflammation has been remedied.

Operational Notes

When taking a sample & hold reference level with the scanner it is important to take the reference sample from a corresponding area on the opposite side of the patient's body. The extremities of the body such as the toes feet fingers and hands will present lower temperature readings.

For example, when scanning carpel tunnel syndrome on the right wrist take the reference sample from the patient's left wrist, or when scanning the liver for hepatitis, take a reference sample from the patient's spleen area. As the blood passes through the spleen then into the liver, under healthy conditions they should be at much the same temperature.

Using The Infrared Bioscanner To Determine The Lux IV Treatment

High Differential Recordings

Scanned readings that show a much higher level when compared against a reference sample taken from a corresponding part of the body are significant and should be investigated further.

Readings greater than perhaps $+1.5 \, °$ C. may indicate localised hypermetabolism, vasodilation, infection or perhaps vascularisation and cancer. When the cause of the inflammation is supported by reported symptoms and patient's history, for example, contusions, fracture, post surgery trauma, injury infections, dermatitis, eczema, psoriasis or burns, then the treatment using the Lux IV will almost certainly be a green lamp filled with emeralds and dark sapphires. This applies to acute and chronic conditions with high readings.

In the case where only a relatively small positive reading is observed and is accompanied with pain but little inflammation, then the treatment would be a violet lamp filled with dark sapphire only or perhaps a reduced number of emeralds. Emerald is specific for cooling, it reduces hypermetabolism and vasodilation whereas dark sapphire is specific for pain, being an analgesic, antispasmodic, muscle relaxant, and reduces hypertension. This type of situation often relates to chronic or old traumas that have been largely physically repaired with the passing of time but still exhibit neuropathy of one sort or another..

The Lux IV should be set to pulse the lamps with a slow calming frequency of Delta. - 1.5 Hz. When the human body is asleep or anaesthetised, the brain frequency is uniformly at around 1.5 Hz. When the Delta brainwave frequency is applied in conjunction with dark sapphire, together they induce a profound relaxed and anaesthetised feeling in the area targeted.

Lux IV medical lamps containing emeralds (beryllium aluminium silicate) and dark sapphires (aluminium oxide) crystalline substrates are extremely effective for reducing localised hyperthermia, hyperperfusion, hypermetabolism and vasodilation as well as dramatically attenuating pain. This type of transducer is electronically modulated at slow analgesic brainwave frequency of sleep (1.5 HZ). They are employed in perhaps 90% of all presented disease or injury. The patient's experience is always very pleasant, regardless of their presented symptoms or disease. As they receive treatment, over 90% of patients report immediate relief from their pain, irritations, uncomfortable or distressing feelings, emotions and symptoms.

Low Differential Recordings

Range And Calibration Accuracy

Typically +/-3.0% of Full Scale Meter Reading on all five ranges. The **Infrared Bioscanner** has two modes of measurement: Standard Temperature Measurement (E). Differential Measurement in four ranges of sensitivity (A, B, C, D). Differential provide readings of great accuracy and on the most sensitive range the reading can be determined down to a twentieth of a degree Celsius. The meter is calibrated in degrees Celsius via a 'Centre Zero' Moving Coil Meter.

Calibrated in Four Ranges of Sensitivity: Modes of Function: The Scanner has two modes of measurement.

A. +40 Zero -40 °C. Differential Temperature Measurement Mode.

B. +10 Zero -10 °C Differential Temperature Measurement Mode.

C. +4.0 Zero -4.0 °C. Differential Temperature Measurement Mode.

D. +1.0 Zero -1.0 °C. Differential Temperature Measurement Mode.

E. Zero -10.0 Zero to +40 °C. Standard Temperature Measurement Mode: Temperature is referenced against Zero degrees Celsius.

Regional Temperature Distribution In The Human

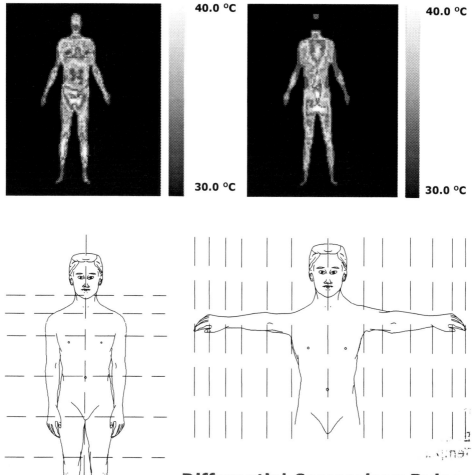

40.0 °C

40.0 °C

30.0 °C

30.0 °C

Differential Comparison Rules

Fig. A3:26 - 29. a) Always take the reference sample for differential measurement comparison from a corresponding area on the opposite side of the patient's body.

b) Alternatively, take a reference sample from an area close to the target area under examination.

289

Infrared Bioscanner Main Panels And Their

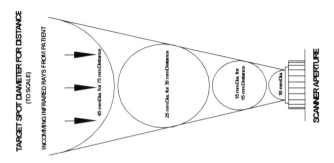

Fig. A3:30. Approximate scale diagram illustrating the spot diameter for different distances from the scanner aperture.

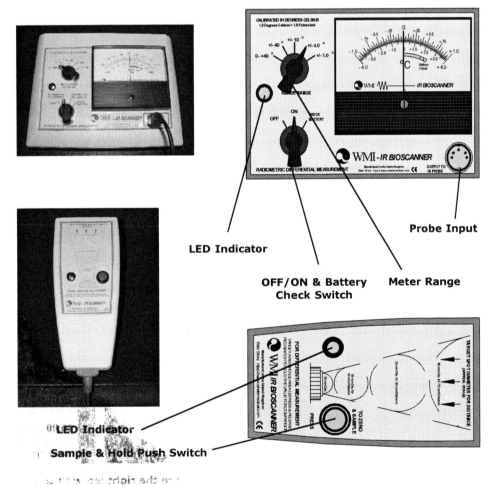

Probe Input

LED Indicator

OFF/ON & Battery Check Switch

Meter Range

LED Indicator

Sample & Hold Push Switch

Fig. A3:31 - 34. The Drawing Below Shows The Normal Switch Positions For Typical Surgery Use.

BACK IN THE SADDLE - THE INVISIBLE RADIATIONS OF INJURIES AND THEIR REPAIR

First Published By Market Place Magazine

The 12th Century Spanish King, Alfonso the Great, translated from Arabic scrolls a book which lists hundreds of medicines prepared from powdered gem stones. The Arabs claimed diamond powder, in addition to healing many diseases, gave a man speed, strength, concentration and bravery. Ruby powder would remedy weakness of the heart, sores, ulcers, and would break up blood clots. Emerald powder was used for fever, injuries, infections, psoriasis and eczema. Medicines prepared from gem stones are today being prescribed in Tibet, India and other parts of the world. Gem medical preparations are potent, powerful, expensive and, like drugs in the wrong hands, can be dangerous.

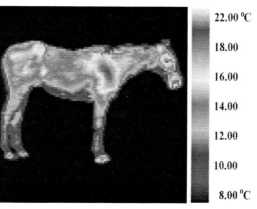

Fig. A3:35. Infrared image showing the heat in a front right foot infection.

Unlike drugs, gem powders are similar to sand in that they do not dissolve and cannot be assimilated by the body - so how do they work? All objects in the universe, including humans and horses, radiate invisible microwave frequencies that can be recorded by infrared cameras. Dying or atrophied cells emit less energy. Injured or infected tissue or organs emit even

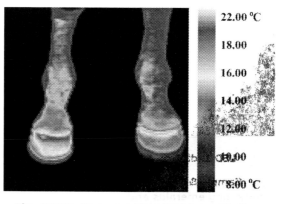

Fig. A3:36. Compare the right leg with the left- the heat from the infection can be seen spreading up the foreleg.

291

more energy than healthy parts. Using infrared imaging the foot infection of a lame horse can be clearly seen by comparing the colours against the temperature scale alongside the image, the heat generated is shown spreading up the right foreleg.

Anne Cawley writes: *Clanfluther is a 12 Year Old, 16 Hand bay gelding by Sherngzar retired sound from 11 years racing. For the last 18 months, I was using him for escorting hacks in riding stables and hunting; he was excellent at both. In the Axe Vale Harrier's Hunt at the end of September, trotting along a narrow Devon lane following a good run, Clanfluther overreached, pulling off a new shoe, and managed to tread on the longest nail, driving it into the sole. He was transported back to the stables where the farrier refitted the shoe. At this point he seemed almost sound. The next day Clanfluther was very lame. After a course of antibiotics, he remained lame and the vet took swabs which revealed an unusual antibiotic resistant infection.*

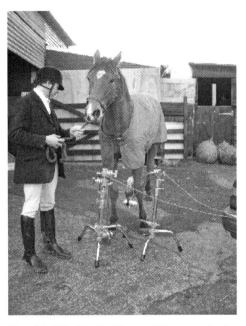

Fig. A3:37. Clanfluther getting ready for treatment.

January three months later the infection had not cleared up and he was still lame. Dr. Jon Whale called at the stables and asked permission to take some infrared scans of horses for his medical research. Minutes later, the scans of Clanfluther's infected foot and leg revealed much higher temperatures than the healthy legs. Dr. Whale said the horse will be in quite some pain but, provided the vet agreed, it might be possible to help and suggested to look at www.whalemedical.com and would return with printed copies of the scans for the vet and farrier.

Fig. A3:38. Treatment using 2 lamps containing emeralds and sapphires to the hoof and a third lamp with carnelians and diamonds to the leg artery.

After seeing the scans, the vet took X-rays to ensure that Clanfluther's injury was free of nails and bone damage. Later, back at the stables, Jon Whale gave an evaluation treatment to Clanfluther's foot and leg with three small electronic medical lamps containing emeralds and sapphires. Clanfluther enjoyed the treatment. Jon said that the Lux IV lamps would relieve the pain and cool and calm the infection and injury. Fifteen minutes into the treatment, Clanfluther moved his foot away from the lamps as if testing the effects. After a moment he placed his foot back under the lamps and went to sleep. For three days, Clanfluther was much better, bucking and galloping in the field, but on the fourth day he returned to the stables slightly lame. Clanfluther's infection was chronic, his evaluation treatment had evidently rendered the infection and pain subclinical for a few days which gave him freedom to play for the first time in months and yet within six weeks he had recovered and was back working again without further treatment. For months, he was pointing his right leg, taking his weight on the left. Once the infection had cleared, he predominately pointed his left leg, resting it from its months of burden, the scans showed this leg now slightly warmer than the right.

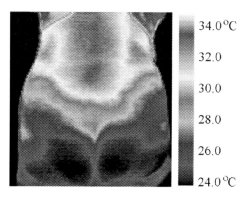

Fig. A3:39. Infra red image of Victoria's back before any treatment.

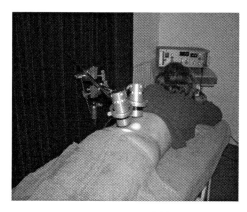

Fig. A3:40. The treatment with red and green lamps.

When electronically excited, crystalline minerals, like humans, radiate, by dielectric resonance, energy at very specific frequencies. Ruby, which is also used in surgical lasers, emits a hot red frequency. Its rays rapidly reduce hypothermia, vasoconstriction, hypometabolism, thereby increasing local

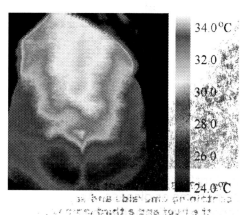

Fig. A3:41. The Infrared scan results two weeks later.

temperature, circulation and biological energy. Emerald and sapphire emit green and violet frequencies which efficiently reduce localized hyperthermia, hyperperfusion, hypermetabolism and vasodilation as well as dramatically attenuating pain and rendering aggressive bacteria docile. When used as medicines, the subjective and cellular effects of gem minerals in layman's terms are:

Ruby - heating, drying, energizing, expanding, increasing circulation.

Carnelian - cooling, moist, harmonizing, anti-allergenic.

Emerald - cold, unifying, contracting, antibiotic, analgesic, relaxant, antispasmodic.

Diamond - stimulating, invigorating, clarifying, antidepressant, anticoagulant.

Sapphire - cool, tranquillizing, soothing, analgesic, sedative, antispasmodic, anti-traumatic.

Powdered gem medicines are eliminated through the intestines, and are therefore very expensive and wasteful. The Lux IV low voltage electronic medical lamps developed by Jon Whale use the medical dielectric resonance properties of gem stone minerals safely without ingestion or side effects. The gems are thereby not destroyed and can be used indefinitely. Whale himself is an autonomous medical scientist. His lamps, which have taken 20 years to develop, can target the injured, infected or diseased parts of the body in animals and humans. The lamps can be defined as transducers that modulate and adjust the biological energy of the selected living cells or organs targeted. Contusions, fractures, burns, psoriasis, eczema, carcinomas, lymphomas, melanomas, prostate cancer, dermatological diseases, rheumatoid arthritis, diabetes mellitus and associated pathology, liver disease and many other common conditions, including bacterial infections, can be accompanied by localized vasodilation, hyperthermia, hyperperfusion, hypermetabolism and or hypervascularisation - all high biological energy conditions which have higher microwave emissions are often accompanied by discomfort and pain.

Lux IV medical lamps containing beryllium aluminium silicate (emeralds) and aluminium oxide (sapphire) crystalline substrates are extremely effective for reducing localized hyperthermia, hyperperfusion, hypermetabolism and vasodilation, as well being capable of dramatically attenuating pain. This type of transducer is electronically modulated at a slow analgesic brainwave frequency of sleep (1.5 Hz, Delta). The lamps can be employed in perhaps 90% of all presented disease or injury. The patient's experience is always very pleasant, regardless of their presented symptoms or disease. As they receive treatment the majority of patients report relief from their pain, irritation, uncomfortable or distressing feelings, emotions and symptoms.

The discovery of targeting and increasing, decreasing and/or modulating the biological energy of internal organs and glands, thereby improving their efficiency and performance, is a quantum leap for medical science, since it has become much more than just theoretically possible to adjust the haematology and biochemistry associated with sinister diseases. This has been demonstrated with palliative management of a terminal patient with stage three lymphoma and lymphoedema. By targeting appropriately selected organs and glands, doctors have produced many excellent results for patients presenting a wide variety of chronic health problems which have not responded to conventional or alternative remedies.

Fractured Pelvis

Victoria writes: *On 16th August 2002, I hacked out with my riding instructor across some common land near our Livery Yard. We were just preparing for a lively canter when my horse bucked and after a swift argument I fell to the ground with a thud . My 50 year old bones were reluctant to resume a vertical position and it quickly became clear that I had sustained an injury. I eventually clambered back on, returned to the yard, then straight home to bed.*

The doctor shook his head, muttering, 'Broken pelvis - complete rest and X-ray immediately, Yuck'. Three weeks later I was walking like a geriatric and still in some considerable pain. Having finished the pain killers and reluctant to take any more I was sent to physio at the local hospital and slowly became convinced that, because of my age and the injury, I would just have to live with it! I was so stiff. Some three months later I was told by a friend of some treatment involving special gem lamps which may help. Prepared to try anything once, off I went full of cold and flu and not really convinced, but I was told that it was painless - pleasant even!

The first treatment was to the area of impact on my right buttock and the pelvic fracture with two analgesic violet lamps to erase the pain and trauma and relax the related muscle groups. This was followed by treatment with an orange lamp direct on my spleen to energize my blood and cardiovascular system for the flu, bronchitis, sinus problems, and to combat my exhaustion. This treatment left me warm but relaxed and returning home I slept for about ten hours. The following day I had to admit the soreness had eased a little and the flu was abating. I returned for another treatment the following week, reported how I had felt and settled down for the second session - well, unbelievable was not an exaggeration! I had green lamp treatment on my middle back and a red lamp simultaneously on my lower back, and within a few minutes felt a rather odd sensation from the tops of my legs to my knees. Infrared scans were taken before and after treatment so that I could see what was actually happening. I am very impressed with the treatment, easier and much less painful than physiotherapy, safer than painkillers and what a result. I finally got back into the saddle on Christmas Eve and enjoyed a gentle hack, and I am sure a lively canter is not far away.

Victoria's case illustrates how different areas of energy are treated. Note the well defined differential high/low energy trauma line on the first infrared back scan. Just below this line is the cold painful area. Perhaps at the time of the fall and injury, the body deliberately created an energy flow constriction to attenuate the pain and shock and, three months on, the trauma was still held in cellular and muscular memory, causing the lower back pain and physical exhaustion. Violet sapphire lamps, within minutes of being applied to injury, will dramatically reduce pain. The upper red high temperature part of Victoria's back was treated with cooling emerald and analgesic sapphire lamps (green). At the same time the lower green cold painful area of her back was treated with warm ruby, combined with analgesic sapphire lamps (red). This combination of 'push-pull' management is very potent and can almost be guaranteed to produce effective and lasting results. The blood is an 'organ' and energizing it with diamond and carnelian substrates rapidly improves the functions of all other organs and glands, including the immune defence system.

Fractured Collarbone

Rachel Jane writes: *Out on a mock hunt over the Salisbury Plains near Stonehenge last December I had a fall. On this occasion I suspected I had broken my right collarbone, so the day was cut short for me with a visit to the Accident and Emergency Unit at Reading. The doctor examined me and sent me for x-rays. By this time I was beginning to feel racking pain in my right shoulder and neck area, as well as turning a nice shade of purple and blue across the chest. Later, on review of the x-rays, the doctor confirmed that I had an open fracture of the right clavicle in three places. I was advised to take paracetamol for the pain and let the bone mend of its own accord with no sudden movement of the right shoulder for the coming weeks. The nurse had put my arm in a sling and I was told to return to the Fracture Clinic.*

By the next day, the paracetamol was ineffective, and I was immobilised in bed with pain and shock. Being reluctant to take any stronger medicines and having had Lux IV lamp treatment on previous occasions I was very keen to get treatment.

At the clinic, I was given treatment with two violet lamps. One was placed directly above my collarbone and the other in the neck area where I was also suffering from a lot of pain. This was done for about forty-five minutes but, as I expected, after the first ten minutes, the pain began to go away, both in the collarbone and neck areas. Next I was given treatment with an orange lamp for the bruising I had suffered as a result of the injury.

The 180 miles return journey was pain free and I did not require any medication. As well as experiencing no further pain I noticed over the next few days that the bruising was rapidly disappearing. A week after my first treatment for my injury I returned for a booster treatment. Two weeks after my fall I was making very good progress. My doctors at the Fracture Clinic were very impressed. I regained movement of my right arm very quickly, and within three and a half weeks of the accident I was able to lift my right hand above my head without too much difficulty. Six weeks after the fall, I was back in the saddle again on Salisbury Plain.

At least with youngsters, sporting injuries given good orthodox treatments and time, will eventually clear up. However, Rachel's case demonstrates how Whale's Lux IV lamps can dramatically accelerate the repair process and eliminate pain.

Fig. A3:42. Treatment for ME and chronic fatigue.

Clanfluther's infection was cleared up with two more treatments and he is now back working and can often be seen trotting along the country lanes and bridal paths of East Devon. It is possible that the same procedures used to treat him could be modified slightly for the management of MRSA and the other escalating antibiotic resistant infections that are occurring in our hospitals and elsewhere.

Contributors:

Anne Cawley and Clanfluther, Stovar Long Lane Riding Stables, Beer, Devon, EX12 3LD, UK. Tel: 001 44 (0) 1297 24278. Victoria Spence-Tomas, Devon, UK, Rachel Jane, Middlesex, UK. Jon Whale Medical Research and Development. E-mail: whalemedicalinc@aol.com.

About Whale Medical Inc.'s Lux IV

The Lux IV has been officially

Fig. A3:43. Triple lamp treatment for prolapsed disc with chronic mobility difficulties.

tested: safety tested in compliance with the European Union legal directive for medical apparatus and is registered as a Class IIA device with Class IIB patient applied lamps. The certificates are pasted on www.whalemedical.com/cd1.html This is a government legal requirement, medical apparatus has to be built from components and parts that have individual certification for medical and dental use. Therefore, the Lux IV specifications, build standard, quality assurance, construction, reliability, mechanical strength, stability, healthy and safety and so on, are the highest possible standards achievable. The Test Report documentation and certificates are available for inspection at our offices and we provide copies of the certificates in the Operating and Training Handbook. The Lux IV is manufactured in the United Kingdom to BS EN ISO9001. Tested and assessed for EMC and electrical safety to standards BS EN 50082-1 and 50081. EC marked labels are fitted.

* Versatile and easy to use. Automatic treatment selection by illuminated 'Push Button' switches, leaving the practitioner free to attend to another client whilst treatment is being given. Treatment may be safely delegated to juniors or trainees.

* Effective by itself, significantly shortening recovery times and improving results of other medical and psychological therapies. It provides an alternative where drug treatment is precluded.

* The energy can be felt on the skin and at deep tissue and bone levels. It improves the patient's complexion, energy levels and mood which becomes apparent after 20 minutes of treatment. Patients find the treatment pleasurable and relaxing as well as effective and enduring.

* The practitioner can observe results as the therapy proceeds. Ninety per cent of patients can feel the energy almost instantaneously and give feedback to the practitioner as their symptoms subside.

Fig. A3:44. Lux IV Electronic Gem Therapy Instrument.

Source Web Site: http://www.whalemedical.com

Other Books by Jon Whale

The Catalyst Of Power - The Assemblage Point Of Man.

Second Edition.

Dragon Rising Publishing. 18 Marlow Avenue. Eastbourne. East Sussex. BN22 8SJ.United Kingdom. Tel: +44 (0)1323 729 666. Fax: +44 (0)8452 804 040. E Mail steve@dragonrising.com. Web Site: http://dragonrising.com.

Also Available in the Dutch and Bulgarian language.

Bulgarian-Links:-http://www.slovo.bg/books/partnerbooks.php?ID=17981 or http://www.bgbook.dir.bg/showsubcat.php?ID=37

Dutch-Links:-http://www.east-westpublications.nl/index.php?p=boek&n=285 or http://winkel.bruna.nl/Auteurs_op_Alfabet/W/Whale,044_J,046/9062290779.htm

ALSO BY DRAGONRISING...

Non-Fiction

- Adventures in EFT: Your Essential Guide to Emotional Freedom by Silvia Hartmann, Ph.D
- The Advanced Patterns of EFT by Silvia Hartmann, Ph.D
- The Art & Science of Emotional Freedom by Ananga Sivyer
- The Patterns & Techniques of EmoTrance Trilogy by Silvia Hartmann, Ph.D
- MindMillion: Let Us Help You Change Your Stars by Silvia Hartmann, Ph.D
- Project Sanctuary by Silvia Hartmann, Ph.D
- Life Without Panic Attacks: Reclaim Your Emotional Freedom, Reclaim Your   Life by Nicola Quinn
- The Energy Odyssey: New Directions in Energy Psychology by Willem   Lammers
- EFT & NLP by Silvia Hartmann
- For You, A Star by Silvia Hartmann

Fiction

- The In Serein Trilogy by StarFields
- Vampire Solstice by StarFields

Online Training Courses

- Sidereus EmoTrance Practitioner Training by Silvia Hartmann, Ph.D

- Sidereus Storyteller Training by Silvia Hartmann, Ph.D
- Sidereus Energy Healing for Animals by Silvia Hartmann, Ph.D
- The Association for Meridian Therapies Meridian Therapy Practitioner Training   by Silvia Hartmann, Ph.D
- The Appollonius Quartet: Improve Psychic Skills, Paranormal Abilities with   Energy Hypnosis by StarFields

Live Training Recordings

- BeautyT Advanced EmoTrance Live Recordings + Self Help with Silvia   Hartmann, Ph.D
- The EmoTrance Gatwick 2006 Live Recordings with Silvia Hartmann, Ph.D,   Nicola Quinn & Sandra Hillawi

Hypnosis CDs, Meditation CDs & HypnoDreams

- The HypnoDreams Trilogy and Reise In Die Heimat by Silvia Hartmann,   Ph.D & Ananga Sivyer
- The HypnoSolutions: Soften & Flow, Fame & Fortune, The Secret Song, The   Journey Home, Life and Love of Life & Star Diamond by Silvia Hartmann, Ph.D & Ananga Sivyer
- Deep Trance Lullaby by Silvia Hartmann, Ph.D & Ananga Sivyey
- Here & Now by Ananga Sivyer

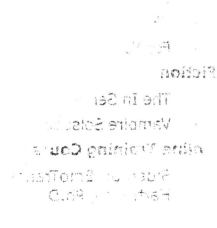